FINANCIAL TRAINING

AAT STUDY PACK

Intermediate Examination Paper 8

ECONOMICS AND STATISTICS / 2

Published August 1989 by Financial Training Courses, Parkway House, Sheen Lane, London SW14 8LS

Copyright © 1989 The Financial Training Company Limited

ISBN 1 85179 009 8 (Vol 1)

ISBN 1 85179 010 1 (Vol 2)

ISBN 1 85179 008 X (Vols 1 and 2)

Printed by Da Costa Print, 111 Salusbury Road, London NW6 6RG

0169z

Contents

0169z

0169z

Introduction

This is the second volume of a two volume Study Pack which has been designed to provide a complete course of study for paper 8, Economics and Statistics, at the Intermediate examination of the Association of Accounting Technicians.

This volume provides comprehensive coverage of the statistics part of the syllabus. Volume 1 covers the economics syllabus.

The order of the Pack follows the syllabus very closely and develops the subject matter of the syllabus from first principles.

At the end of most sessions in the Pack you will find objective test items and written test questions. The latter are all of examination style and standard and must be attempted under exam conditions if you are to obtain the maximum benefit. You must write out a full answer as you would in the examination and not simply audit the suggested answers or merely write out an answer in note form.

0169z

Syllabus

Aims

To develop:

(a)   an understanding of the basic principles of economics; and

(b)   the statistical knowledge acquired in studying Numeracy and Statistics - with special reference to the analysis, interpretation and application of statistical data.

Syllabus

Economics

10%   **Demand and Supply Analysis:**   demand theory, utility and indifference curves; price and income elasticity of demand.

10%   **Price Theory:**   theory of the firm; perfect and imperfect competition; monopoly; equilibrium analysis.

10%   **Monetary and Fiscal Policy:**   propensity to consume and save, liquidity preference; the multiplier; the accelerator; an awareness of the significance of interest rates; the distinction between direct and indirect taxation.

10%   **National Income:**   the measurement of national output and income, definitions of GDP, GNP and National Income.

10%   **Money and Banking:**   nature of money; functions of money and credit; an outline role of central and commercial banks; an appreciation of the money and capital markets.

10%   **International Trade:**   the theory of comparative advantage; free-trade; tariffs; exchange rates; balance of payments accounts; terms of trade.

Statistics

5%   **Collection of Data:**   internal sources of data; external sources of data (a detailed knowledge is not required but a candidate should be aware of major publications containing statistical information).

25%   **Presentation of Data:**   tabulation; treatment of class-intervals for discrete and continuous data, guidelines for the construction of tables, frequency distributions, cumulative frequency distribution.   Graphs, histograms, frequency polygons, bar-charts (simple, composite and compound), pie-charts, pictograms, ogives, Gantt charts, ratio-scale, Z charts, Lorenz curves.

10%   **Summary Measures:**   measures of average: arithmetic mean, median and mode. Measures of dispersion: range, interquartile range, quartile deviation, mean deviation, standard deviation variance, regression, correlation, time series and probability. Sampling, significance testing and quality control.

0169z

Exam format

This examination is split into two sections.

Section A - Economics

This consists of four questions. Candidates must answer three questions in the section, all carrying 20 marks.

Section B - Statistics

This consists of three questions. Candidates must answer two questions in the section, all carrying 20 marks.

Candidates will be expected to memorise the statistical formulae relevant to Paper 8. No tables may be taken into the examination.

0169z

Publisher's note

Financial Training - the only publisher to have AAT approved status - have tailored this Study Pack closely to the needs of students studying for the exam for Paper 8 at the intermediate stage. Studied properly, it will help you cover all parts of the syllabus in detail. However, the AAT examiners have repeatedly stressed the need for candidates to have a real understanding of the topics being examined, and of their relevance in real-life situations, rather than merely reproduce information from memory.

You should try to read round the subject as widely as you can; and, ideally, work through the Study Pack in the structured context provided by a correspondence course or (even better) classroom tuition.

Financial Training Courses offer a range of correspondence, revision and link courses tailored to the individual student's needs. For full details, write or phone us at Parkway House, Sheen Lane, London SW14 8LS. Telephone: 01 876 0499. Fax: 01 878 1749.

0169z

How to study

An accountancy qualification is not something that is automatically awarded to you after a specified period of time. You must make it happen by taking the decision at the start of your studies to commit yourself 100%.

Having made the commitment you must then get the best from your study time. The following tips should help you:

- Do not leave studying to impulse - work out a feasible timetable covering, say, a two week period and then **stick** to it.

- Work in short bursts up to a maximum of 45 minutes. After this your attention falls away and study becomes less effective.

- Keep your breaks short and do not allow them to overrun.

- Try to get into a study routine, always starting work and breaking off at the same times.

- Make sure that your timetable is a mixture of different types of study - taking notes, reading, doing questions. Too much of one type gets monotonous.

- Make your **own** notes on any material that must be learnt. Notes in your own hand will be easier to revise from later.

- Your notes should consist of lots of short, sharp sentences and paragraphs, well spaced out with concise headings. Do not just copy from the Study Pack.

- Use tricks to ease the memorising process - brief notes or headings on index cards to carry with you, mnemonics to learn a list of points, test yourself regularly or get someone else to quiz you.

- Revise what you have learnt constantly. Do not leave revision to the last minute.

Each individual must develop the method of study that suits him best and we hope that the ideas given above will help you to do this. Remember - plan, work consistently and above all, be committed to success.

SESSION 1

Collection of data

In this first introductory session we shall outline the sources from which statistical data may be drawn.

1.1 Introduction

Running any business organisation requires statistical information to be obtained. For example, planning future sales targets requires past sales data to be obtained; making up employees' wages requires data from clock cards to be obtained. Once statistical information is available it can be used by managers to obtain the best results consistent with the objectives of the organisation. The information available falls into two categories: internal sources of data and external sources of data.

1.2 Internal sources of data

1.2.1 Some simple examples

Business organisations themselves produce huge amounts of data. For example:

(a) There are 25 employees in the Export Department.

(b) Last year's budget for the Personnel Department was £265,000.

(c) In December 19X8, 1,500 Type LA31 engines were produced.

(d) Last month 358 expense claims were submitted.

These are obviously all items of data internal to the organisation. Data such as the rate of inflation or the number of motor cars imported into the UK are external to the organisation and will be considered in section 1.3.

1.2.2 Try this example

(a) **Question**

For the organisation where you work or study, list some types of data internal to the organisation which are useful for its efficient operation.

(b) **Answer**

The areas where data arise within an organisation will obviously vary from organisation to organisation. For a 'typical' organisation, five major activities might be considered:

(i) *Production* - amount of stock available, quality of goods produced, productivity, frequency of machine breakdowns;

(ii) *Marketing* - sales figures, expenditure on advertising and promotion, results from market research surveys, travelling expenditure by representatives;

(iii) *Purchasing* - price of raw materials, consumption of stationery, occurrence of overdue deliveries;

(iv)   *Finance* - wage rates of employees, cash in hand, bad debt details, details of loans held;

(v)   *Administration* - number of employees, costs of maintenance, number of mailings.

1.2.3   Data and information

Although the terms data and information are commonly used to mean the same thing (and have been in paragraph 1 of this session), it is important to distinguish between the two.

(a)   **Data** are raw facts, unassembled and frequently unrelated to one another.

(b)   Only by processing the data in some way do we obtain **information**. We can thus define information as a collection of related pieces of data. In general, data may be transformed into information in a number of ways:

(i)   bringing related pieces of data together;
(ii)   summarising data;
(iii) tabulation and diagrammatic techniques;
(iv)   statistical analysis;
(v)   financial analysis.

1.2.4   Who wants the information?

We have seen that data arises in many different situations within an organisation. Having transformed the data into information, there will be a variety of interest groups within the organisation and their needs will differ widely. It would thus be difficult to precisely define all interest groups and the information they use.

We can, however, identify three levels of management and their information needs.

(a)   **Strategic level management**

This is the executive or top level management and deals largely with issues of long range planning. For such decision-making access to all internal information is required and, in addition, information external to the organisation is also employed.

(b)   **Tactical level management**

This middle management level tends to make decisions on a periodic basis (annually, quarterly, monthly) and deals primarily with issues that require information of a historical or financial nature which is generated within the organisation. Many tactical level management decisions are the result of decisions made at the strategic level.

(c)   **Operational decisions**

These involve recurring problems, such as the need to schedule staff for a particular production line each week. The information required is precise, normally not financial and also usually related to a policy prescribed by higher level management.

In addition to these management levels having access to data and information, other groups within an organisation also require information. For example, employees in general obtain information from bulletins and newsletters on job security and income; shareholders require information on present and expected earnings from company reports.

1.3   External sources of data

1.3.1   Primary and secondary data

Organisations frequently need to make use of data obtained outside the organisation itself. For example:

(a)   A survey may be undertaken to determine customer satisfaction with service arrangements in a large store.

(b)   To determine the number of potential customers for a product, data on the size and characteristics of the population is useful.

(c)   If a company is to remain competitive details on the activities (sales, reinvestment, etc) of its competitors are necessary.

This data will fall into the categories of primary and secondary data.

Any data which is used solely for the purpose for which it was collected is termed primary data (as in example (a) above). Data that is taken from some other source is called secondary data (as in examples (b) and (c)). An important distinction is made here since, as in example (a), the data collected by the store might be used by them for some other purpose and would then no longer be primary data. The terms thus refer, not to the data itself, but to the purpose for which it was collected.

Example 1.1

Decide which of the following are primary data and which are secondary data:

(a)   Information from clock cards when used for making up wages.

(b)   Data from a government publication on the toy industry when used by a new toy shop in determining which items to stock.

(c)   Expense claim forms submitted by sales representatives when it is used to estimate the car mileage travelled by the reps.

(d)   Results of an election opinion poll published in a newspaper.

Solution

(a)   Obviously this is primary data since the data is collected to make up the wages.

(b)   This is secondary data. Government statisticians collate data from various sources and the data is used for various reasons.

(c)   This is again secondary data because the expense claim data is collected for a different reason.

(d)   Primary data since the data was collected specifically for the purpose. If you said secondary data you were probably thinking that the results were being used to predict the result of the election. This is different to the reason why it was collected.

1.3.2   The problem of using secondary data

We would naturally prefer to use primary data if this is possible since data collected for a specific purpose is likely to be better. In paragraph 1.3.5 we will look at some of the methods of collecting data oneself. However it is not always possible to use primary data and the problems of using secondary data need highlighting. Some problems are listed below:

(a)   The data has been collected by someone else. We have no control over how it was collected. If a survey was used, was a suitable questionnaire used? Was a large enough sample taken? Was it a reputable organisation who carried out the data collection?

(b)   Is the data up to date? Data quickly becomes out of date since, for example, people's consumer tastes change. Price increases may drastically alter the market.

(c)   The data may be incomplete. Certain groups of people are sometimes omitted from the published data. For example, which groups are included in unemployment figures?

(d)   Is the information actual, seasonally adjusted, estimated or a projection?

(e)   The reason for collecting the data may be unknown. Statistics published by an organisation on motor cars may include or exclude three-wheeled cars, vans and motor-caravans. We need to know which categories are included in the data.

If we are to make use of secondary data we need to have answers to these questions. Sometimes the answers will be published with the data itself or sometimes we may be able to contact the people who carried out the data collection. If not, we must be aware of the limitations of making decisions based on information produced from secondary data.

1.3.3   Sources of secondary data

These will obviously be very numerous and can be broadly categorised as of two forms:

(a)   Those produced by individual companies, local authorities, trades unions, pressure groups, etc. Some examples are:

    (i)   *South Yorkshire Statistics* (annual) - an annual selection of statistics relevant to the area.

(ii) *Bank of England Quarterly Bulletin* - reports on financial and economic matters.

(iii) *Company Reports* (usually annual) - information on performance and accounts of individual companies.

(iv) *Labour Research* (monthly) - articles on industry, employment, trades unions and political parties.

(v) *Financial Times* (daily) - share prices and information on business.

(b) Those produced by Government departments. This is an extensive source of data and is considered in the following paragraphs.

1.3.4 Government statistics

(a) **The Government Statistical Service**

This comprises the statistics divisions of all the major government departments plus the two large collecting agencies, these being the Business Statistics Office and the Office of Population Censuses and Surveys. The service is co-ordinated by the Central Statistical Service and exists primarily to solve the needs of government. However, much of the information compiled is readily usable by business and other organisations. In recent years the service to business has been extended and booklets, such as Profit from Facts, have been published encouraging businesses to make more use of government statistics.

The service works in the following way. Each government department (eg, Trade, Industry, Employment, Environment and the Treasury) prepares and publishes its own statistics via Her Majesty's Stationery Offices. If any series of data from these departments is of sufficient interest it is usually included in more general publications like the Monthly Digest of Statistics. As mentioned earlier, the Government Statistical Service publishes an extensive range of statistical digests. To help find the publication most suitable to anyone's needs two useful guides are available. *Government Statistics - a brief guide to sources* lists all the main publications and departmental contact points. A more comprehensive list is available in *Guide to Official Statistics*. The following two sections indicate some of the important general and specific digests produced.

(b) **General digests**

(i) *Monthly Digest of Statistics* - a collection of the main series of data from all government departments.

(ii) *Annual Abstract of Statistics* - similar to Monthly Digest but containing more series and over longer periods of time.

(iii) *Social Trends* - a collection of key social and demographic statistics, presentation using colour charts and tables.

(c)   **Specific digests**

(i)   *Economic Trends* - from the Central Statistical Office this provides a broad background to trends in the UK economy, presented via commentary, tables and charts.

(ii)   *British Business* - contains statistics and commentary from the Departments of Trade and Industry. The contents varies (weekly) but includes statistics on, for example, capital expenditure, investment intentions, industrial production, food, chemicals, engineering sales and orders, company liquidity, acquisitions and insolvencies, regional development grants.

(iii)   *National Income and Expenditure 'Blue Book'* - detailed estimates of the national accounts, including consumer expenditure; produced by the Central Statistical Office.

(iv)   *Overseas Trade Statistics of the UK* - gives detailed statistics of exports and imports; produced by the Department of Trade.

(v)   *Employment Gazette* - from the Department of Employment this includes articles, tables and charts on manpower, employment, unemployment, earnings, labour costs and stoppages due to disputes.

(vi)   *New Earnings Survey* - again from the Department of Employment this contains statistics relating to earnings from employment by industry, occupation and region.

(vii)   *Financial Statistics* - contains key financial and monetary statistics of the UK.

(viii)   *Business Monitors* - this is a series of publications from the Business Statistics Office. A wide variety of statistics are produced, examples of which are:

MAZ   Annual data relating to cinemas.

MM1   Monthly data on road vehicles and new registrations.

MQ5   Quarterly data on insurance companies and private pension funds.

MA3   Annual analysis of the accounts of listed and unlisted companies.

MM1   Monthly list of price indices for current cost accounting.

Data from the Census of Production and the Census of Distribution are also included in the Business Monitor series, these being broken down giving different publications for each industry.

1.3.5 Methods of collecting data

As explained earlier, primary data is usually preferable to using secondary data. If the data is to be collected by the organisation itself one, or a combination, of the following methods may be employed.

(a) *Direct observation* - This is generally considered to be the best method since it reduces the chance of incorrect data being recorded. For practical reasons and due to high cost it is not always possible to use this method. Useful in, for example, scientific surveys, determining customer service patterns or road traffic surveys.

(b) *Postal questionnaires* - The main problem here is that a poor response rate is frequently obtained, though this can be improved by reminders (increased cost). Other difficulties are that the source of the response is unknown and only simple questions can be asked. It is, however, relatively cheap.

(c) *Telephone interviewing* - This is also a relatively cheap method of collecting data though the results overall may be biased since not everyone has a telephone. It is also easy to be refused.

(d) *Interviewing* - Provided a well-trained team of interviewers is employed this method has advantages over (b) and (c) above. Face-to-face contact with respondents frequently results in more information being obtained.

1.4 Conclusion

As well as showing that data may be obtained from sources both external and internal to an organisation we have also considered, briefly, the methods by which data may be collected in the first place.

1.5   Questions

1.5.1   Written test questions

1.1   Briggs (Carpets) Limited

Assume you are a statistician working for a firm of management consultants and receive the following letter.

Brigg's (Carpets) Limited
Pattern House
Pile Road
Bradford
West Yorkshire

Dear Sir/Madam

As you may know our company is a medium sized manufacturer of carpets, based in Bradford. Recently, a business associate made the suggestion that we could be making more use of published statistics.

In the past we have occasionally received publications of a general nature but have not seriously used them in business planning. Below I have listed some of our needs and would be very grateful if you could advise us where (ie, which publications) to obtain the relevant data.

1   What is the demand for our range of carpets?

2   How competitive are we? (We have some information on prices from simple observation, are there any published statistics on this?)

3   How do our wage rates compare with other manufacturers (our labour force is almost entirely non-union)?

4   Is too much overtime being worked in our company (again, compared to others nationally)?

5   Is there information available on the retail outlets of carpets throughout the UK?

6   Shortly we hope to expand into the overseas market. Thus, what quantities of our products are currently imported and exported?

I hope these brief details will give you some idea of our needs and I look forward to hearing from you in the near future.

Yours faithfully

B Brigg
Managing Director

Required

Write a letter in reply giving precise details of the sources of the required information.

1.2   Data collection

Data may be collected using direct observation, postal questionnaires, interviewing or telephone interviewing.   List fully the advantages and disadvantages of using each of these methods. For each of the scenarios given below, suggest which would be the most appropriate method for data collection.

(a)   Becco plc wish to launch a new product but are uncertain of what customer response will be.

(b)   The local Chamber of Commerce wish to determine how many companies in the area have job vacancies.

(c)   An office has a vending machine in an adjoining corridor for staff to obtain drinks. Management feel that too much time is being wasted by staff in using the machine.

SESSION 2

Tabulation

Once collected, data must be presented in a neat, easy to
follow form if further analysis is to be facilitated. In this
session we shall see how to tabulate raw data. At this
early stage we shall also define continuous and discrete
variables.

2.1 The purpose of tabulation

Any method of data collection will often result in large amounts of data being available. This is the case when an organisation's own internal sources are used or when the data collection is by either a survey, abstraction from secondary sources or by any of the methods explained in paragraph 1.3.5 of the previous session. These large amounts of data will need to be examined to obtain relevant information. This means we must discard any irrelevant details, usually leaving us with a number of categories and sub-categories from which we wish to obtain some overall impression. The data remaining from the elimination of irrelevant details can be summarised using either narrative or by use of tables.

As will be seen in the following paragraph, a major drawback of the narrative approach is that the information required is not clearly presented and only a limited amount of data can be presented. A properly constructed tabular presentation, however, gives the required information immediately and clearly.

2.2 Examples of tabulation

2.2.1 The narrative approach

(a) Consider the following example:

A major bank is interested in the types of accounts held by its customers. The information below has recently been collected:

A sample of 5,000 accounts was taken each belonging to a different customer. 729 accounts were held by customers aged under 25 of whom 522 held current accounts, the remainder holding ordinary deposit accounts. 1,383 of the accounts were held by customers aged between 25 and 44, 1,020 being current accounts, 271 were ordinary deposit accounts and the remainder were high interest deposit accounts. There were 1,621 accounts belonging to customers aged between 45 and 59, of these 61% were current accounts, 29% were ordinary deposit accounts and 10% high interest deposit accounts. Of customers aged 60 and over, 628 held current accounts, 410 held ordinary deposit accounts and the remainder held high interest deposit accounts.

(b) Here the data on the 5,000 accounts has already been examined and irrelevant details on, for example, sex of customer or length of time the account has been held for have been eliminated. We are thus left with a reasonable amount of data and, by reading the narrative a few times, we are able to gain some useful information. The main drawbacks, however, in using this approach to present the data are:

(i) What if the two eliminated variables, sex of customer and age of account, are considered relevant? This would make the narrative much longer and more cumbersome.

(ii) What if other categories were included? For example, an investment account. This would have a similar effect to (i).

(iii) Perhaps we might like to make comparisons with another major bank or a similar sample of customers. We would then have two pieces of narrative to consider.

These points highlight the problems of using solely a narrative approach and hence point us to the benefits of tabulation.

2.2.2 Using tables

Reconsidering the above example we will work through the process of constructing a single table to summarise all the information contained in the narrative.

(a) A simple one-way table

A major point of interest in the given data is obviously the age breakdown of account holders. Working through the narrative, this could be presented as follows:

under 25	729
25-44	1,383
45-59	1,621
60 and over	1,267

The figure for the 60 and over group is given by 5,000 - (729 + 1,383 + 1,621) since there are a total of 5,000 accounts each held by different customers.

(b) Title and headings

The table in (a) gives us a clear breakdown of the ages of the customers but leaves the reader to guess what the columns mean. Clearly the left-hand column is age but it is better to clearly label both columns and to tell the reader what the subject of the table is. Also it is useful to show relevant totals, ie, in this case the total number of accounts.

An improvement on the table given in (a) is thus as follows:

Ages of customers

Age	Number of customers
under 25	729
25-44	1,383
45-59	1,621
60 and over	1,267
Total	5,000

(c) Another one-way table

Another major point of interest in the data is the number of accounts held of each type. A table of this information is more difficult to extract from the narrative and some steps of working may be helpful.

(i) There are three types of account: current accounts, ordinary deposit accounts and high interest deposit accounts.

(ii) Current accounts:

522 (age under 25)

1,020 (aged 25 - 44)

989 (aged 45 - 59; 61% of 1,621 accounts = 0.61 x 1,621 = 988.81 or 989 accounts by rounding to nearest whole number of accounts)

628 (aged 60 and over)

(iii) Ordinary deposit accounts:

207 (aged under 25; 729 minus the number of current accounts = 729 - 522 = 207)

271 (aged 25 - 44)

470 (aged 45 - 59; 29% of 1,621 accounts = 0.29 x 1,621 = 470.09 = 470 accounts)

410 (aged 60 and over)

(iv) High interest deposit account:

0 (aged under 25; we must assume this since no other detail is given)

92 (aged 25 - 44; 1,383 minus the number of current and ordinary deposit accounts = 1,383 - (1,020 + 271) = 1,383 - 1,291 = 92)

162 (aged 45 - 59; 10% of 1,621 accounts = 0.1 x 1,621 = 162.1 = 162 accounts)

229 (aged 60 and over; total aged 60 and over minus number of current and ordinary deposit accounts = 1,267 (from (a)) - (628 + 410) = 229)

Summing the number of accounts in (ii) to (iv) gives the required table.

Number of different accounts held

Type of account	Number of customers
Current	3,159
Ordinary deposit	1,358
High interest deposit	483
Total	5,000

(d)   **A two-way table**

Our objective at the start of this paragraph was to construct a single table to summarise all the information contained in the narrative. Having carried out the simple calculations in (c) above, this is now easily done by employing a two-way table (sometimes called a cross-tabulation). In this example the two 'variables' are obviously age of customers and type of account held. These become the headings for the following required two-way table:

Ages and types of accounts held by sample of 5,000 customers

Type of Account	under 25	25-44	45-59	60 and over	Total
			Age		
Current	522	1,020	989	628	3,159
Ordinary deposit	207	271	470	410	1,358
High interest deposit	0	92	162	229	483
Total	729	1,383	1,621	1,267	5,000

2.3   Guidelines for constructing tables

There are no set rules for constructing tables since tables often vary markedly in content and format. The following guidelines should however be adhered to:

(a)   Always give the table a title and suitable headings.

(b)   If the date contains a number of categories or sub-categories use a two-way table.

(c)   Give column and row sub-totals where appropriate.

(d)   If the draft table contains too much detail it will fail in its objective of summarising the data. Further simplified tables should then be constructed each dealing with different aspects of the data.

(e)   It is important to state the source of the data. This may be included in the title or given beneath the table.

(f)   The units in the table should be 'manageable'. This can be accomplished by, for example, dividing particular column entries by 1,000 and including this fact in the column heading.

(g)   It is sometimes useful to show percentages in the table in addition to the actual figures.

In analysing large amounts of data, tables similar to those already considered prove very useful. However, it is often the case that the data is in such a basic form (what is known as raw data) that using tables of this type is not possible. This problem is considered in the following session where the ideas of tally charts and frequency distribution is presented.

2.4 Discrete and continuous data

2.4.1 Raw data

Raw data is the term used for the numerical information or figures that are initially collected together and written down. This is before any sort of analysis has been carried out on the figures either using the narrative approach or a tabular presentation. Without some sort of analysis this raw data can be rather unhelpful since it is just about impossible to see any trends in a mass of figures. As an example look at the following figures:

NUMBER OF TRANSACTIONS AT A SHOP ON 72 CONSECUTIVE DAYS

24	27	13	34	7	31	23	41
16	9	30	17	29	20	12	15
10	18	12	5	13	20	10	24
44	21	23	32	26	15	27	16
19	15	24	14	11	27	20	34
7	36	20	24	16	25	24	6
23	32	10	23	27	18	20	39
13	10	21	27	15	28	31	26
28	23	24	25	20	9	27	12

2.4.2 Variables

A variable is a measurement which varies from one individual to another or from one item to another. Examples of variables are the length of time a contract takes to fulfil, the number of mistakes in a set of accounts, the weight of a steel bar, age and so on. Variables can be one of two types depending on what values they can take.

(a) **Discrete variables**

Discrete variables are those variables which can only take whole number or integer values. When we count things the answers we get are whole numbers, these are the most common examples of discrete variables. The number of people who use a micro-computer in an hour, the number of cars sold in a day, are examples of discrete variables.

(b) **Continuous variables**

Continuous variables are variables which can take any value within a certain range, so a decimal or fractional value can be obtained for continuous variables. Most physical measurements can take decimal values and so are continuous variables. Examples include the width of a component, temperature and time to produce an item.

Example 2.1

(a) Are the following variables discrete or continuous?

(i) Volume of a bottle.

(ii) Number of radios produced in a day.

(iii)   Number of people absent from work on a workday.

(iv)   Average number of people absent from work on a workday.

(b)   **Solutions**

(i)   As volume can take decimal values, it is a continuous variable.

(ii)   As this is a count it will be a whole number, it is a discrete variable.

(iii)   As this is also a count it will be a discrete variable.

(iv)   This is not a count but an average of counts so this variable can take decimal values. It is therefore a continuous variable.

2.5   Step by step illustration 1

Smith plc manufacture bed linen. In 19X2 their total sales were £126,000 and these sales increased by £28,000 in 19X3 and then again by £41,000 in 19X4. In comparison Brown plc, one of Smith's competitors, had total sales of £206,000 in 19X2 and their sales reduced by 10% each year in 19X3 and 19X4. Present this information in tabular form.

Solution

(a)   It is useful in any problem where construction of a table is required to first write down the headings in the table. In this example this is easy:

Year	Sales of Smith plc	Sales of Brown plc

(b)   The next stage in problems of this kind is to work out the individual entries in the table:

Smith plc: 19X2   £126,000
             19X3   126,000 + 28,000 = £154,000
             19X4   154,000 + 41,000 = £195,000

Brown plc: 19X2   £206,000
             19X3   206,000 - (0.1 x 206,000) = 206,000 - 20,600 = £185,400
             19X4   185,400 - (0.1 x 185,400) = 185,400 - 18,540 = £166,860

(c)   The draft table is now easily formed:

Year	Sales of Smith plc (£)	Sales of Brown plc (£)
19X2	126,000	206,000
19X3	154,000	185,400
19X4	195,000	166,860

(d)   Since the units are all of the same order of magnitude, we can make the units more manageable by dividing by 1,000. Also a title should be added to the table. The final table might thus have the form:

Sales of Smith plc and Brown plc for 19X2-X4

Year	Sales of Smith plc £1,000s	Sales of Brown plc £1,000s
19X2	126	206
19X3	154	185.4
19X4	195	166.86

2.6 Step by step illustration 2

The table below shows figures of employees in employment for 19W2 to 19X3. Interpret this data by commenting on the trend in employment in motor vehicle manufacturing and comparing it to what happened in 'manufacturing' and 'all industries and services'.

Total employees in employment

Year	Motor Vehicle Manufacturing ('000s)	Manufacturing ('000s)	All industries and services ('000s)
19W2	490	7,779	22,121
19W3	510	7,830	22,663
19W4	497	7,873	22,790
19W5	457	7,524	22,710
19W6	448	7,281	22,543
19W7	464	7,328	22,619
19W8	471	7,290	22,777
19W9	459	7,258	23,158
19X0	412	6,940	22,972
19X1	355	6,221	21,871
19X2	318	5,912	21,473
19X3	306	5,641	21,210

Solution

(a) Questions of this type are a little vague in what is required. For each of the three columns of data on employment we could, for example, comment on every year to year change, eg, employment in motor vehicle manufacturing increased by 20,000 from 19W2 to 19W3, fell by 13,000 from 19W3 to 19W4, etc. This is clearly a long-winded way of describing the trend in employment and should be avoided.

(b) What is required is some comment on the changes in employment, without the repetitive detail of (a). For all questions of this type this is best achieved by picking out the 'peaks' and 'troughs' in the data and also by commenting on the overall change in the data between the beginning of the period and the end. In this example suitable comments might be as follows.

The total number of employees in motor vehicle manufacturing rose to a peak in 19W3, gradually fell until 19W6, increased slightly until 19W8 and then fell dramatically until 19X3 when it was over 37% down on the 19W2 figure.

The total number of employees in manufacturing industries rose slowly between 19W2 and 19W4 but then fell sharply until 19W6, when after a small increase in 19W7, it fell rapidly until 19X3. Overall between 19W2 and 19X3 there was a 27.5% fall in employment in manufacturing industries.

The total number of employees in all industries and services rose between 19W2 and 19W4, fell back between 19W4 and 19W6, rose again to peak in 19W9 and then fell fairly sharply until 19X3 when it was just over 4% below the 19W2 figure.

Workings: Percentage changes in employment between 19W2 and 19X3:

$$\text{motor vehicle manufacturing} = \frac{490 - 306}{490} \times 100\%$$

$$= 37.55\% \text{ fall}$$

$$\text{manufacturing} = \frac{7,779 - 5,641}{7,779} \times 100\%$$

$$= 27.48\% \text{ fall}$$

$$\text{all industries and services} = \frac{22,121 - 21,210}{22,121} \times 100\%$$

$$= 4.12\% \text{ fall}$$

(c) It is also useful in questions of this type to give some overall comment about what appears to be happening (as indicated by the data).

In this example, there has obviously been a large movement of employees out of motor vehicle manufacturing between 19W2 and 19X3. On the limited evidence of the data available, this movement of employees does not seem to have been significantly into other manufacturing industries since there has also been a 27.5% fall in employment in this area.

2.7   Step by step illustration 3

The following table is an extract from the *Monthly Digest of Statistics* and gives detail on consumer expenditure between 1980 and 1984. Study this table and then answer the following questions:

(a) Calculate the percentage change in consumer expenditure between 1980 and 1984 for the following categories:

> total consumers' expenditure
> cars, etc
> food
> beer
> energy products
> rent, etc

What do these figures suggest?

(b) What do the 'revalued at 1980 prices' figures indicate? Make reference to the categories listed in (a).

£ million

	Durable goods				Other goods						Energy prod-ucts	Other goods	Services	
Total consu-mers' expend-iture	Total	Cars, motor cycles and other vehicles	Furnit-ure and floor cover-ings	Other durable goods	Food (house-hold expend-iture)	Beer	Other alcohol-ic drink	Toba-cco	Cloth-ing other than foot-wear	Foot-wear			Rent, rates and water charges	Other services
At current prices														
1980 136 789	13 320	6 307	3 429	3 584	22 873	5 320	4 634	4 822	8 103	1 760	10 957	14 369	16 044	34 587
1981 152 125	13 885	6 511	3 513	3 861	24 170	5 970	5 183	5 515	8 406	1 853	13 367	15 538	19 465	38 773
1982 166 538	15 165	7 064	3 698	4 403	25 590	6 453	5 554	5 882	8 854	2 067	14 954	16 809	22 399	42 811
1983 182 420	18 310	9 142	4 150	5 018	27 148	7 140	6 232	6 208	9 804	2 310	16 212	18 292	23 576	47 188
1984 194 654	18 858	9 088	4 398	5 372	28 151	7 734	6 585	6 631	10 637	2 536	16 958	19 873	25 250	51 441
Revalued at 1980 prices														
1980 136 789	13 320	6 307	3 429	3 584	22 873	5 320	4 634	4 822	8 103	1 760	10 957	14 369	16 044	34 587
1981 136 429	13 486	6 366	3 354	3 766	22 676	5 000	4 612	4 470	8 189	1 696	10 992	14 420	16 279	34 609
1982 137 581	14 193	6 510	3 424	4 259	22 587	4 838	4 545	4 128	8 329	1 810	11 038	14 624	16 530	34 959
1983 143 011	16 459	7 909	3 724	4 826	22 858	4 914	4 816	4 082	8 892	1 948	11 129	14 968	16 764	36 181
1984 145 192	16 298	7 302	3 754	5 242	22 468	4 943	4 962	3 948	9 392	2 051	11 254	15 541	16 978	37 357

Solution

In questions of this type data from a government publication is presented. If the question asks for interpretation of the data in general then it requires surprising effort to see what the data are actually saying since so much information is presented. In this question (as is often the case) well-defined questions are asked making the task easier.

The solution to this question is as follows:

(a) The percentage changes in consumer expenditure between 1980 and 1984 are:

$$\text{Total consumer's expenditure \% change} = \frac{194,654 - 136,789}{136,789} \times 100$$

$$= 42.3\%$$

$$\text{Cars, etc, \% change} = \frac{9,088 - 6,307}{6,307} \times 100$$

$$= 44.1\%$$

$$\text{Food \% change} = \frac{28,151 - 22,873}{22,873} \times 100$$

$$= 23.1\%$$

$$\text{Beer \% change} = \frac{7,734 - 5,320}{5,320} \times 100$$

$$= 45.4\%$$

$$\text{Energy products \% change} = \frac{16{,}958 - 10{,}957}{10{,}957} \times 100$$

$$= 54.8\%$$

$$\text{Rent, etc, \% change} = \frac{25{,}250 - 16{,}044}{16{,}044} \times 100$$

$$= 57.4\%$$

The figures indicate that the increase in consumer expenditure has been greater in some categories than others. If total consumers' expenditure is taken as the 'average' then, for the categories listed, food is the only category where the increase in expenditure is less than this average. On the other hand expenditures on cars, beer, energy and rent are all higher than the average increase.

These figures highlight a trend that has actually been taking place over a number of years. In general, the public has been spending less money on food items and more money on other goods and services.

(b) The figures entitled 'revalued at 1980 prices' are presented to remove the effect of inflation from the unadjusted data. Reconsidering the categories listing in (i) and calculating the percentage changes between 1980 and 1984 for this data, we have

Total consumers expenditure % change = 6.1%

Cars, etc, % change = 15.8%

Food % change = 1.8% decrease

Beer % change = 7.1% decrease

Energy products = 2.7%

Rent, etc, = 5.8%

These percentage change figures are very revealing. If the effect of inflation is removed then the amount spent on both food and beer have decreased. Additionally, expenditure on cars, etc, has seen the largest increase in expenditure between 1980 and 1984. These facts are not revealed by using the data considered in part (i).

2.8 Conclusion

It is important that you remember the guidelines for tabulation set out in section 2.3. Refer back to them now. You should also make sure that you can recall several examples of continuous and discrete variables.

2.9 Questions

2.9.1 Written test questions

2.1 Bunny and Hutch

The total number of employees of Bunny and Hutch Limited on 31 December 19X4 was 3,984, of which 2,124 were men. During 19X4, 221 men had been engaged and 185 resigned. The corresponding figures for women were 97 and 108 respectively. The average wage rate paid to male employees in 19X4 was £121.32 and to female employees £87.93. The company worked for 50 weeks in 19X4. Tabulate this data, including in your table an estimate of the total wage bill.

2.2 Discrete and continuous

(a) What is the difference between a discrete variable and a continuous variable?

(b) State which of the following are discrete variables and which are continuous variables?

    (i) Number of passengers on a train.

    (ii) Weights of bags of sweets filled by an automatic machine.

    (iii) Daily rainfall in Sheffield.

    (iv) Time taken to complete a simple task on a production line.

    (v) Stocks of sugar held by a biscuit manufacturer.

2.3 Motor policies

The following table gives details of the motor insurance policies of an insurance company in 19X3:

Region	Number of claims	Number of policies held
North	1,330	16,223
Midlands	1,384	18,210
South	1,377	22,581
East Anglia	234	9,363
London	1,401	32,580
Wales	180	10,005
Scotland	118	7,388
Northern Ireland	659	6,276

Provide a brief interpretation of the information contained in this table.

2.4   Unemployment

The following tables on unemployment are extracted from the *Monthly Digest of Statistics*. Study these tables and answer the questions that follow:

Thousands

	United Kingdom					Students regis-tered for vacation employ-ment	Great Britain				Northern Ireland			
	Unemployed		Unemployed excluding school-leavers				Unemployed							
	Total	Per-centage rate	Total un-adjusted	Seasonally adjusted[3]			Total	Per-centage rate[1]	Males	Females	Total	Per-centage rate	Males	Females
				Total	Per-centage rate									
1983 January 13	3 225.2	13.4	3 087.4	2 983.8	12.4	21.9	3 109.0	13.3	2 270.6	838.4	116.2	20.1	84.2	32.0
February 10	3 199.4	13.3	3 075.6	2 997.2	12.5	4.0	3 084.7	13.2	2 252.7	832.0	114.7	19.8	83.9	30.8
March 10	3 172.4	13.2	3 060.2	3 023.9	12.6	1.9	3 058.7	13.0	2 236.0	822.7	113.7	19.6	83.4	30.2
April 14	3 169.9	13.2	3 035.4	3 024.4	12.6	75.2	3 053.5	13.0	2 221.1	832.5	116.4	20.1	85.3	31.1
May 12	3 049.4	12.7	2 923.7	2 969.3	12.4	10.6	2 934.4	12.5	2 115.0	819.4	115.0	19.9	84.4	30.6
June 9	2 983.9	12.4	2 865.0	2 963.0	12.3	13.9	2 870.5	12.2	2 061.8	808.7	113.4	19.6	82.9	30.5
July 14	3 020.6	12.6	2 905.0	2 947.0	12.3	182.1	2 903.5	12.4	2 059.4	844.1	117.1	20.2	84.6	32.6
August 11	3 009.9	12.5	2 897.8	2 935.8	12.2	188.7	2 892.9	12.3	2 040.6	852.4	117.0	20.2	84.5	32.5
September 8	3 167.4	13.2	2 952.8	2 944.4	12.3	223.7	3 043.7	13.0	2 116.3	927.4	123.7	21.4	88.3	35.4
October 13	3 094.0	12.9	2 925.9	2 944.8	12.3	26.6	2 974.2	12.7	2 075.9	898.3	119.8	20.7	86.5	33.4
November 10	3 084.4	12.8	2 946.7	2 947.2	12.3	3.7	2 964.7	12.6	2 072.4	892.2	119.7	20.7	86.6	33.2
December 8	3 079.4	12.8	2 961.3	2 958.3	12.3	3.3	2 960.9	12.6	2 080.7	880.3	118.4	20.5	86.2	32.2
1984 January 12	3 199.7	13.2	3 082.9	2 975.3	12.3	27.5	3 077.4	13.0	2 156.6	920.9	122.2	21.0	88.8	33.5
February 9	3 186.4	13.2	3 080.9	2 999.4	12.4	2.1	3 063.8	13.0	2 147.4	916.5	122.5	21.1	89.5	33.0
March 8	3 142.8	13.0	3 048.0	3 013.6	12.5	1.3	3 021.9	12.8	2 116.6	905.3	120.9	20.8	88.4	32.4
April 5	3 107.7	12.8	3 022.4	3 012.0	12.5	39.6	2 987.6	12.7	2 092.5	895.2	120.1	20.7	87.6	32.5
May 10	3 084.5	12.8	2 980.3	3 026.2	12.5	6.9	2 963.9	12.6	2 073.4	890.5	120.6	20.8	87.7	32.8
June 14	3 029.7	12.5	2 934.5	3 031.8	12.5	22.9	2 910.8	12.3	2 033.5	877.3	118.9	20.5	86.1	32.8
July 12	3 100.5	12.8	3 008.1	3 049.4	12.6	177.9	2 978.9	12.6	2 063.2	915.7	121.6	20.9	87.0	34.7
August 9	3 115.9	12.9	3 025.9	3 066.3	12.7	194.7	2 995.2	12.7	2 064.6	930.5	120.7	20.8	86.5	34.2
September 13	3 283.6	13.6	3 101.7	3 090.6	12.8	219.0	3 156.6	13.4	2 155.6	1 000.9	127.1	21.9	90.0	37.1
October 11	3 225.1	13.3	3 074.6	3 093.6	12.8	30.8	3 103.2	13.1	2 130.8	972.4	122.0	21.0	87.2	34.8
November 8	3 222.6	13.3	3 094.7	3 097.1	12.8	6.5	3 101.6	13.1	2 135.7	965.9	121.0	20.8	87.0	34.0
December 6	3 219.4	13.3	3 108.1	3 106.4	12.8	2.9	3 100.0	13.1	2 145.8	954.2	119.4	20.5	86.7	32.7
1985 January 10	3 341.0	13.8	3 231.5	3 123.9	12.9	20.3	3 217.9	13.6	2 226.8	991.0	123.1	21.2	89.2	33.9
February 14	3 323.7	13.7	3 225.9	3 144.0	13.0	2.1	3 200.7	13.6	2 220.1	980.6	123.0	21.2	89.8	33.2
March 14	3 267.6	13.5	3 179.6	3 148.0	13.0	2.1	3 145.9	13.3	2 180.3	965.6	121.7	20.9	88.9	32.8
April 11	3 272.6	13.5	3 188.9	3 176.2	13.1	46.1	3 150.3	13.3	2 181.8	968.5	122.3	21.0	88.9	33.3
May 9	3 240.9	13.4	3 133.2	3 179.6	13.1	5.0	3 120.0	13.2	2 155.8	964.2	120.9	20.8	87.9	33.0

2.13

0171z

Unemployed
Analysis by standard regions

Thousand

		North	Yorkshire and Humber-side	East Midlands	East Anglia	South East	South West	West Midlands	North West	Wales	Scotland	Northern Ireland
1980		140.8	154.6	98.7	39.2	328.1	106.9	170.1	242.1	102.7	207.9	
1981	Monthly	192.0	237.2	155.3	61.4	547.6	155.6	290.6	354.9	145.9	282.8	74.5
1982	averages	214.6	273.2	176.6	72.2	664.6	179.0	337.9	407.8	164.8	318.0	98.0
1983		225.7	288.7	188.0	77.5	721.4	188.6	354.7	437.1	170.4	335.6	108.3
1984		230.5	291.9	194.3	77.3	747.5	193.7	345.4	442.9	173.3	341.6	117.1
												121.4
1984	January 12	230.9	293.7	193.8	80.0	750.9	199.3	349.6	451.0	174.7	353.4	122.2
	February 9	228.0	292.2	195.2	81.1	748.1	198.4	346.6	448.7	174.2	351.3	122.5
	March 8	225.9	287.1	193.8	79.4	739.5	194.8	342.9	443.1	171.9	343.5	120.9
	April 5	224.7	284.9	192.1	77.8	732.0	191.0	340.3	437.5	169.9	337.4	120.1
	May 10	225.9	285.3	190.3	76.4	724.8	185.5	339.6	435.0	169.1	331.8	120.6
	June 14	223.1	279.1	186.5	73.5	716.1	179.1	334.9	426.1	163.2	329.3	118.9
	July 12	227.0	286.2	191.6	74.4	735.2 26	183.8	341.1	435.5	167.5	336.7	121.6
	August 9	226.6	285.7	192.3	74.3	744.6	185.8	342.1	439.2	167.7	336.8	120.7
	September 13	243.1	308.4	202.2	77.6	777.7	198.6	360.4	457.2	182.3	349.2	127.1
	October 11	236.6	300.8	199.0	77.2	767.4	200.3	353.0	446.9	178.9	343.1	122.0
	November 8	237.9	300.1	196.8	77.7	767.5	203.5	347.3	447.5	180.0	343.4	121.0
	December 6	236.5	298.8	198.3	78.5	766.2	204.4	346.9	447.0	180.4	343.1	119.4
1985	January 10	243.5	309.6	207.0	83.2	795.6	213.2	357.1	461.5	185.9	362.2	123.1
	February 14	237.1	307.7	207.6	84.5	797.0	213.7	355.3	456.8	183.8	357.2	123.0
	March 14	233.6	302.9	204.1	82.2	784.0	208.1	349.3	449.3	180.6	351.9	121.7
	April 11	236.5	303.8	203.7	82.4	784.2	205.5	348.2	451.3	180.0	354.7	122.3
	May 9	237.3	303.0	202.1	81.0	772.2	200.8	347.0	450.3	178.5	347.9	120.9
Unemployment rate												
May 9		*18.8*	*14.9*	*12.7*	*10.6*	*9.8*	*11.8*	*15.4*	*16.2*	*16.8*	*15.4*	*20.8*

(a) What was the total number of unemployed in the UK on May 9 1985? What percentage of the population of the UK was this?

(b) When was the last fall in seasonally adjusted total number of unemployed excluding school leavers?

(c) Which region had the highest rate of unemployment on May 9 1985?

(d) In what month in 1984 did unemployment in Yorkshire and Humberside reach 300,000? Was this level of unemployment maintained in the region for the remainder of 1984?

(e) Which region had the lowest number of unemployed in January 1985?

(f) It is often said that the figure for the total number of unemployed presented each month underestimates the true level of unemployment. What arguments are there for saying this?

SESSION 3

Frequency distributions

In the previous session we shaw how raw data may be presented concisely in tabular form. We now go even further and see how the variables may be expressed in the form of a frequency distribution. This will be important in future sessions when we look at ways of analysing the characteristics of distributions.

0172z

3.1 Description of a frequency distribution

In paragraph 2.4.1 of the previous session we introduced the concept of raw data. When we have a set of raw data we usually wish to summarise the figures into something more manageable and comprehensible. As was suggested, tabular methods previously presented are not suitable for such data. If we have raw data the first step is often to put the values into their numerical order. This tells us something about the range of values we have and whether there are any concentrations of values. However, we still have the main problem of too many values. We can start to reduce this problem by grouping together all similar values. The value can then be written down just once followed by the number of occurrences of that value (ie, its frequency). If this does not reduce the data to a suitable form we can go a stage further by grouping different values into class intervals. We then determine the frequencies for each class interval. The resulting table is known as a frequency distribution or frequency table.

3.2 Constructing a frequency distribution from raw data

3.2.1 Tally charts

The original raw data can be tabulated using a tally sheet and tally marks. List the different observed values down the left hand side and then put a tally mark every time a value is found in the raw data. A useful tip is to use every fifth tally mark to 'cross out' the previous four, so allowing us to add up the tally marks easily at the end. The total number of tally marks for each value is entered in the frequency column. The tally marks give a rough picture of the distribution of values.

Consider the transactions carried out during a day.

NUMBER OF TRANSACTIONS AT A SHOP ON 72 CONSECUTIVE DAYS

24	27	13	34	7	31	23	41
16	9	30	17	29	20	12	15
10	18	12	5	13	20	10	24
44	21	23	32	26	15	27	16
19	15	24	14	11	27	20	34
7	36	20	24	16	25	24	6
23	32	10	23	27	18	20	39
13	10	21	27	15	28	31	26
28	23	24	25	20	9	27	12

The tally sheet will look like this:

NUMBER OF TRANSACTIONS	TALLY MARKS	FREQUENCY
5	1	1
6	1	1
7	11	2
8		0
9	11	2
10	1111	4
11	1	1
12	111	3
13	111	3
14	1	1
15	1111	4
16	111	3
17	1	1
18	11	2
19	1	1
20	~~1111~~ 1	6
21	11	2
22		0
23	~~1111~~	5
24	~~1111~~ 11	7
25	11	2
26	11	2
27	~~1111~~ 1	6
28	11	2
29		0
30	1	1
31	11	2
32	11	2
33		0
34	11	2
35		0
36	1	1
39	1	1
41	1	1
44	1	1
		72

This is a frequency table of individual values. The total of frequencies should always be checked to make sure it totals the same as the number of original values.

Example 3.1

Using individual values draw up a frequency table, by tally marks, of the following data. A company has recorded the number of complaints received per week for a period of twenty-five weeks. The figures are:

2	13	10	8	4
18	6	0	15	2
7	15	22	3	11
9	14	14	5	6
6	3	8	17	8

3.3

Solution

NUMBER OF COMPLAINTS PER WEEK	TALLY MARKS	FREQUENCY
0	1	1
1		0
2	11	2
3	11	2
4	1	1
5	1	1
6	111	3
7	1	1
8	111	3
9	1	1
10	1	1
11	1	1
12		0
13	1	1
14	11	2
15	11	2
16		0
17	1	1
18	1	1
19		0
20		0
21		0
22	1	1
		—
		25

3.2.2 Grouped data

The frequency table obtained above is an improvement on the original list of figures but it is still much too long a table for us to be able to obtain very much information from it. To obtain a more concise and useful presentation we can go a stage further and group the values into bands or classes. The frequency quoted is then for all the values in the class interval.

For the transactions data from 3.2.1 we obtain:

NUMBER OF TRANSACTIONS	TALLY MARKS	FREQUENCY
1-5	1	1
6-10	4111 1111	9
11-15	4111 4111 11	12
16-20	4111 4111 111	13
21-25	4111 4111 1111 1	16
26-30	4111 4111 1	11
31-35	4111 1	6
36-40	11	2
41-45	11	2
		—
		72

3.4

It is worth considering the implications of such a table. It is more concise and gives us a clearer view of the distribution of our data. However, we should also realise that by setting up such a table we have lost detailed information. Whilst the table tells us there are nine values from 6-10 inclusive, it does not tell us what those values might be. This will present us with problems when we calculate statistics from grouped data. Also, the choice of intervals was arbitrary, we could just as easily have chosen intervals 1-6, 7-12 and so on.

Example 3.2

For the complaints data from Example 3.1 above draw up a frequency table using intervals 0-4, 5-9, etc.

Solution

NUMBER OF COMPLAINTS (per week)	FREQUENCY
0-4	6
5-9	9
10-14	5
15-19	4
20-24	1
	25

3.2.3 Choosing class intervals

Many guidelines are suggested as aids to choosing class intervals and deciding how many intervals to choose. These include:

(a) *The minimum number of intervals should be five.*

This is used because if you use any fewer than five intervals the data gets so concentrated we cannot make meaningful comparisons between the frequencies for intervals.

(b) *The maximum number of intervals should be twelve.*

This is a guideline which has come about from experience. When looking at a table we can just about take in twelve lines at one time. Of course, there will be situations where we have to use more than twelve intervals (eg, a list of the number of accountants in each county of the United Kingdom).

(c) *There should be an even distribution of values in an interval.*

Ideally, we would want an even spread of values through the interval so making the frequency for the whole interval relate directly to individual values within the interval. Although this is a sensible idea it is very difficult to achieve in practice.

(d)   *The values counted in an interval should average to the mid-point of that interval.*

This is so that assumptions we shall make when calculating statistics from class interval data are reasonable. Again, this is a difficult guideline to follow in practice.

(e)   *To find class interval limits divide the range of values into the number of intervals required.*

This is to ensure we get equal width intervals and that they cover the full range of our raw data. The problem with this approach is that the intervals we obtain usually make very little sense. When computers are used to draw up frequency tables this approach is used and often very odd-looking intervals like 8.376-13.088, 13.088-17.811, etc, are obtained.

All these are only guidelines and should be taken as such. It would be quite impossible to ensure any table we draw up will meet all of these requirements. Whilst we should try and observe guidelines (a)-(d), if practical, guideline (e) is usually ignored in favour of the following approach.

One of the most important rules when drawing up a table with interval data is to use common sense. People naturally think in units of 10 or multiples linked to 10 so if we have no real reason for using alternatives, use intervals based on this size of interval. In our example above, intervals of five units width have been used (two intervals giving ten units). In many situations there are values which have special importance. If we were drawing up a table showing people's taxable income, important values would be those taxable incomes where the different tax bands operate. When we have values of special importance these should always be arranged to be at the beginning or ending of an interval.

So far the intervals we have seen have been for discrete variables. If we decided to use intervals covering 10 units we might pick any of the following:

(a)   43-52, 53-62, etc;

(b)   45-54, 55-64, etc;

(c)   41-50, 51-60, etc;

(d)   40-49, 50-59, etc;

as our set of inclusive intervals. Whilst any one of these is perfectly acceptable from a practical point of view, the last set (d) is the easiest to use. This is because we count all the 'forties', all the 'fifties', etc, to obtain the frequencies for each interval. In each of the other examples we have to count some and ignore others. Just taking the first possibility (a) we would need to check all the 'forties' but ignore the 40, 41, 42 figures, then check all the 'fifties' but only count 50, 51 and 52 figures.

3.2.4   Choosing class intervals for continuous variable

For continuous variables we set up our intervals using the same approach. However, we need to be careful that all possible values are allowed for without the danger of ambiguity (not knowing which interval to count a value in). Look at the following choices of intervals concerning weekly earnings.

(a)	£	(b)	£	(c)	£
	121-130		120-130		120 but less than 130
	131-140		130-140		130 but less than 140
	141-150		140-150		140 but less than 150
	151-160		150-160		150 but less than 160

The first grouping seems all right but remember the lower limit of the interval is the lowest value which should be included in that interval, the upper limit of the interval is the highest value which should be included in that interval. Taking the top two intervals, which one would you count an earnings figure of £130.61 in? Unfortunately, it does not fit into either, it is above the top limit of the first interval and below the bottom limit of the second interval. These forms of interval should not be chosen because they do not allow for all possibilities.

The second grouping appears to get over this problem. However, it has created another problem. In which interval would you count an earnings figure of exactly £130? It fits into the first interval because the top value of the interval is £130, but it also fits into the second interval because the bottom value of that interval is also £130. We have an ambiguity so these intervals are not suitable either.

The third grouping gets over both problems. The intervals are '£120 but less than £130', '£130 but less than £140', etc, which means a value of exactly £130 will be counted in the second interval. Any value just below £130, eg, £129.99 would go into the first interval. This form of interval allows for all values without ambiguity and so should be used.

Notice that the first example is acceptable for discrete variables since all whole numbers are covered, it is only when dealing with continuous variables that this problem occurs.

3.2.5   Illustration

To draw up a frequency table for the package weights of boxes of sweets given below we can use intervals 5 grams wide.

WEIGHTS OF 48 BOXES OF SWEETS (in grams)

502.5	496.3	500.3	500.6	499.2	504.6	496.5	603.7
497.6	502.3	507.7	487.2	503.0	507.4	501.8	493.8
500.0	503.2	490.5	511.4	501.7	494.6	497.0	504.1
505.8	513.0	504.2	496.2	508.1	500.3	503.5	507.2
503.3	498.6	506.2	497.9	504.8	514.8	509.4	502.9
506.3	501.1	498.2	502.5	497.2	501.1	499.6	500.8

Choose intervals '490 but less than 495 grams', etc, so the table we obtain is:

WEIGHT OF PACKAGE	FREQUENCY
485 but less than 490 grams	1
490 but less than 495 grams	3
495 but less than 500 grams	12
500 but less than 505 grams	22
505 but less than 510 grams	8
510 but less than 515 grams	2
	—
	48
	—

Example 3.3

A firm has recorded the time it takes to serve 55 individual customers. These times have been measured to the nearest $1/10$th of a minute.

12.3	27.3	10.5	21.8	8.6	6.1	19.6	12.8	6.9	15.1	11.4
9.4	14.1	17.9	5.9	4.5	15.7	8.0	27.2	14.8	12.4	16.8
24.6	16.0	11.9	37.9	7.5	17.3	13.9	7.8	28.5	6.3	12.9
10.2	25.6	6.7	19.9	16.2	11.2	52.1	5.0	18.4	10.5	9.3
8.9	13.5	16.5	8.7	10.7	18.5	13.0	7.1	11.6	14.5	23.3

Draw up a frequency table with intervals of 5 minutes width.

Solution

Choose intervals '0 but less than 5 minutes', '5 minutes but less than 10 minutes', etc. The table obtained is

TIMES TO SERVICE CUSTOMERS

SERVICE TIME (in minutes)	FREQUENCY
0 but less than 5	1
5 but less than 10	15
10 but less than 15	18
15 but less than 20	12
20 but less than 25	3
25 but less than 30	4
30 but less than 35	2
	—
	55
	—

3.2.6 Unequal width class intervals

The emphasis so far has been on choosing intervals which have the same width as one another. In many practical situations it is not sensible to stick rigidly to this approach. Looking back at our example on transactions the table would look better (and lose very little detail) if we combined some of the intervals as:

NUMBER OF TRANSACTIONS	FREQUENCY
1-5	1
6-10	9
11-15	12
16-20	13
21-25	16
26-30	11
31-40	8
41-50	2
	—
	72

The second and third last intervals have been combined into a double width interval and the final interval expanded so that it is also the same double width. This combining of intervals or use of unequal width intervals is used to avoid situations where lots of intervals have few values in them. It also makes it easier to arrange for values of special importance to be the limits of the intervals chosen.

3.2.7 Open-ended class intervals

A final technique we can use is to make the first and/or last interval open-ended. This means we use an interval such as £70 or over, or less than 5 metres. The purpose of these open-ended intervals is to tidy up the extremes in our table. These intervals are to pick up extreme values in our raw data so should only have low frequencies in them. The table has been drawn up incorrectly and is likely to be misleading if an open-ended interval has a high frequency. In our example of transactions it would be reasonable to use:

NUMBER OF TRANSACTIONS	FREQUENCY
1-5	1
6-10	9
11-15	12
16-20	13
21-25	16
26-30	11
31-40	8
41 or over	2
	—
	72

but would be very misleading if we presented the table as:

NUMBER OF TRANSACTIONS	FREQUENCY
1-5	1
6-10	9
11-15	12
16-20	13
21 or over	37
	—
	72

giving the impression that all 37 values in the last interval are sometimes near 21.

Example 3.4

Incorporate open-ended intervals into the table found for service times in Example 3.3.

Solution

Open-ended intervals could be used at either end of the table giving:

SERVICE TIME (in minutes)	FREQUENCY
Under 5	1
5 but less than 10	15
10 but less than 15	18
15 but less than 20	12
20 but less than 25	3
25 but less than 30	4
30 or over	2

3.3 Cumulative frequency distributions

On occasions we sometimes wish to know the number of times a variable takes a value above (or below) a specific value. For example, using the transactions data we may wish to know the number of days when 23 transactions or less were recorded or perhaps the percentage of days when more than 32 transactions took place. One way to answer such questions is to refer to the original raw data and simply count up the relevant number of data values. This is, however, often not possible because the original data is not available and the only source of data is the frequency distribution. Using the frequency distribution we would clearly have to perform some calculations before we could answer the required questions. An alternative method is to use a cumulative frequency and its graphical representation, the ogive. We will here just consider the cumulative frequency distribution and leave the ogive until a later session.

To construct a cumulative frequency distribution we simply use the frequency distribution and add another column of cumulative frequency or running total. For our example on transactions at a shop the cumulative frequency distribution is formed as follows:

NUMBER OF TRANSACTIONS	FREQUENCY	CUMULATIVE FREQUENCY
1-5	1	1
6-10	9	1 + 9 = 10
11-15	12	10 + 12 = 22
16-20	13	22 + 13 = 35
21-25	16	35 + 16 = 51
26-30	11	51 + 11 = 62
31-35	6	62 + 6 = 68
36-40	2	68 + 2 = 70
41-45	2	70 + 2 = 72
	72	

In practice, the frequency column and the additions are omitted. Also, since we are now only really interested in the upper limits of the class intervals, the lower limits are omitted. The cumulative frequency distribution thus has the form:

NUMBER OF TRANSACTIONS (Class Limits)	CUMULATIVE FREQUENCY
- 5	1
- 10	10
- 15	22
- 20	35
- 25	51
- 30	62
- 35	68
- 40	70
- 45	72

The final cumulative frequency figure should always be the total number of results (72 in this case).

The cumulative frequency distribution can now be used to answer questions involving class limits. For example, on how many days did 25 or less transactions occur? Without calculations we still cannot however answer the questions originally posed, ie, questions involving values other than the class limits. These are answered using the ogive (described later).

Example 3.5

Draw up a cumulative frequency distribution for the example on customer service times (Example 3.3) and hence find the number of customers served in under 20 minutes.

Solution

SERVICE TIMES (in minutes)	CUMULATIVE FREQUENCY
Less than 5	1
Less than 10	16
Less than 15	34
Less than 20	46
Less than 25	49
Less than 30	53
Less than 35	55

From this cumulative frequency distribution, 46 customers are served in under 20 minutes.

3.4   Step by step illustration 1

Twenty-five employees from the finance department of a large organisation took an introductory course in computing. The test at the end of the course resulted in the following marks by the employees.

Test marks of 25 employees (out of 50)

12	19	8	21	32
25	34	22	30	20
43	21	16	45	32
27	38	39	21	18
33	11	28	26	27

Construct a frequency distribution of this data.

Solution

The first thing to note is that the variable is discrete (or can be assumed to be). This influences our choice of class intervals. The figures given are obviously all in the range 0 to 50 and are fairly evenly spread within this range. This makes the problem easier and removes the necessity of using open-ended classes. Since there are only 25 data values we only need a few class intervals (say about 5). It is logical, because the variable is marks, to also use boundaries of width 10 marks. A first attempt at the frequency distribution thus might be:

MARKS OBTAINED		FREQUENCY
0-9	1	1
10-19	~~IIII~~	5
20-29	~~IIII IIII~~	10
30-39	~~IIII~~ 11	7
40-49	11	2
		—
		25

This seems a satisfactory first attempt (although by no means the only way the data could have been presented), the data values being evenly distributed through the classes. The only minor criticism might be that the value 50 marks could not appear in this frequency distribution (the range of possible marks being 0 to 50). The frequency distribution for the data given thus has the form:

Test marks of 25 employees

MARKS OBTAINED	FREQUENCY (No of employees)
0- 9	1
10-19	5
20-29	10
30-39	7
40-49	2
	—
	25

3.5   Step by step illustration 2

The wage distribution of manual employees of Hols Limited is as follows:

WEEKLY WAGE (£)	NUMBER OF EMPLOYEES
Less than 60	5
60 but less than 80	22
80 but less than 100	41
100 but less than 120	46
120 but less than 140	28
140 but less than 160	20
160 but less than 180	13
180 but less than 200	9
200 but less than 220	4
220 but less than 240	2
240 but less than 260	2
260 but less than 280	1

Comment on the merits of this frequency distribution for presenting this data and also comment on the information actually given in the table.

Solution

Points to be noted about the frequency distribution include:

(a)   Class intervals are based on width 10 (2 x 10 = 20) which is logical.

(b)   'But less than' classes have been suitably used to avoid the problem of £99.99 (for example).

(c)   An open-ended class 'less than 60' has been used to include the low paid employees - instead of using 3 separate classes.

(d)   Main criticism is that the frequency distribution is too long and that the last few classes are sparsely populated in comparison to the other classes. An improvement would be to group the last four classes into a class of '200 but less than 280' or alternatively '200 and over'.

Interpretation of the frequency distribution:

(a)   Most employees have a weekly wage in the lower range of the table, say around £100.

(b)   A few employees have very low wages.

(c)   The table shows a peak in number of wages early on (in the £100-£120 class) and then there is a gradual fall in the number of employees as the wage increases.

(d)   No manual employees earn £280 or above.

3.6   Step by step illustration 3

The production line at a large factory is frequently breaking down. The following data has been collected for a particular month's production:

LENGTH OF BREAKDOWN (minutes)	FREQUENCY
less than 15	23
15 but less than 30	18
30 but less than 45	11
45 but less than 60	7
60 but less than 90	5
90 but less than 120	3
120 but less than 180	1
over 180	1

Construct the cumulative frequency distribution of length of breakdowns and hence determine:

(a)   the number of breakdowns lasting less than one hour;

(b)   the number of breakdowns lasting for $1\frac{1}{2}$ hours or more;

(c)   the percentage of breakdowns which last under half an hour.

Solution

The cumulative frequency distribution is formed by adding another column of the running total of frequencies.

LENGTH OF BREAKDOWN (minutes)	CUMULATIVE FREQUENCY
less than 15	23
less than 30	41 (23 + 18)
less than 45	52 (41 + 11)
less than 60	59 (52 + 7)
less than 90	64 (59 + 5)
less than 120	67 (64 + 3)
less than 180	68 (67 + 1)

Note that the unequal class intervals cause no problems here, the class limits are simply written down from the original frequency distribution. Also note, the last class of 'over 180' is not included in the cumulative frequency distribution since its class limit cannot be written down. This omission will not cause problems unless the questions asked to use the last class. Answers to the individual questions are:

(a)   59 breakdowns last less than one hour;

(b)   reference to the original frequency distribution should be made here. 5 breakdowns last for $1\frac{1}{2}$ hours or more;

(c)   41 breakdowns last under half an hour.   Altogether there were 69 breakdowns.
Therefore:

$$\frac{41}{69} \times 100 = 59.4\% \text{ of breakdowns last under half an hour.}$$

3.7   Conclusion

Make sure that you are able to construct a frequency distribution, especially grouped, for any set of raw data. Pay particular attention to the setting up of class intervals. Lastly, be aware of the loss of detail and accuracy caused by grouping items together.

3.8 Questions

3.8.1 Objective test questions

(1)   A frequency polygon is

    A   a special type of bar chart, the areas of the bars being proportional to the frequencies

    B   A graphical representation of a frequency distribution, plotting frequencies against mid points of the classes

    C   a graphical representation of a frequency distribution, plotting cumulative frequencies against the end points of each class

    D   a diagram showing how the cumulative percentage frequencies relate to the cumulative percentage values

(2)   A discrete variable is one which

    A   takes its values independently of any other variable
    B   can take any value within a given range
    C   has a value dependent on the value of another variable
    D   can only take certain separate values

3.8.2 Written test questions

3.1 Pusto Limited

Pusto Limited produce potato crisps in packets of nominal weight 25 grams. During a quality control check a sample of 58 packets was taken from the production line and each packet weighed. The following were the results:

29.8	28.3	28.5	29.6
28.8	29.6	29.2	35.6
28.2	28.3	27.5	29.2
32.1	27.9	30.3	31.8
30.1	26.9	27.3	37.1
30.7	34.9	28.9	28.4
27.0	29.7	29.6	28.9
25.9	28.4	27.7	33.5
29.3	27.8	28.8	29.6
28.5	31.6	26.2	24.8
30.1	28.6	28.9	26.1
26.6	25.5	26.9	26.7
29.0	28.8	25.7	26.5
33.1	29.5	25.9	
34.2	33.8	30.1	

Using this data form a frequency distribution with class intervals of unit width. To improve the frequency distribution, combine any class interval you feel appropriate.

3.2 **Socio-economic status**

A person's socio-economic status can be classified as either A, B, C1, C2, D or E in descending order. A random sample of 70 individuals taken in 1981 gave the following information on weekly earnings (£'s) in relation to socio-economic class:

75 (C1)	140 (A)	81 (B)	69 (C2)	121 (D)	60 (D)	62 (D)
100 (C2)	110 (C2)	83 (C2)	86 (E)	50 (E)	125 (B)	89 (C2)
78 (E)	150 (B)	84 (C2)	122 (C1)	125 (C2)	110 (C1)	60 (E)
78 (E)	135 (C1)	110 (B)	79 (D)	100 (D)	122 (C1)	55 (E)
82 (C1)	82 (C1)	122 (C2)	55 (E)	89 (D)	140 (C1)	135 (C1)
85 (D)	76 (C2)	90 (C2)	95 (C2)	102 (C2)	125 (C2)	100 (C1)
130 (B)	121 (B)	75 (C2)	79 (E)	75 (D)	121 (B)	59 (E)
59 (C2)	84 (C2)	125 (B)	85 (C1)	125 (C2)	102 (C2)	90 (C2)
130 (C1)	130 (C2)	79 (E)	125 (B)	138 (C1)	90 (C1)	85 (D)
56 (D)	55 (D)	125 (C1)	75 (E)	130 (C1)	95 (C2)	72 (D)

By considering earnings to fall into one of the three classes of less than £80, £80-£120 and over £120 compile a two-way frequency distribution showing the frequencies in each earnings group/socio-economic class combination. Comment on the pattern of frequencies shown.

3.3 **Business monitor**

The following partly-completed table has been taken from the extract from *Business Monitor PA381.1* shown overleaf:

Motor Vehicle Manufacturing - Analysis of Establishments

	Establishments			Employees		
Size of group of Establishments	Number	Cumulative Frequency	Percentage Cumulative Frequency	Number	Cumulative Frequency	Percentage Cumulative Frequency
1 - 10	930	930	47.8	4,772	4,772	1.0
11 - 19	345	1,275	65.5	4,870	9,642	2.1
20 - 49	264	1,539	79.1	7,968	17,610	3.8
50 - 99	119	1,658	85.2	8,395	26,005	5.6
100 - 199	101	1,759	90.4	14,813	40,818	8.8
200 - 299	42	1,801	92.5	10,320	51,138	11.1
300 - 399	21	1,822	93.6	7,141	58,279	12.6
400 - 749	47	1,869	96.0	24,774	83,053	18.0
750 - 999	19	1,888	97.0	15,919	98,972	21.4
1000 -1499	21	1,909	98.1	26,428	125,400	27.1
1500 - 1999	13	1,922	98.8	21,671	147,071	31.8
2000 - 2499	6	1,928	99.1	13,352	160,423	34.7
2500 - 3999						
4000 - 7499						
7500 and over						
Total	1,946	1,946	100.0	462,153	462,153	100.0

(a) Complete the table for the last three class intervals.

(b) Using the completed table determine:

    (i) the proportion of establishments that employ less than 200 employees and the proportion of total employment in motor vehicle manufacturing that they account for;

    (ii) the proportion of establishments that employ 2,500 or more employees and the proportion of total employment that they account for.

3.4 Office form

It is desired to evaluate a newly developed form for use in an office. The following table gives the performance in time to complete the old form 81C/A and the new form 81C/B.

TIME TAKEN TO COMPLETE THE FORM IN MINUTES	NUMBER OF EMPLOYEES COMPLETING THE FORM	
	81C/A	81C/B
10 but less than 15	3	3
15 but less than 20	20	25
20 but less than 30	46	34
30 but less than 45	50	26
45 but less than 60	23	10
60 but less than 90	18	5
90 but less than 120	15	5
120 and over	7	2
Total	182	110

Interpret this data, giving an indication as to whether the new form 81C/B is an improvement over the old form.

SESSION 4

Graphs

Graphs, charts and diagrams are an important part of the
Paper 8 Syllabus. In the next three sessions we shall
examine an array of diagrams which can be conveniently
used to represent the frequency distributions described
earlier.

We begin with simple straight line graphs.

4.1 Introduction

Graphs and charts are very useful in business as a means of presenting and interpreting data. In this session we introduce graphs of simple relationships and in later sessions consider more detailed charts and diagrams used in business. Graphs are also very important in economics for illustrating, for example, cost and profit functions. Further, in more complicated statistical techniques, graphs are often used as a starting point in the analysis.

4.2 Examples of graphs

4.2.1

Production line costs for AM Engineering Limited

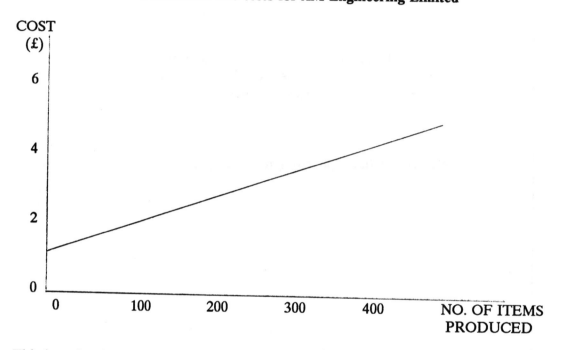

This is a simple straight line graph showing the costs for producing a number of items on a production line. It shows that, even if no items are produced, there is a cost of £1 to 'set up' the production line. After that, costs increase as production increases at a direct rate.

0173z

Sales of Rocco Ice-cream

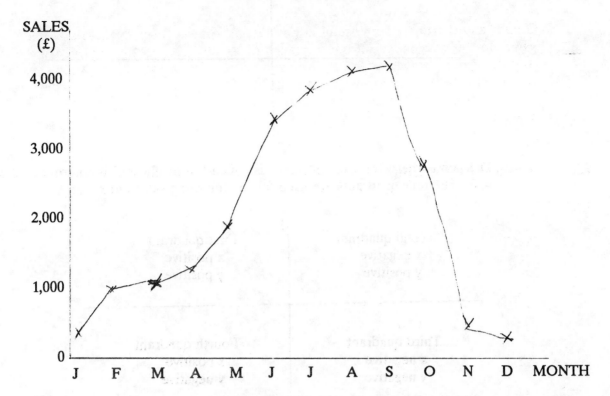

This graph illustrates the sales of Rocco Ice-cream for the twelve months of a particular year. It shows that, as expected, sales increase over the summer months. The data in such a graph is called a **time series** and is considered in detail in Session 9.

The two graphs shown here are significantly different. The first has a clear, direct relationship from which it would be fairly easy to obtain an expression explaining how costs and number of items produced were related. The pattern shown in the second graph is more complicated and it would be very difficult to obtain a relationship in this case.

4.3   How to draw a graph

In many graphs we wish to draw we will have two measurements, x and y, which are related. The major points to be remembered when drawing such graphs are given below.

1   Since there are two variables we require two axes. The vertical axis is used to represent y, the **dependent variable** in the relationship. The x variables are represented on the horizontal axis, these being the **independent variables**.

2   The horizontal and vertical axes are used to represent both positive and negative values. This is done by dividing the graph into four quadrants.

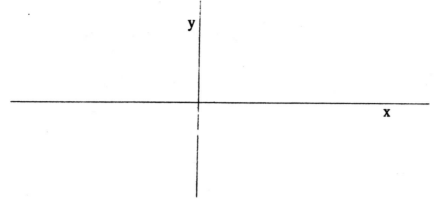

The point where the axes intercept is called the **origin** and is where x = 0 and y = 0. The four quadrants are used for the following values of x and y.

Second quadrant x negative y positive	First quadrant x positive y positive
Third quadrant x negative y negative	Fourth quadrant x positive y negative

For example, the point   x = 2,   y = 3   falls in the first quadrant.
"   "   x = -2,   y = 3   falls in the second quadrant.
"   "   x = -2,   y = -3   falls in the third quadrant.
"   "   x = 2,   y = -3   falls in the fourth quadrant.

3   Choosing suitable scales for the axes is very important. When using graph paper, the squares are divided up in multiples of ten and it is therefore logical to use multiples of ten for the intervals on the scale. It is not practical to use intervals of, say, 3 or 7 on an axis.

4   The intervals for the scales need not be the same for both the x and y axes. For example, an interval of 5 units on the x-axis and 100 units on the y-axis is permissible. Care should, however, be taken to examine the scales of the x and y axes when interpreting a graph.

5   Always remember to label the axes on a graph. The minimum requirement is to label them x and y (or some other letters). If the graph has a practical meaning, then label the axes the actual title of the variable. This was done in both examples in section 4.2.

Example 4.1

Draw a graph of the following values:

x	5	-10	-5	-2	10	15
y	50	-100	-50	20	75	25

Solution

In this data, the x values range from -10 to +15, while the y values range from -100 to +75. Our scales, logically based on intervals of a multiple of 10, must therefore cover these ranges. It would not be sensible in this example to use the same scale for both the x and y axes because of the very different ranges.

A suitable graph is as follows:

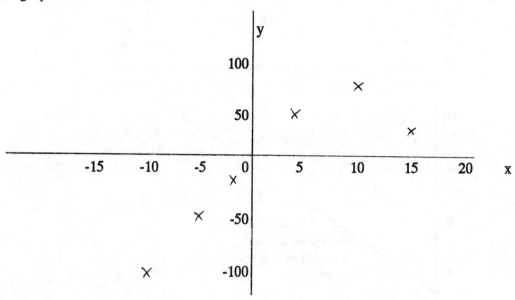

4.4   The graph of a straight line

4.4.1   The equation of a straight line

If, when we plot values of x and y on a graph, we obtain a straight line this is called a straight line or linear relationship.

Suppose:

$$y = 2x + 3$$

then we can work out values of y from values of x. Using a table we have

x	0	1	2	3	4	5	6
2x	0	2	4	6	8	10	12
3	3	3	3	3	3	3	3
y	3	5	7	9	11	13	15

If we now draw this on a graph we obtain a straight line

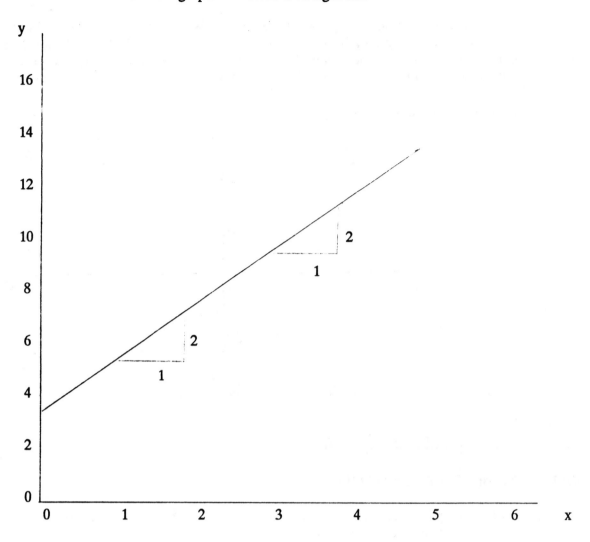

A straight line has two characteristics, it has a slope and it cuts the y-axis at a certain value, called the intercept. In this example we see the intercept is y = 3 and the slope is 2.

A straight line equation is

$$y = (SLOPE .x) + INTERCEPT$$
or
$$y = mx + c$$

(m is used for slope and c is used for the intercept).

Any equation which has this form is a straight line equation so the following are examples of straight lines.

(a) y = x + 5   since m = 1,   c = 5

(b) y = -2x + 10   since m = -2,   c = 10

(c) y = 8   since m = 0,   c = 8

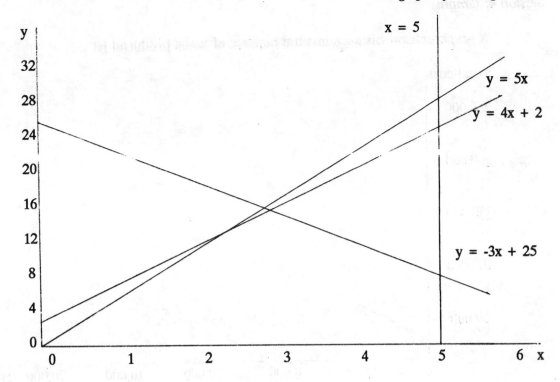

The idea of a straight line relationship occurs in calculation of costs or in depreciation calculations. Suppose a company produces just one product. If the fixed costs are £20,000 and the unit cost of one item of each product is £10, the costs of producing x items of the product are

$$
\begin{aligned}
\text{TOTAL COST} &= \text{FIXED COSTS} + \text{UNIT COST X NUMBER OF ITEMS} \\
&= 20{,}000 + 10x
\end{aligned}
$$

Note that fixed costs are defined as those costs that do not vary with the level of output. Thus rent and rates are examples of fixed costs.

Unit costs are also referred to as 'variable costs'. These are costs that vary with the level of output. An example would be the material that makes up each product. The more products we produce, the more material is used and hence the greater the cost.

4.9

A graph of total costs against the number of items produced is:

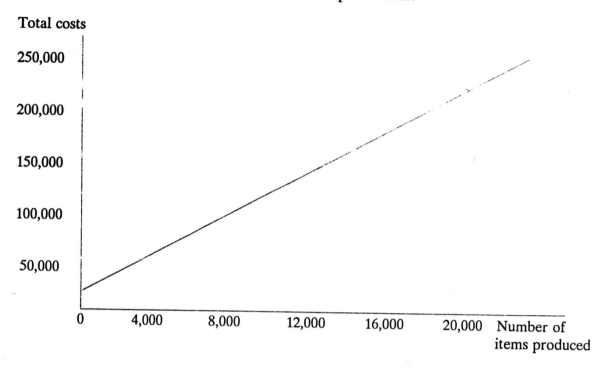

When no items are produced costs equal £20,000, when 20,000 items are produced costs equal £20,000 + £200,000 = £220,000.

If we want to find the costs for producing a number of items we simply read it off the graph or substitute in the equation. For production of 8,000 items the costs are

$$\text{COSTS} = 20,000 + 10 \times 8,000 = £100,000$$

This is also the value if we read the value from the graph. (The value vertically at the 8,000 point is 100,000).

If we know total cost we can work backwards to find the number of items produced either from the graph or by solving an equation. Suppose total cost is £140,000 and we wish to know the number of items, we have

$$140,000 = 20,000 + 10x$$
$$120,000 = 10x$$
$$12,000 = x$$

so, if 12,000 items are produced, the total cost is £140,000. (Again, using the graph we obtain 12,000 items).

Now suppose a firm has bought a piece of machinery for £150,000. It is to be depreciated by straight line depreciation over 9 years. Straight line depreciation is used to reduce the cost of an asset to its eventual written down value by equal amounts each year. We do not know the equation for the value of the machinery through time but we do know two points on it so can draw the graph.

4.5   The graph of a curve

4.5.1   The equation of a curve

In business, perhaps the most important curve or non-linear relationship is the quadratic relationship. The equation of a quadratic is similar to a straight line relationship but it has an extra term of x squared. An example of a quadratic equation is:

$$y = 24 - 10x + x^2$$

In general a quadratic equation is:

$$y = ax^2 + bx + c$$

and must have an x squared term, that is 'a' cannot be zero. The following are examples of quadratic equations.

(a) $y = x^2$ where a = 1, b = 0, c = 0

(b) $y = -10 + 12x - 2x^2$ where a = -2, b = 12, c = -10

(c) $y = 30 - 2x - 0.5x^2$ where a = -0.5, b = -2, c = 30

Many other curves arise in business situations, perhaps most notably being the exponential curve:

$$y = a^x$$

where a is a constant.

These are not considered in detail here.

4.5.2   Plotting the graph of a curve

There are no short-cuts for plotting quadratic relationships, each point must be worked out and plotted separately. To plot the graphs of the quadratics shown above, the following calculations are required.

(a) x	0	1	2	3	4	5	6
$y = x^2$	0	1	4	9	16	25	36

(b)

x	0	1	2	3	4	5	6
-10	-10	-10	-10	-10	-10	-10	-10
12x	0	12	24	36	48	60	72
$-2x^2$	0	-2	-8	-18	-32	-50	-72
y	-10	0	6	8	6	0	-10

(c)

x	0	1	2	3	4	5	6
30	30	30	30	30	30	30	30
-2x	0	-2	-4	-6	-8	-10	-12
$-0.5x^2$	0	-0.5	-2	-4.5	-8	-12.5	-18
y	30	27.5	24	19.5	14	7.5	0

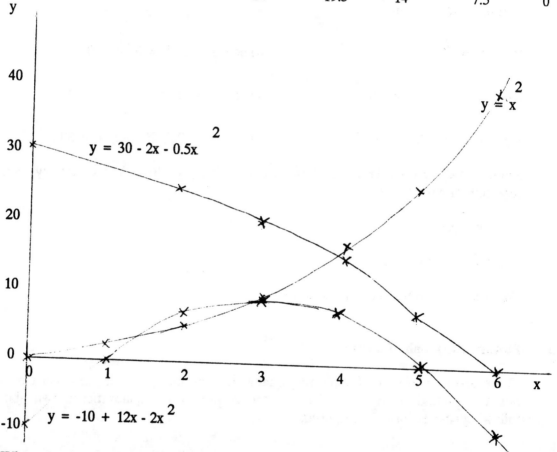

When the full graph for a quadratic is drawn it is either a 'U-shape' or an 'upside down U-shape'. In our examples we have drawn only part of the full graph (for x = 0 to x = 6) so for some of the curves we can't see the 'U' or 'upside-down U' fully, only part of the shape.

Example 4.3

Draw the following equations on the same graph for x = 0 to x = 6

(a) $y = 1 + x + 3x^2$

(b) $y = 12x - 2x^2$

(c) $y = 100 - x^2$

Solution

The calculations are

(a)

x	0	1	2	3	4	5	6
1	1	1	1	1	1	1	1
x	0	1	2	3	4	5	6
$3x^2$	0	3	12	27	48	75	108
y	1	5	15	31	53	81	115

(b)

x	0	1	2	3	4	5	6
12x	0	12	24	36	48	60	72
$-2x^2$	0	-2	-8	-18	-32	-50	-72
y	0	10	16	18	16	10	0

(c)

x	0	1	2	3	4	5	6
100	100	100	100	100	100	100	100
$-x^2$	0	-1	-4	-9	-16	-25	-36
y	100	99	96	91	84	75	64

and the graphs are

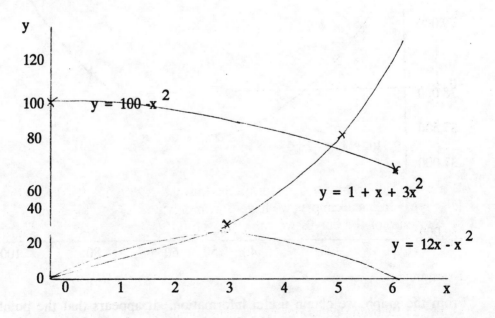

4.5.3   Practical examples of quadratic relationships

In business, quadratic relationships arise most frequently in cost and profit functions. Suppose a firm has established that its costs can be found, overall, from the equation

$$\text{Total costs} = 40{,}000 - 100x + x^2$$

where x is the number of items produced. To plot a graph of this function we must again work out the total costs for various numbers of items produced. Determining the range of x values is the problem here. The number of items produced cannot be negative so start at x = 0. Trial and error indicates that the following x values are suitable:

x	0	20	40	50	60	80	100
40,000	40,000	40,000	40,000	40,000	40,000	40,000	40,000
-100x	0	-2,000	-4,000	-5,000	-6,000	-8,000	-10,000
$+x^2$	0	400	1,600	2,500	3,600	6,400	10,000
Total costs	40,000	38,400	37,600	37,500	37,600	38,400	40,000

The graph of the total cost function is thus as follows:

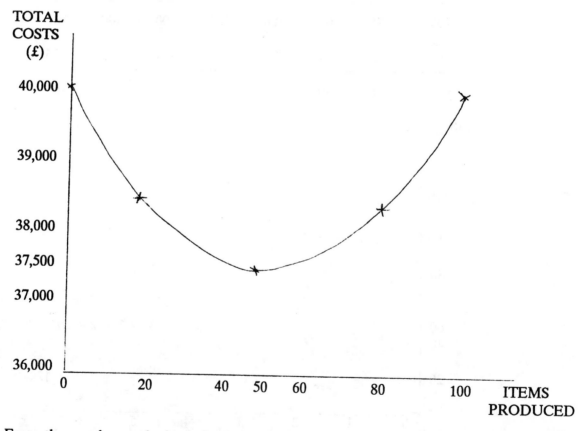

From the graph, we obtain useful information. It appears that the point at which total costs are at a minimum is when 50 items are produced. At this level of output, total costs are 37,500 units.

When finding maximum or minimum points from a graph as above the results obtained will often only be approximate. For example, for a certain graph the maximum profit might be when 10,251 items are sold. This level of accuracy is difficult to obtain from a graph.

4.6 Step by step illustration 1

To hire a certain piece of equipment an initial charge of £10 is made and a fee of £2.50 per day is charged to retain this equipment. Write down the relationship between C, the cost of hiring the equipment, and n, the number of days the equipment is hired for. Plot this function on a graph.

Solution

The relationship between cost and the number of days the equipment is hired for is quite simple to write down:

Cost C = initial charge + daily charge x number of days hired for

Cost C = £10 + (£2.50 x n)

or simply <u>C = 10 + 2.5n</u>

This relationship is obviously a straight line relationship and we thus need two points to plot the graph:

when n = 0   C = 10

when n = 10   C = 10 + 25 = 35.

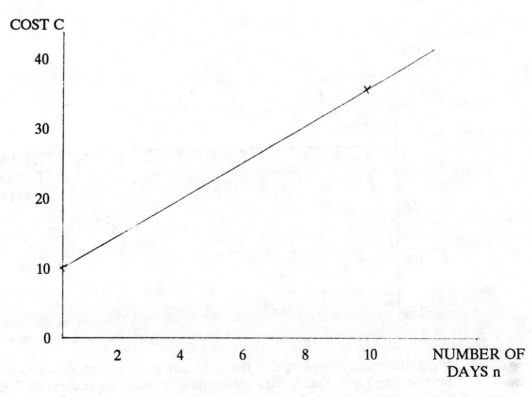

4.7   Step by step illustration 2

A company's profit P, in thousands of pounds, is related to the quantity produced q, in thousands of units, by:

$$P = 95q - 10q^2 - 120$$

Plot this relationship on a graph for a range of values of q between 0 and 10.

What is the optimum amount to produce and what is the associated profit?

Solution

The profit equation is a quadratic and thus requires a table of values to be formed before plotting is possible.

q	0	1	2	3	4	5	6	7	8	9	10
95q	0	95	190	285	380	475	570	665	760	855	950
$-10q^2$	0	-10	-40	-90	-160	-250	-360	-490	-640	-810	-1,000
-120	-120	-120	-120	-120	-120	-120	-120	-120	-120	-120	-120
P	-120	-35	30	75	100	105	90	55	0	-75	-170

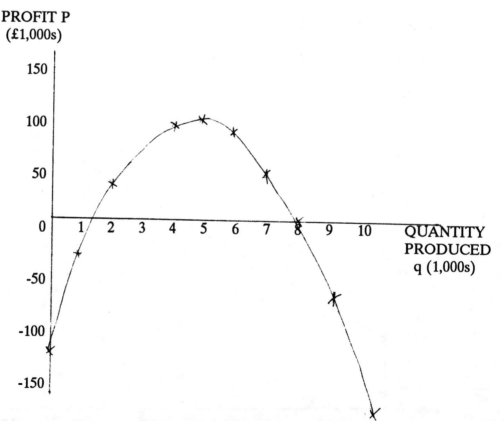

From the graph, it appears that the maximum point is somewhere near q = 5. The best we can say is that profits are maximised when approximately 5,000 units are produced when the profit is approximately £105,000.

(The exact answer is in fact q = 4,750.)

4.8   Step by step illustration 3

A firm has found that their total costs and total revenue for a product in their range are as follows:

Total costs = 20,000 + 10x

and

Total revenue = $50x - 0.01x^2$

where x is the total production. Draw a graph to illustrate the total costs and total revenue and explain what your diagram shows.

Solution

The total cost equation is a straight line relationship, passing through the points:

x = 0   Total costs = 20,000

x = 5,000   Total costs = 70,000

The total revenue equation is a quadratic relationship, giving the following table of values:

x	0	1,000	2,000	3,000	4,000	5,000
50x	0	50,000	100,000	150,000	200,000	250,000
$-0.01x^2$	0	-10,000	-40,000	-90,000	-160,000	-250,000
Total revenue	0	40,000	60,000	60,000	40,000	0

The range 0 to 5,000 for the x values has been used because it spans the practical range of the total revenue equation. It can be found by trial and error or by the following algebraic manipulation of the quadratic equation:

TR = $50x - 0.01x^2$ = 0

x (50 - 0.01x)   = 0

therefore   x = 0 or 50 - 0.01x   = 0

50 = 0.01x

therefore   x = 5,000

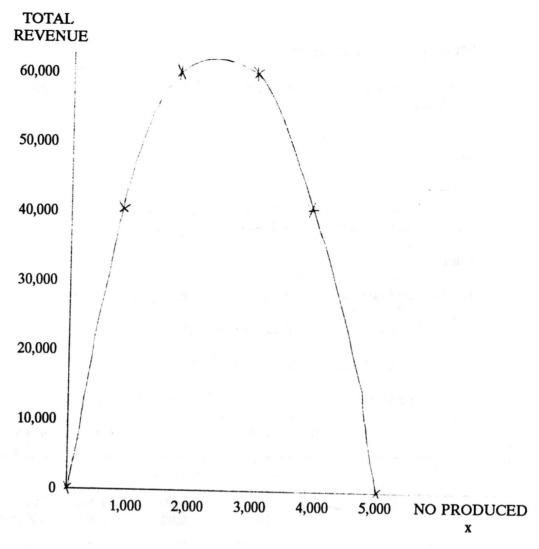

The graph of the two functions shows two main points:

(a) It indicates the break-even points. The areas of profit and loss are marked on the diagram.

   The firm makes a profit when production is in the approximate range 550 to 3,400.

(b) Maximum revenue occurs at x = 2,500.

   Note that this is **not** the point of maximum **profit**.

4.9   Conclusion

Before moving on to look at charts and diagrams with specific statistical uses, make sure that you have understood the mechanics of straight line graphs and simple curves.

4.10   Questions

4.10.1   Written test questions

4.1   Printer

A printer charges a standard rate of £3 for each job to cover the cost of making out the plate. The printer then charges $1^1/2$p for every copy taken. To make photocopies on a commercial machine, the cost per copy is 5p.

Write down the relationships between the cost C, and the number of copies taken n, if:

(a)   the work is printed; and

(b)   the photocopier is used.

Draw a graph of the two functions and discuss, from the point of view of costs, which method is preferable.

4.2   Ball bearings

The profit P (in £s) in manufacturing and selling 1,000 ball bearings of a certain grade of steel is given by:

$$P = 4 + 2r - r^2$$

where r is the radius of the ball bearings which must lie in the range 0.5 to 3.0 mm inclusive. Plot the graph of the profit relationship P and use your graph to determine which size of ball bearing gives maximum profit. What is the value of this maximum profit?

4.3   Product revenue

A company produces a product for which the fixed production costs are £400 and the production costs per item are known to be £5. The revenue R produced from the product is given by:

$$R = 60q - q^2$$

where q is the quantity sold.

(a)   Write down an expression for the total costs of producing the product.

(b)   Determine an expression for the profit for the product.

(c)   Draw a graph of the profit relationship and use it to estimate what quantity gives the optimum profit.

4.4   **Agricultural use**

In a particular continent the land available for agricultural use is declining slowly, due to industrialisation and urban expansion. In 1900, 0.645 million hectares were available and since then the amount has been reduced by 0.001 million hectares per year. Write down an expression for L, the amount of land available, in terms of t, the number of years since 1900.

Because the population is increasing rapidly the land needed to produce enough food is also increasing. In 1900, 0.054 million hectares were sufficient but this requirement doubles every 25 years. Construct a table of values of the land required R, for the period 1900 to 2000 and hence write down an expression for R in terms of t.

Draw the graphs of L and R on the same axes and use them to determine when more land is required than is available.

SESSION 5

Charts and diagrams

There are a variety of ways in which statistical data may be represented pictorially. In this session we shall consider the mechanics and merits of:

- pictograms;

- pie charts; and

- bar charts.

5.1 Introduction

Charts and diagrams are frequently used to present data in a clear and eyecatching way. Large masses of complicated data can be presented in such a way as to be readily understood. There are many different charts and diagrams which can be used. The choice depends on:

(a)   the type of data;

(b)   the amount of data; and

(c)   what factors should be emphasised, if any.

You should always ensure that the end result is a chart or diagram which is clear and intelligible. Also, remember that charts and diagrams give visual information for comparing relative size. As such, they are unsuitable for conveying precise numerical information, where precision is required, tables of data should be used.

5.2 Pictograms

5.2.1 Introduction

A pictogram is a simple diagram which uses pictures to represent numbers. Suppose we have the number of letters received by mail-order firms in the following table:

FIRM	ANNUAL NUMBER OF LETTERS
Grand Galaxy	3,475,000
Commonwealth	8,122,000
Largeforests	5,108,000
Ells	4,427,000
Berties	6,381,000

We could use a picture of a letter to represent a number of actual letters. In this case if we use a picture of a letter to represent 1,000,000 letters received, we obtain the following pictogram:

ANNUAL NUMBER OF LETTERS

FIRM

Great Galaxy

Commonwealth

Largeforests

Ells

Berties

represents 1,000,000 letters

Always remember to include the key on your diagram.

As can be seen fractions in the pictogram are difficult to show accurately, but that is not the purpose of these diagrams. They are to give us a quick, rough idea of relative size and as such are fairly successful.

An alternative approach sometimes adopted is to magnify the picture so that its size represents the figure being illustrated. The preceding pictogram might look like this:

Great Galaxy

Commonwealth

represents 1,000,000 letters

Largeforests

Ells

Berties

This diagram uses area of the pictured letter to represent size but it is not all clear that the figure for Commonwealth represents almost double the figure for Ells. If we had increased each dimension in proportion to the relative size of the figures it would be very misleading. Just taking the figures for Commonwealth and Ells, these would be represented by:

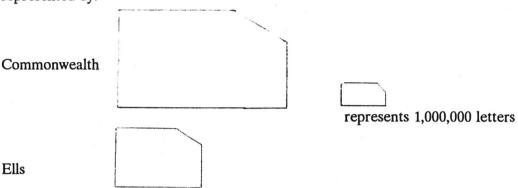

Commonwealth

represents 1,000,000 letters

Ells

and as can be seen the visual impression given by the first is that it is well over double the second. If magnification is to be used the earlier method should be used and not this method!

Example 5.1

Draw an appropriate pictogram for the following beer sales figures:

BREWERY	QUARTERLY SALES FIGURE (in £)
Soprano	542,00
Blackdough	397,000
Empties	56,000
Browns	315,000

Solution

Probably the easiest picture to use is a glass of beer:

Soprano

Blackdough

= £100,000 sales

Empties

Browns

5.3 Pie charts

5.3.1 Introduction

A pie chart consists of a circle split into segments. The circle represents a total and the segments represent the parts which go to make up the total. The 360° of the circle is divided in proportion to the figures making the total. Suppose a family's income in 19X5 is £1,000 per month. If their expenditure splits down as:

	Amount (£)	Proportion (%)	Angle
Mortgage and Insurance	300	30	108
Electricity and Gas	50	5	18
Food and Drink	200	20	72
Clothes	40	4	14
Car and Petrol	150	15	54
Telephone	10	1	4
Savings	70	7	25
Fares	60	6	22
Miscellaneous	120	12	43
	1,000	100	360

then the corresponding pie chart would look like this:

You can replace the names in the segments by different colours or shadings provided a key is given. Again, we do not obtain a precise idea of expenditure on certain items or services, just an idea of their relative proportions.

5.3.2 Illustration

Sometimes we wish to compare the breakdown at two different times or in two different situations. We can then draw two pie charts next to each other with the area of the pie chart representing the totals. If we have income and expenditure figures for the same family in 19W5 as:

	Amount (£)	Proportion (%)	Angle
Mortgage and Insurance	100	40	144
Electricity and Gas	10	4	14
Food and Drink	50	20	72
Clothes	10	4	14
Car and Petrol	40	16	58
Telephone	5	2	7
Savings	10	4	14
Fares	15	6	22
Miscellaneous	10	4	14
	250	100	

then comparable pie charts are:

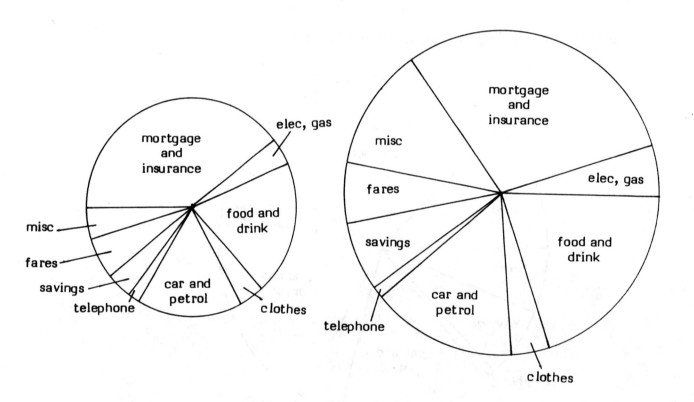

In an illustration like this always draw the segments in the same order and same part of the circle (or as closely as possible). This makes direct comparison a great deal easier.

Example 5.2

Draw a pie chart for the following data:

BREAKDOWN OF GROCERY MARKET SHARE

Food Inc	29%
Grub plc	22%
Cookers	15%
Troughers	13%
Others	21%

Solution

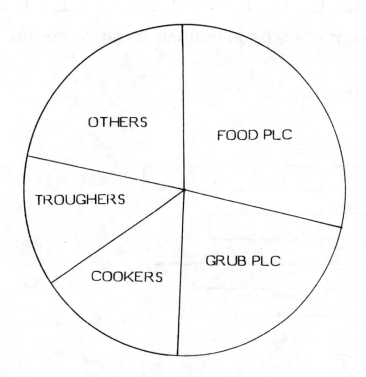

5.4 Simple bar charts

5.4.1 Introduction

In a simple bar chart the figures we wish to compare are represented by bars. These can either be drawn vertically or horizontally. The height or length of a bar is proportional to the size of the figure being illustrated. If we know that production figures of different car companies are as follows:

FIRM	NUMBER OF CARS PRODUCED
Ausota	180,000
Vauxsun	145,000
Moruar	165,000
Trihall	160,000
Fortin	170,000

the vertical bar chart for these figures is:

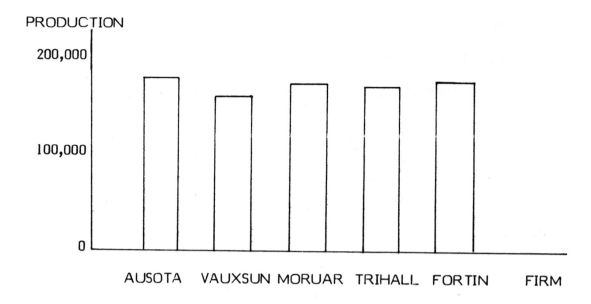

or, as a horizontal bar chart:

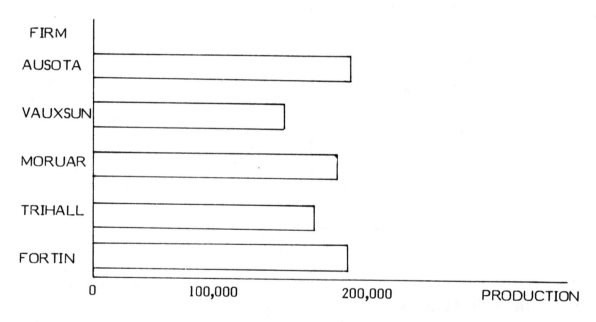

We can put the appropriate identification either in the bar itself, immediately adjacent to the bar, or use a key for shadings or colours. When drawing these charts it is very important to start the scale from zero. A very misleading picture may be shown otherwise. This is, in fact, a very common way in which readers are misled. Look out for the trick in your newspaper!

Example 5.3

Draw a simple bar chart for the following figures concerning the number of branches of certain chain stores:

CHAIN STORE	BRANCHES
AZX	360
Blazes	245
D & L	185
Cottonvalue	290
Allsorts	410

5.8

0174z

Solution

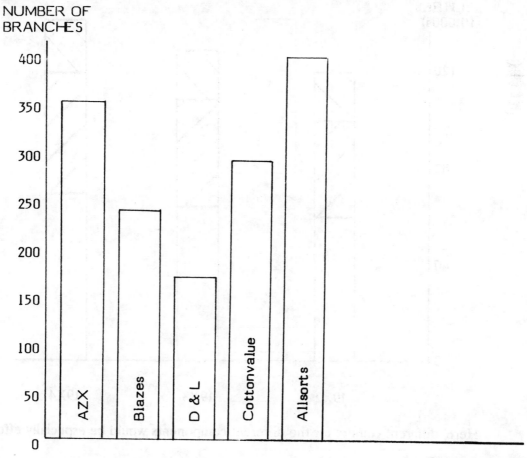

5.4.2 Component bar charts

When we draw bar charts the totals we wish to illustrate can often be broken down into sub-divisions or components. Suppose we have the following table of wine consumption by type and year:

CONSUMPTION FIGURES (in 10,000 litres)

WINE

	WHITE	RED	ROSE	TOTAL
19X2	59.3	46.5	14.2	120.0
19X3	63.6	47.0	14.4	125.0
19X4	72.3	48.2	14.5	135.0

We start by drawing a simple bar chart of the total figures. The columns or bars are then split up into the component parts. Remember to put the key on the diagram otherwise it is useless. This chart can still be drawn either vertically or horizontally.

WINE CONSUMPTION

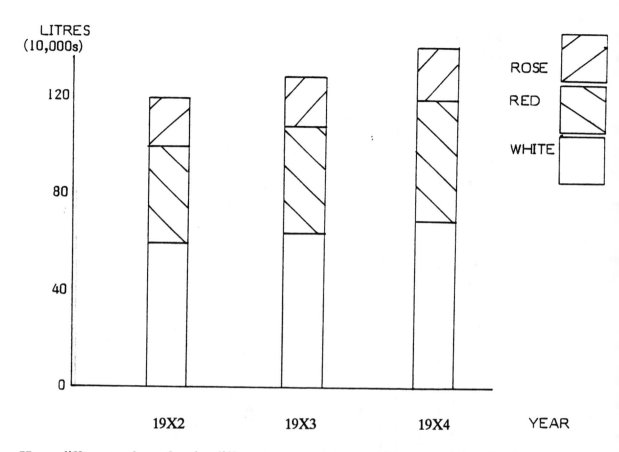

Here, different colours for the different components would be especially effective.

Example 5.4

A shoe firm has three factories. The output of pairs of shoes by factory is:

	19X1	19X2	19X3	19X4
Leicester	350,000	300,000	550,000	400,000
Northampton	200,000	300,000	400,000	500,000
Nottingham	200,000	300,000	300,000	400,000

Draw a suitable diagram to illustrate this information.

Solution

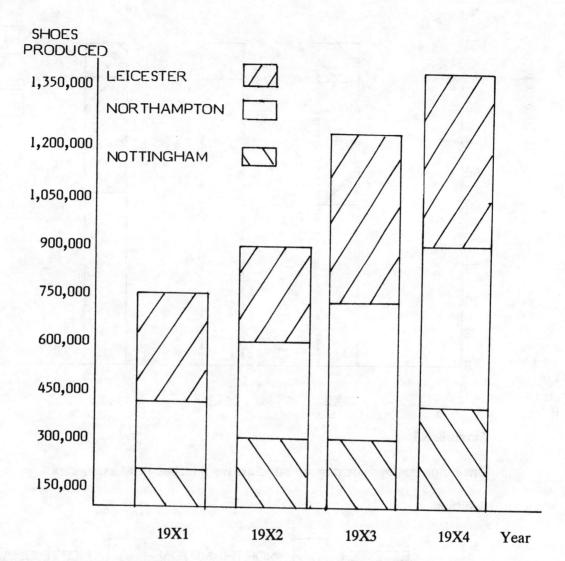

5.4.3   Percentage component bar chart

If we wish to know what proportion of a total each component represents, we can use a percentage component bar chart in place of a pie chart. All the columns of the bar chart are the same height or length representing 100%. These are then divided in the appropriate proportions.

The proportions for the wine consumption example are calculated as:

	WHITE			RED			ROSE		
19X2	$\frac{59.3}{120.0}$	x 100	= 49.4%	$\frac{46.5}{120.0}$	x 100	= 38.8%	$\frac{14.2}{120.0}$	x 100	= 11.8%
19X3	$\frac{63.6}{125.0}$	x 100	= 50.9%	$\frac{47.0}{125.0}$	x 100	= 37.6%	$\frac{14.4}{125.0}$	x 100	= 11.5%
19X4	$\frac{72.3}{135.0}$	x 100	= 53.6%	$\frac{48.2}{135.0}$	x 100	= 35.7%	$\frac{14.5}{135.0}$	x 100	= 10.7%

and the chart is drawn as:

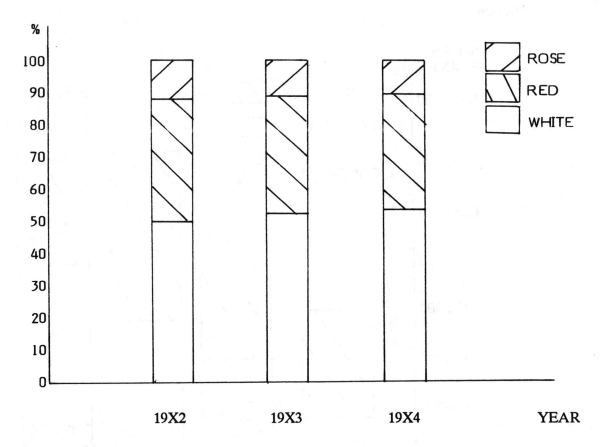

Example 5.5

Draw a percentage component bar chart for the shoe production data.

Solution

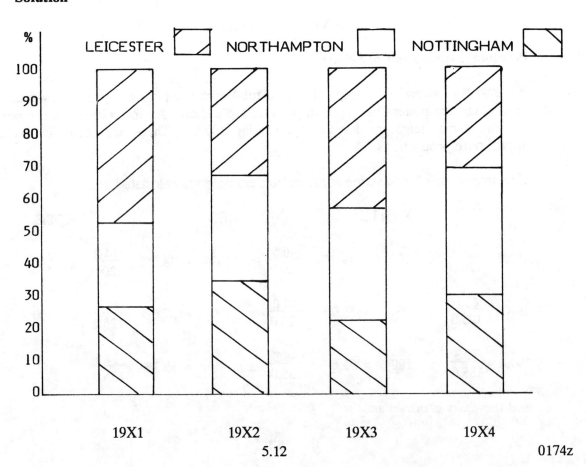

5.12

The proportions are worked out using the totals for each year, giving:

	LEICESTER	NORTHAMPTON	NOTTINGHAM
19X1	$\frac{350,000}{750,000}$ x 100 = 46.7%	$\frac{200,000}{750,000}$ x 100 = 26.7%	$\frac{200,000}{750,000}$ x 100 = 26.7%
19X2	$\frac{300,000}{900,000}$ x 100 = 33.3%	$\frac{300,000}{900,000}$ x 100 = 33.3%	$\frac{300,000}{900,000}$ x 100 = 33.3%
19X3	$\frac{550,000}{1,250,000}$ x 100 = 44.0%	$\frac{400,000}{1,250,000}$ x 100 = 32.0%	$\frac{300,000}{1,250,000}$ x 100 = 24.0%

5.4.4 Compound bar charts

Our concern may not be with proportional comparisons but rather with comparisons of the component figures themselves. If this is the case we can use a compound bar chart. The wine consumption data could be illustrated as:

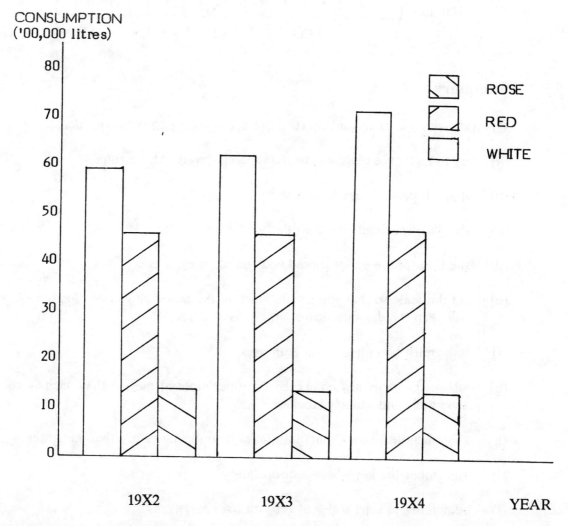

This type of chart allows us to follow trends of each individual component as well as make comparisons between the components. It does not, however, give any direct indication of total consumption.

Example 5.6

Draw a compound bar chart for the shoe production example.

Solution

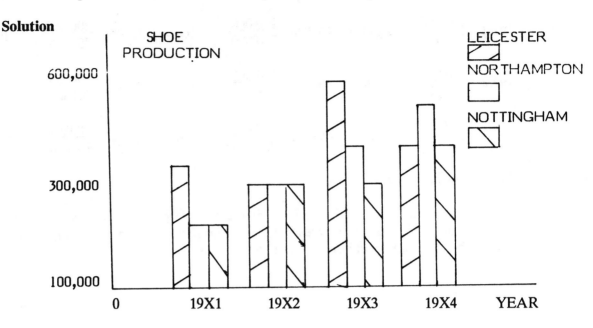

5.5 Summary

When drawing diagrams and charts there are several points to consider:

(a) try to make the diagrams neat and uncluttered. Use a ruler!!;

(b) if graph paper is available, **use** it;

(c) the diagram should have a title;

(d) the titles of the scales should be printed on each axis;

(e) set the scale so that you use as much of the paper as you can for the diagram: this will keep the diagram neater and assist accuracy;

(f) units must be indicated on both axes;

(g) where diagrams are combined or superimposed ensure that each is recognisable separately and suitably labelled;

(h) too much detail on a diagram makes it confusing rather than enlightening;

(i) remember the key where appropriate;

(j) remember to start scales at zero on bar charts;

(k) remember that component and compound bar charts become less and less effective the more sub-divisions you use. It is often worth considering a pie chart as an alternative.

5.6   Step by step illustration 1

In the financial year 19X3/X4 Sheffield City Council had the following major items of expenditure:

	£m
Education	175
Housing	84
Family and Community Services	41
Policy and General Purposes	17
Recreation and Amenities	11
Environmental Health and Cleansing	11
Corporate Estate	8

Illustrate this information using a pie chart.

Solution

Adding the figures up, the total expenditure was £347. We must now work out the proportions of each category of expenditure and its angle.

	%				Angle			
Education	$\frac{175}{347}$	x 100	=	50	$\frac{50}{100}$	x 360	=	180
Housing	$\frac{84}{347}$	x 100	=	24	$\frac{24}{100}$	x 360	=	86
Fam & Comm Serv.	$\frac{41}{347}$	x 100	=	12	$\frac{12}{100}$	x 360	=	43
Policy & GP	$\frac{17}{347}$	x 100	=	5	$\frac{5}{100}$	x 360	=	18
Rec & Amen.	$\frac{11}{347}$	x 100	=	3	$\frac{3}{100}$	x 360	=	11
Env Health & Cl	$\frac{11}{347}$	x 100	=	3	$\frac{3}{100}$	x 360	=	11
Corp Estate	$\frac{8}{347}$	x 100	=	2	$\frac{2}{100}$	x 360	=	7

The pie chart for the Sheffield City Council items of major expenditure is thus:

Major Expenditure of Sheffield City Council 19X3/X4

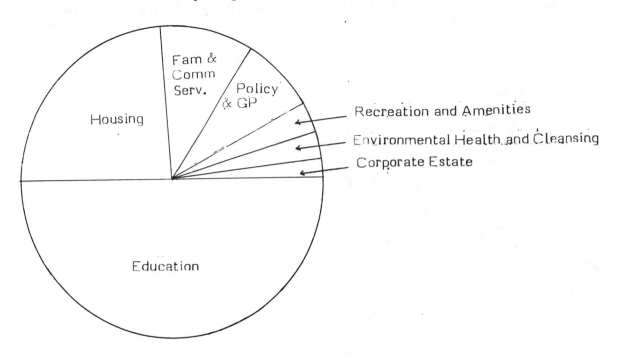

Note: The problem of rounding errors is well illustrated by this example. The % column sums to 99% (not 100%) and the angle column sums to 356° (not 360°), making the illustration only approximate.

5.7   Step by step illustration 2

A computer company has three factories, located in Nottingham, Leicester and Derby. The production records of each factory are:

Number of computers produced (hundreds)

Factory	19X2	19X3	19X4
Nottingham	3	5	14
Leicester	11	14	27
Derby	18	26	55
Total	32	45	96

Compare the production at the three factories using component and percentage component bar charts. Comment on these diagrams.

Solution

Component bar chart:

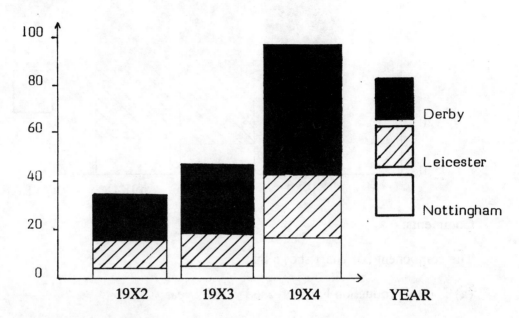

Percentage component bar chart:

Changing the data to percentages gives:

Factory	19X2			19X3			19X4		
Nottingham	$\frac{3}{32}$ x 100	=	9.4	$\frac{5}{45}$ x 100	=	11.1	$\frac{14}{96}$ x 100	=	14.6
Leicester	$\frac{11}{32}$ x 100	=	34.4	$\frac{14}{45}$ x 100	=	31.1	$\frac{27}{96}$ x 100	=	28.1
Derby	$\frac{18}{32}$ x 100	=	56.2	$\frac{26}{45}$ x 100	=	57.8	$\frac{55}{96}$ x 100	=	57.3

PERCENTAGE BREAKDOWN OF COMPUTER PRODUCTION AT THREE FACTORIES

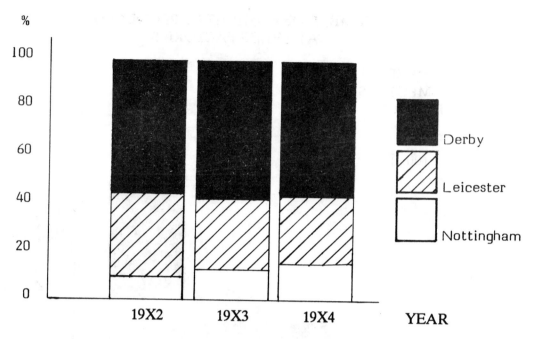

Comments:

The component bar chart shows that:

(a)   total production has increased year by year;

(b)   production at the three factories has increased year by year;

(c)   production was greatest at Derby, second highest at Leicester and smallest at Nottingham in each of the three years.

The percentage component bar chart shows that Nottingham has been producing an increasing proportion of total production, whilst Leicester's proportionate production has declined. Derby's proportionate production stayed about the same for each of the three years.

5.8   Step by step illustration 3

The following chart shows the average wage of employees of BS Limited for 19X1 to 19X3. List the major points of information shown by this diagram.

AVERAGE WAGES OF EMPLOYEES OF BS LIMITED

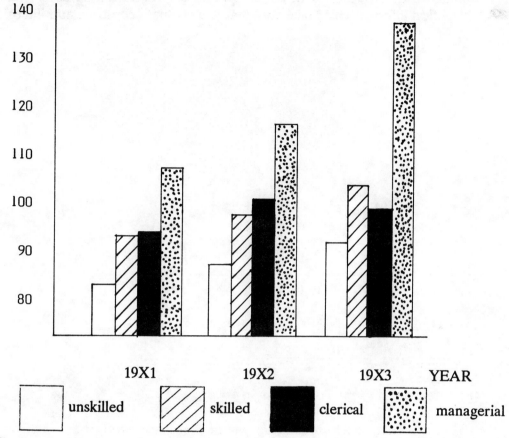

AVERAGE
WAGE (£)

19X1   19X2   19X3   YEAR

unskilled   skilled   clerical   managerial

Solution

(a)   The compound bar chart is misleading because the vertical scale does not start from zero (starts presumably from £70).

(b)   BS Limited employees were assumed to fall into four category: unskilled, skilled, clerical and managerial.

(c)   All categories of employees had a wage increase each year, except clerical staff in 19X3 when their wages fell from the previous year. No account for inflation was taken.

(d)   The chart is limited in the amount of information it gives since no percentage figures are given. Year to year percentage increases could be calculated for each category by reading figures from the diagram. However, it appears that unskilled and skilled employees have seen about the same percentage increases whilst managerial staff have had much the larger percentage increase in wages.

0174z

5.9 Conclusion

Of the three main types of chart examined in this session the first, pictograms, are of very limited use. However, both pie charts and bar charts can be used effectively to display statistical information. Make sure that you can both construct and interpret these.

5.10 Questions

5.10.1 Written test questions

5.1 Energy consumption

The table below shows the total UK inland energy consumption, measured in millions of tonnes of coal equivalent, for coal, petroleum and natural gas in the years 19X1 and 19X9.

Energy type	19X1	19X9
Coal	139.3	129.6
Petroleum	151.2	139.0
Natural gas	28.8	71.3

Illustrate this data pictorially using (i) a component bar chart; and (ii) a compound bar chart. Discuss the benefits in using each method.

5.2 FSS and Co

The annual accounts of FSS and Co Limited have been published and the following information has been extracted from the Value Added Statement:

	19X3/X4 £m	19X2/X3 £m
Value added	750.0	620.0
Distributed as follows:		
Pay, pensions and social security contributions	478.3	351.0
Corporation taxes	49.4	42.2
Interest on borrowed money	53.7	48.4
Dividends to shareholders	58.9	32.2
Depreciation	54.6	65.3
Retained profits	55.1	80.9

Illustrate this data pictorially.

5.3 ICI profits

Interpret the following diagram.

ICI TRADING PROFITS BY DIVISION (£ millions)

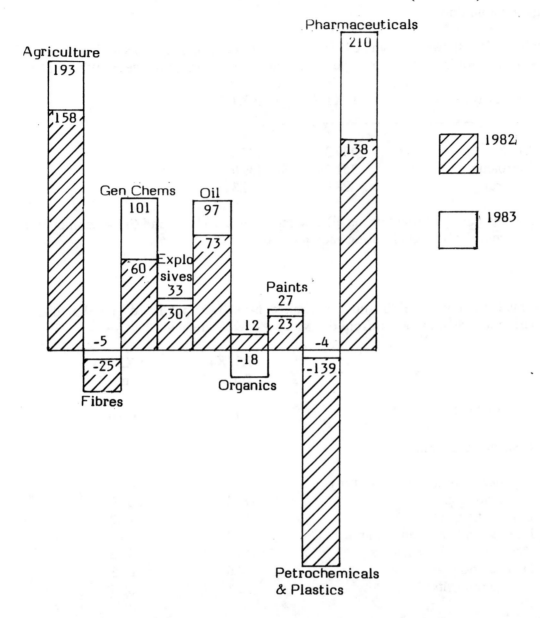

5.4 Pydec

Pydec Limited are a British company manufacturing television sets and audio equipment. The attached is a section from their company report for 19X1/X2.

You have been asked by the co-ordinating committee of a trades union at the Leicester factory of Pydec to critically comment on this report.

PYDEC LIMITED

DIFFICULT TIMES AHEAD?

As you all know this has been a very difficult year for the company. The following diagrams illustrate this all too clearly.

1 **Profits tumble**

From the graph below you can see just how badly we have done in respect of profits. There are two main reasons for this vast reduction in profits (down by almost 20%). Firstly, and most important, we have sold fewer of our products. Secondly, we have to contend with inflation which has greatly increased both our costs of production and our overhead costs (not least of which has been the increase in wages - see later).

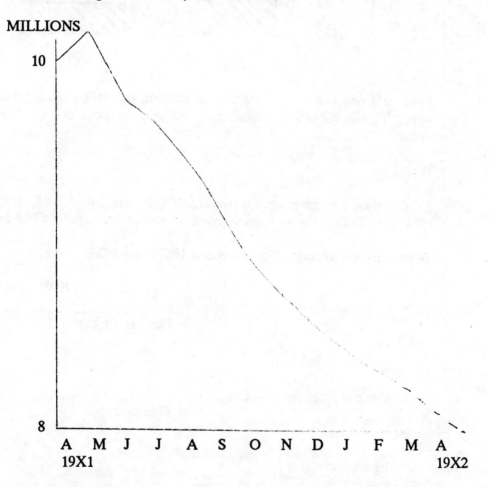

2 **Production falls**

As you know, we have three factories, at Dundee, London and here at Leicester (Head Office). The following bar chart gives a breakdown of the production of TV sets at the 3 factories.

0174z

NO. SETS
PRODUCED
(thousands)

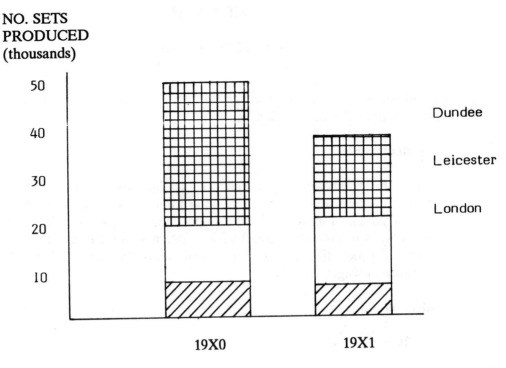

From this one can clearly see that production has fallen significantly over the last year. This is disturbing - since some of our competitors have been doing much better.

3   **Wages up**

In the past we have always rewarded our employees well; last year was no different. In fact, the average wage of all employees rose by £7.23 per week.

If we compare average wages between 19W5 and 19X0:

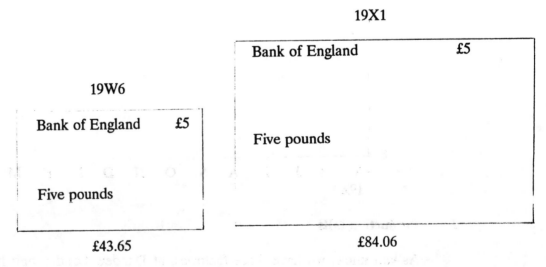

Prospects for the future are not good and any wage increases must be earned by increasing our efficiency.

4   **The future**

The above diagrams give a gloomy forecast for the coming years. To remain competitive we may have to reduce our workforce significantly. However, in some respects we can help ourselves quite a lot.

Our major overhead cost is employees wages. If wage increases are kept to a minimum this can only do us good and may help us retain staff.

Our aim for the coming year must be to try and become more competitive.

I look forward to your support.

James Telly
Chairman

SESSION 6

Other charts

Concluding our examination of statistical charts we shall look at a group of charts for very specific purposes:

- histograms

- ogives

- Z-charts

- semi-logarithmic graphs

- Lorenz curves

6.1 Introduction

In Session 5 we considered various charts which are used to illustrate data. If, however, the data is contained in a frequency distribution then bar charts, pie charts and pictograms are limited in the amount of data they can illustrate.

When frequency tables or distributions are drawn up the intention is that the tables should tell us what sort of data and spread of data we have. Some people find it easy enough to spot these characteristics from a table but for many people it is still a mass of numbers so an alternative simpler method of presentation is required. As we are trying to picture what our data is like we use pictures or pictorial representations of frequency tables.

6.2 Histograms

6.2.1 Introduction

The usual diagram used to illustrate a frequency distribution is a histogram. The horizontal scale is used for the variable or measurement of interest and the vertical scale to indicate relative frequency.

Consider the following data:

WEIGHT OF PACKAGE (grams)	FREQUENCY (no of packages)
485 but less than 490	1
490 but less than 495	3
495 but less than 500	12
500 but less than 505	22
505 but less than 510	8
510 but less than 515	2
	—
	48

The histogram for this frequency distribution would be drawn as follows:

DISTRIBUTION OF SWEET BOX WEIGHTS

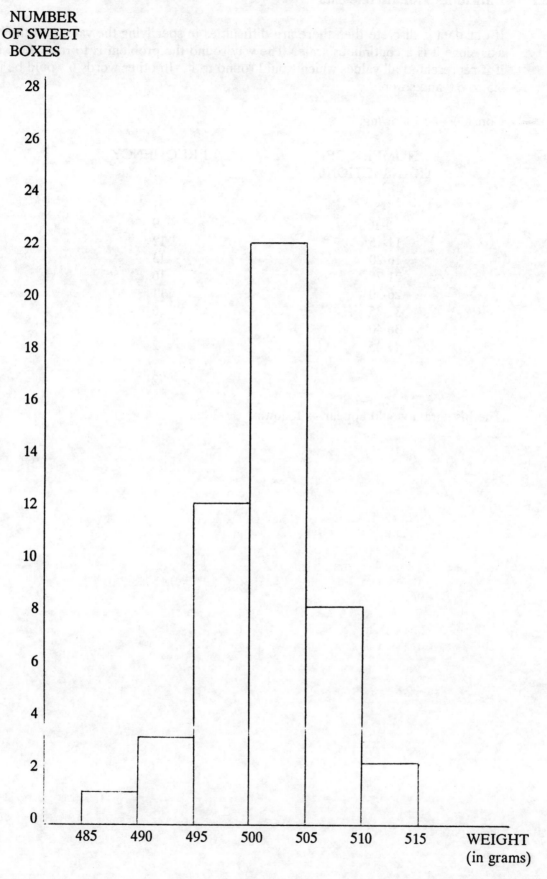

The columns are drawn up from the horizontal axis and, because the intervals we have are of equal width, are drawn to a height representing frequency on the vertical scale.

0175z

6.2.2 Difficulties with discrete data

If our data is discrete then there are difficulties in specifying the values on the horizontal axis since it is a continuous scale. The way round the problem is to treat each integer as if it represented all values which would round to it. In other words 6 would be treated as 5.5 to 6.5 and so on.

Consider the following:

NUMBER OF TRANSACTIONS	FREQUENCY
1-5	1
6-10	9
11-15	12
16-20	13
21-25	16
26-30	11
31-35	6
36-40	2
41-45	2
	—
	72

The histogram would appear as follows:

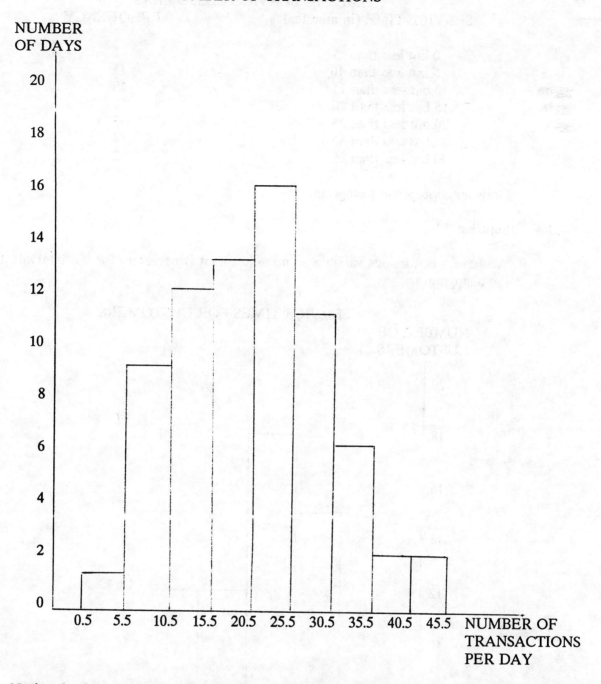

NUMBER OF TRANSACTIONS

Notice the frequency of '1' for the interval 1 to 5 has been drawn in at height equal to 1 for an interval 0.5 to 5.5 using the principle already mentioned. The other intervals are treated similarly.

6.2.3 Illustration with continuous data

For the service time data the following frequency table was obtained:

TIMES TO SERVICE CUSTOMERS

SERVICE TIME (in minutes)	FREQUENCY
0 but less than 5	1
5 but less than 10	15
10 but less than 15	18
15 but less than 20	12
20 but less than 25	3
25 but less than 30	4
30 but less than 35	2

Draw an appropriate histogram.

6.2.4   Solution

We have a continuous variable so no adjustment is necessary for the intervals, therefore the histogram is:

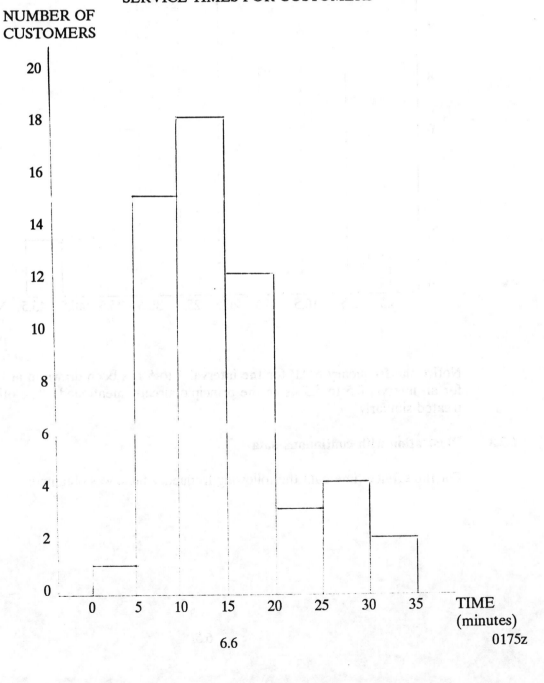

6.2.5 Illustration with discrete data with unequal class intervals

In all the histograms seen so far the class intervals used have had equal widths. Consider the following data that does not use equal intervals, so how do we draw the histogram? Remember the vertical scale on a histogram represents relative frequency. In histograms it is the **area** of the columns which represents frequency, not the column heights. This being the case, if an interval is four times as wide as another interval, its column height would be drawn to a height one quarter of frequency so that the columns are comparable. If the heights obtained involve fractions they should be drawn in at that height, not rounded. The histogram for the following example frequency table is:

NUMBER OF TRANSACTIONS	FREQUENCY
1-5	1
6-10	9
11-15	12
16-20	13
21-25	16
26-30	11
31-40	8
41-50	2

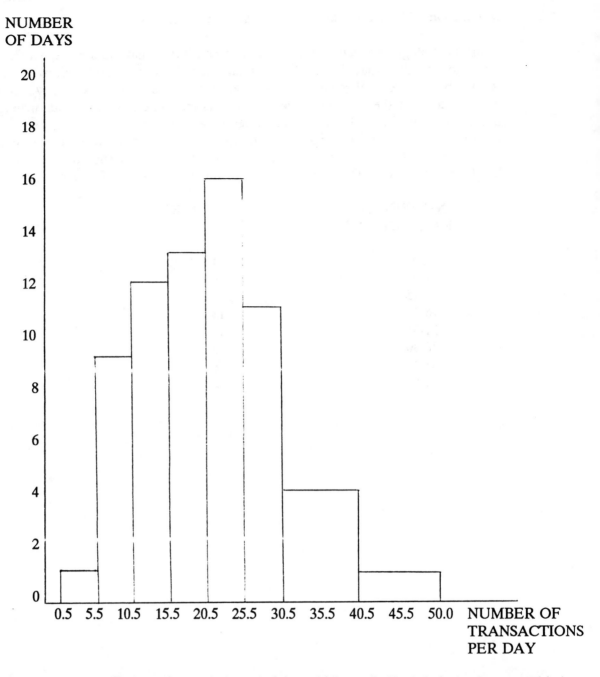

Notice how the final two intervals have heights which are half of their frequency. This is because both intervals are double the width of the other intervals (ten units rather than five units). The area of the column representing 30.5 to 40.5 is 8 square units, correctly matching the number of transactions.

6.2.6 Open-ended class intervals

The final problem is to draw in open-ended intervals when producing a histogram. The accepted convention is to treat the open-ended interval as if it were the same width as the adjacent interval. This allows us to draw in the height of the column. On the scale for the horizontal axis we remove the scale under the interval's column and replace it with a description of what interval the column represents.

(a) Example

For the service time frequency table given below draw the appropriate histogram:

SERVICE TIME (in minutes)	FREQUENCY
Under 5	1
5 but less than 10	15
10 but less than 15	18
15 but less than 20	12
20 but less than 30	7
30 or over	2
	—
	55

(b) **Solution**

The interval 'Under 5' is treated as if it had the same width as its adjacent interval. The next interval is '5 but less than 10', so draw the open-ended interval as if from zero to 5 but note we write in 'Under 5' on the scale. As five units is the width of most intervals we draw in the open-ended interval height equal to its frequency (ie, a height of one).

At the other end the adjacent interval is '20 but less than 30', so draw in '30 or over' from 30 to 40 but write on the scale '30 or over'. As both these intervals are drawn in as double width intervals their columns are drawn in with height as half the frequency, ie, $3^{1}/2$ and 1 respectively.

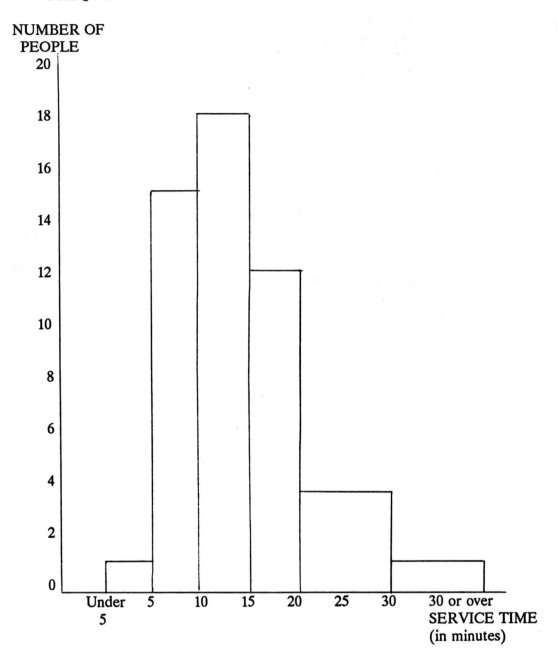

FREQUENCY DISTRIBUTION FOR SERVICE TIMES

6.3   Frequency polygons

6.3.1   Introduction

As an alternative to histograms we may use **frequency polygons**. This diagram attempts to emphasise the 'shape' of our data. The easiest way to illustrate the frequency polygon is to assume we have already drawn a histogram. To obtain the frequency polygon mark the mid-point of the top of each histogram column, then join them up. This is treating each interval as if all its frequency were at the mid-point of the interval.

The histogram for the transactions illustrated in 6.2.5, with a frequency polygon superimposed, is shown overleaf:

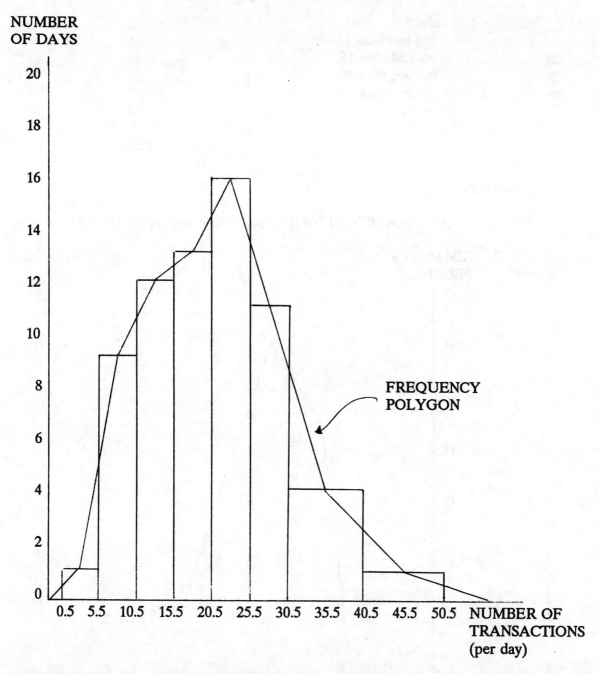

NUMBER OF TRANSACTIONS

The polygon has been neatened up at the ends of the distribution by bringing it down to meet the horizontal axis at what would have been the mid-point of the adjacent class interval if it had existed. If you do not have a histogram to work from then follow the same rules as were used in the construction of the histogram as regards treatment of unequal class intervals and open-ended class intervals.

Example 6.1

Draw a frequency polygon for the service time frequency table given overleaf:

SERVICE TIME (in minutes)	FREQUENCY
Under 5	1
5 but less than 10	15
10 but less than 15	18
15 but less than 20	12
20 but less than 30	7
30 or over	2
	—
	55
	—

Solution

FREQUENCY DISTRIBUTION FOR SERVICE TIMES

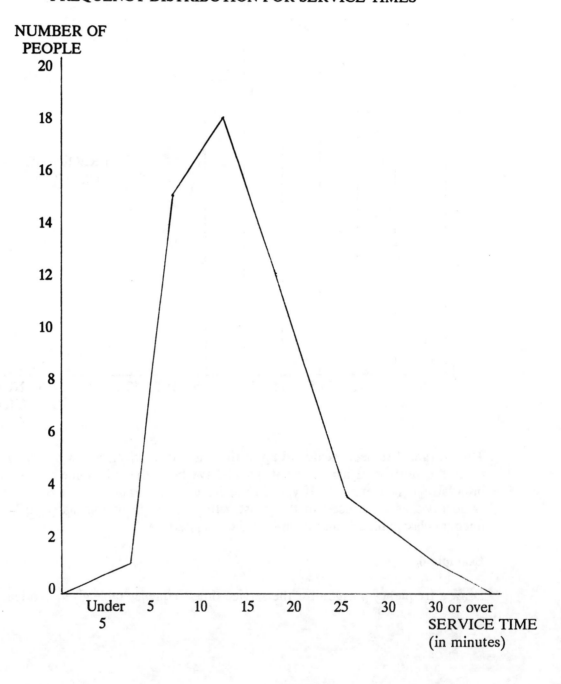

6.3.2　Frequency curves

The frequency polygons we have obtained were rather jagged figures. If we had a histogram with very small class intervals, and therefore with very many columns, then points of the frequency polygon would be close together. This has a smoothing effect on the polygon and if we continued the process we should eventually arrive at a smooth curve, called a **frequency curve**.

6.4　Cumulative frequency curves (ogives)

6.4.1　Introduction

We sometimes wish to be able to answer questions like 'how many people earn less than £200 per week?', 'how many machine breakdowns last longer than 35 minutes?', etc. If we have a frequency distribution or histogram we would need to do some calculations before we could answer such questions. An alternative is to draw an ogive and read off the answers directly.

The ogive (or cumulative frequency curve, or polygon) is drawn with the cumulative frequency total plotted against the upper limit of the corresponding interval. Hence, the curve gives numbers less than a specified value. This diagram is also called a 'less than' ogive. For the sweet boxes weight example we have the following cumulative totals appended to the frequency table:

SWEET BOX PACKAGE WEIGHTS

WEIGHT OF PACKAGES (in grams)	FREQUENCY	CUMULATIVE FREQUENCY	
Under 490	1	1	
490 but less than 495	3	4	(1 + 3)
495 but less than 500	12	16	(4 + 12)
500 but less than 505	22	38	(16 + 22)
505 but less than 510	8	46	(38 + 8)
510 or over	2	48	(46 + 2)
	48		

The final cumulative frequency figure should always be the total number of results. The cumulative frequency can be seen overleaf:

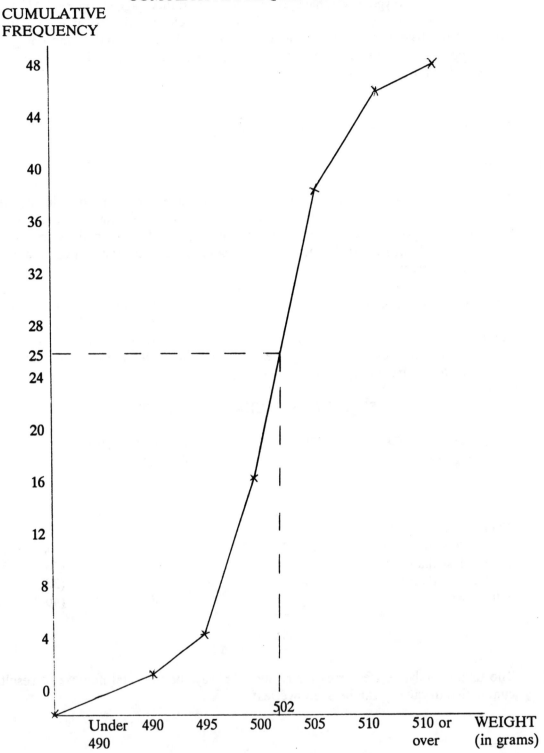

SWEET BOX WEIGHTS
CUMULATIVE FREQUENCY CURVE

The points are joined with straight lines. Open-ended intervals are treated in the same way as when drawing a histogram.

This curve can now be used to read off 'less than' figures. For example, to find the number of packages weighing under 502 grams, look up 502 grams on the horizontal scale and read off the corresponding value on the vertical scale. In this case we obtain about 25, so we can say approximately 25 packages were below 502 grams in weight. To obtain the exact answer we would need to go back to the original raw data.

0175z

To answer questions about how many are 'greater than', we can use this curve to find the number 'less than', subtract this from the total number and obtain our answer. Suppose we wished to know how many packages were greater than 498 grams in weight, then look up 498 grams and obtain approximately 11 on the vertical scale, ie, 11 are less than 498 grams. If 11 are 'less than' we can calculate that:

$$48 - 11 = 37$$

are greater than 498 grams.

An alternative approach is to draw a 'greater than' ogive. Instead of the cumulative frequency total work out a 'greater than' total by taking the cumulative totals from the total number of results. These figures are plotted at the upper limit of the interval. In the sweet box example we obtain:

WEIGHT OF PACKAGES (in grams)	FREQUENCY	'GREATER THAN' TOTAL
Under 490	1	47
490 but less than 495	3	44
495 but less than 500	12	32
500 but less than 505	22	10
505 but less than 510	8	2
510 or over	2	0

and the 'greater than' ogive, superimposed on our original graph, gives:

SWEET BOX WEIGHTS
OGIVES

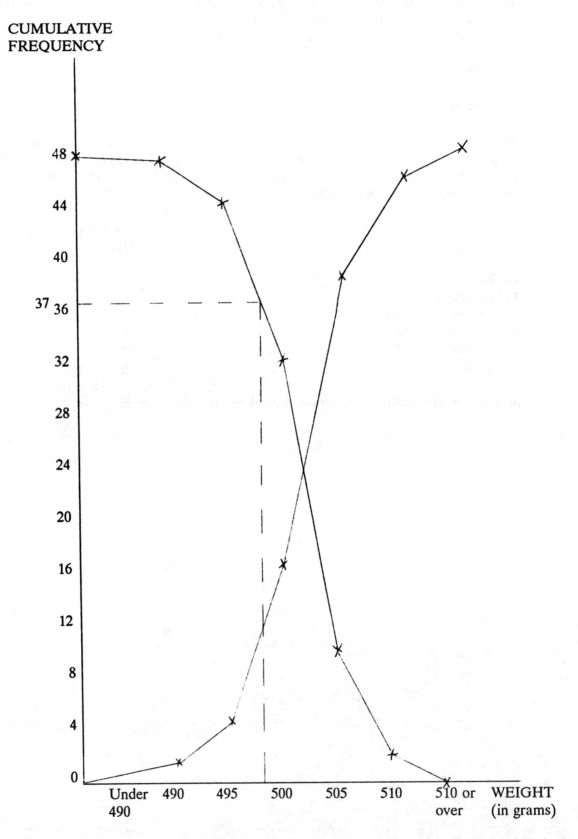

Using the 'greater than' ogive we see that it gives 37 directly as the number of packages greater than 498 grams.

6.16

0175z

A final refinement which can be added to these curves is a percentage scale for cumulative frequency so allowing answers to questions like 'what proportion of packages weigh less than 502 grams?'.

Example 6.2

For the service times table draw a cumulative frequency curve.

SERVICE TIME (in minutes)	FREQUENCY
Under 5	1
5 but less than 10	15
10 but less than 15	18
15 but less than 20	12
20 but less than 30	7
30 or over	2
	55

Determine from the curve the number of service times:

(a)   under 18 minutes;

(b)   under $7^1/2$ minutes; and

(c)   over 12 minutes.

Solution

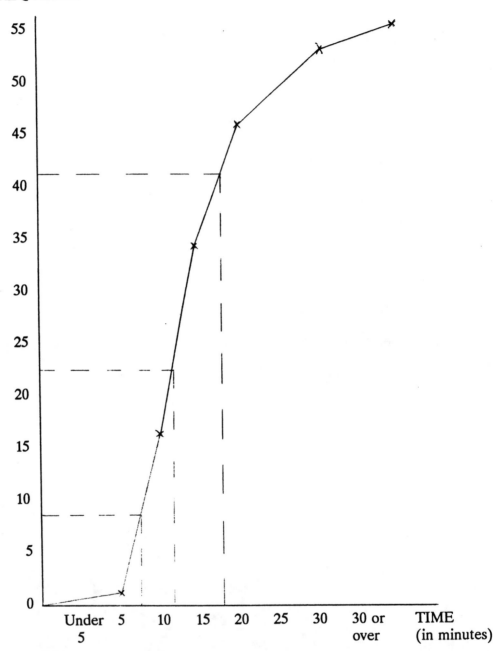

(i) Looking up 18 minutes on the graph, we obtain 41 from the vertical axis so 41 customers had service times of under 18 minutes.

(ii) Looking up $7^1/2$ minutes on the graph, we obtain 8 from the vertical axis so 8 customers had service times of under $7^1/2$ minutes.

(iii) Looking up 12 minutes on the graph, we obtain 22 from the vertical axis so 22 customers had service times of under 12 minutes. This means 33 customers had service times of over 12 minutes.

0175z

6.5   Z-charts

6.5.1   Introduction

A Z-chart is really three graphs combined into one diagram. When plotted the three graphs form a shape similar to a Z, hence the name. Z-charts are used for measurements taken regularly through time, a time series. We usually use one year's figures in the chart. Let us look at each graph in turn.

6.5.2   Time series plot

This is the first line on the chart. Suppose we have the monthly sales figures for RJG Products plc during 19X4 (in £100,000s):

	Jan	Feb	Mar	Apr	May	Jun	Jul	Aug	Sep	Oct	Nov	Dec
Sales:	7	8	12	11	12	9	7	7	3	8	10	11

Remembering to use time as the independent variable, we obtain:

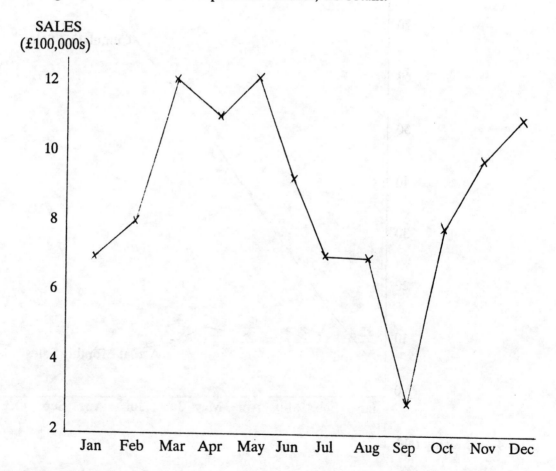

6.5.3   Cumulative figures

The second line on the chart is the running total for sales (or cumulative sales) through the year. It is plotted over the same periods as the time series graph and for this example we need to plot:

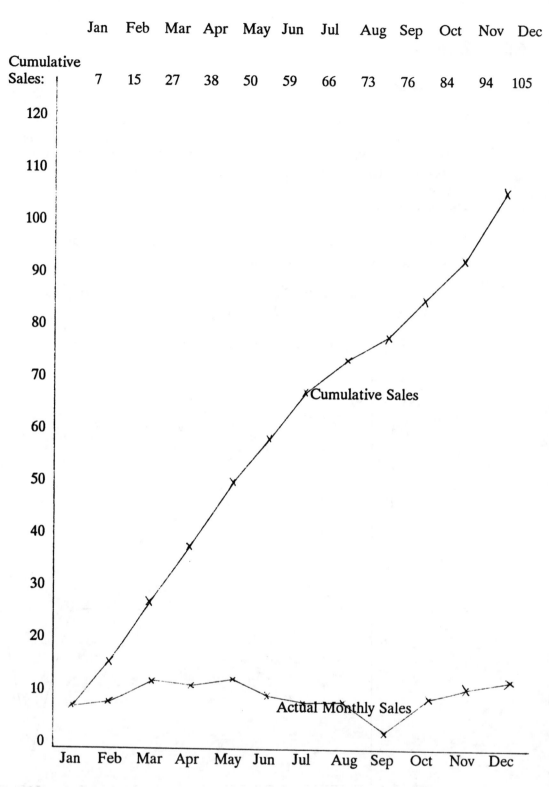

	Jan	Feb	Mar	Apr	May	Jun	Jul	Aug	Sep	Oct	Nov	Dec
Cumulative Sales:	7	15	27	38	50	59	66	73	76	84	94	105

6.5.4 Moving tables

The final line on the graph is an attempt to show the general trend of sales figures. We have already seen how this can be done with moving averages. Moving totals are dealt with in a slightly different way. Before we can start we need the sales figures for the previous year as well. For RJG Products plc the 19X3 sales figures (in £100,000s) were:

	Jan	Feb	Mar	Apr	May	Jun	Jul	Aug	Sep	Oct	Nov	Dec
19X3 Sales:	8	7	9	9	8	10	11	8	6	8	9	10

The moving total is worked out for each month in 19X4 and constitutes the total sales including that month, for the most recent 12 months. For April 19X4, for instance, we would add the figures from May 19X3 to April 19X4 inclusive, giving 108.

There is a short-cut method we can use to do the calculations. Set out the figures as:

	19X3	19X4	MOVING TOTAL		
Jan	8	7	103 + (7-8)	=	102
Feb	7	8	102 + (8-7)	=	103
Mar	9	12	103 + (12-9)	=	106
Apr	9	11	106 + (11-9)	=	108
May	8	12	108 + (12-8)	=	112
Jun	10	9	112 + (9-10)	=	111
Jul	11	7	111 + (7-11)	=	107
Aug	8	7	107 + (7-8)	=	106
Sep	6	3	106 + (3-6)	=	103
Oct	8	8	103 + (8-8)	=	103
Nov	9	10	103 + (10-9)	=	104
Dec	10	11	104 + (11-10)	=	105
	103				

Add up the first year's figures. When you have this total move it to the top of the moving total column and add the latest year's figure for January minus first year's January figure, ie:

103 + (7-8) = 102

This is the moving total for January. Then, move this total down and follow the same process, add the latest year's February figure and subtract the first year's February figure, ie:

102 + (8-7) = 103

Continue this process to the end of the year. These moving total figures are then plotted to complete the Z-chart.

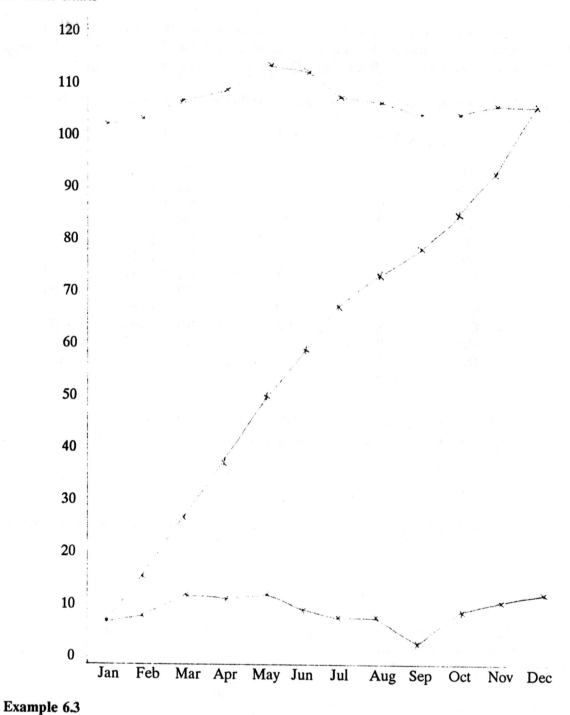

Example 6.3

The production figures, recorded monthly, of Largo Enterprises were:

	19X3	19X4
Jan	4,700	5,000
Feb	5,200	5,000
Mar	3,800	4,600
Apr	3,600	4,500
May	3,600	4,900
Jun	4,300	5,200
Jul	5,500	5,700
Aug	5,900	6,000
Sep	5,600	6,000
Oct	5,600	6,200
Nov	5,300	5,700
Dec	5,100	5,600

Draw a Z-chart for the data.

Solution

The calculations are:

	19X3	19X4	MOVING TOTALS		19X4 CUMULATIVES
Jan	4,700	5,000	58,200 + (5,000-4,700) =	58,500	5,000
Feb	5,200	5,000	58,500 + (5,000-5,200) =	58,300	10,000
Mar	3,800	4,600	58,300 + (4,600-3,800) =	59,100	14,600
Apr	3,600	4,500	59,100 + (4,500-3,600) =	60,000	19,100
May	3,600	4,900	60,000 + (4,900-3,600) =	61,300	24,000
Jun	4,300	5,200	61,300 + (5,200-4,300) =	62,200	29,200
Jul	5,500	5,700	62,200 + (5,700-5,500) =	62,400	34,900
Aug	5,900	6,000	62,400 + (6,000-5,900) =	62,500	40,900
Sep	5,600	6,000	62,500 + (6,000-5,600) =	62,900	46,900
Oct	5,600	6,200	62,900 + (6,200-5,600) =	63,500	53,100
Nov	5,300	5,700	63,500 + (5,700-5,300) =	63,900	58,800
Dec	5,100	5,600	63,900 + (5,600-5,100) =	64,400	64,400

58,200

This gives the graph:

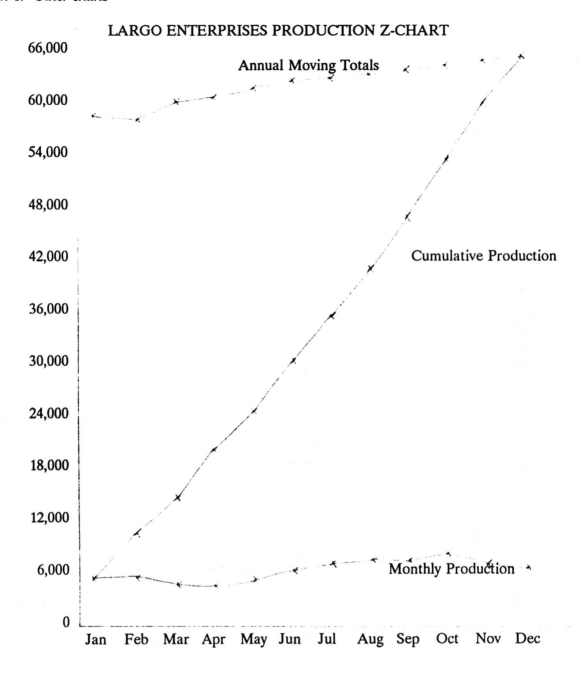

LARGO ENTERPRISES PRODUCTION Z-CHART

6.6 Semi-logarithmic graphs

6.6.1 Introduction

When we draw an ordinary graph it shows us the absolute changes in a measurement so a change from 50 to 100 or from 5,000 to 5,050 is represented by the same distance. However, sometimes we would like to see the percentage or proportional changes illustrated directly. In other words the change from 50 to 100 is a 100% change whereas from 5,000 to 5,050 is a change of 1% and we would like a graph to show this. If we plot the measurements using a logarithmic or ratio scale then this will show us the proportional changes and the slope of the line on our graph will represent the rate or percentage change. The graph is called a semi-logarithmic graph because one scale is logarithmic but the other is an ordinary scale. The vertical axis is usually the logarithmic scale.

Suppose a factory has measured its electricity consumption over a number of years. The figures (in 1,000,000 kW) were:

	19X0	19X1	19X2	19X3	19X4
Electricity	3.51	3.87	4.25	4.69	5.14
Logarithm	0.5453	0.5877	0.6284	0.6712	0.7110

The semi-logarithmic graph is as follows, with a vertical logarithmic scale:

SEMI-LOGARITHMIC GRAPH OF ELECTRICITY CONSUMPTION

LOGARITHM OF
ELECTRICITY
   USAGE

  0.8

  0.7

  0.6

  0.5

     19X0   19X1   19X2   19X3   19X4   YEAR

The line we obtain looks like a straight line. On a semi-logarithmic graph this tells us there is a constant proportional change.

There are special graph papers called semi-logarithm or linear x logarithm or ratio-scale graph paper. These have one scale set out as a logarithm scale. Using this graph paper we would obtain the same as above, since we plot the actual figures and the variations in the vertical scale do the logarithms for us. Another example drawn on semi-logarithmic graph paper is shown overleaf.

6.25

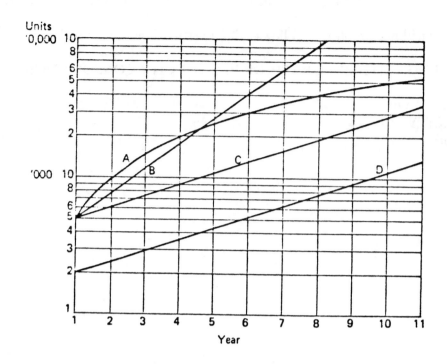

Curve A starts at 5,000 and increases by 5,000 every year. Curve B starts at 5,000 and increases by 50 per cent every year. Curve C starts at 5,000 and increases by 20 per cent every year. Curve D starts at 2,000 and increases by 20 per cent every year. Note that although Curve D is parallel to Curve C the actual size of each year's increase is considerably smaller, e.g. in year 2, 400 as against 1,000.

Example 6.4

Draw a graph illustrating the rate of growth in sales for RPP Manufacturing if their recorded figures are:

Year	19W8	19W9	19X0	19X1	19X2	19X3	19X4
Sales (£100,000s)	1.51	3.07	6.12	11.57	20.48	36.97	62.50

Solution

As we are looking at growth rate we wish to illustrate proportional changes. This suggests using a semi-logarithmic graph.

Year	19W8	19W9	19X0	19X1	19X2	19X3	19X4
Sales	1.51	3.07	6.12	11.57	18.48	26.97	32.50
Logarithm	0.1790	0.4871	0.7868	1.0633	1.2667	1.4309	1.5119

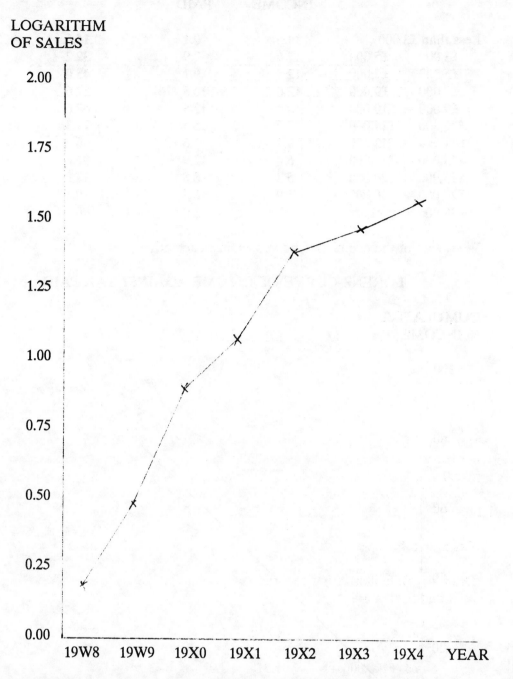

SEMI-LOGARITHMIC GRAPH SHOWING RATE
OF GROWTH OF SALES

We can see from the graph a fairly steady rate of growth up until 19X2 but then the
growth rate has dropped giving a less steep upwards slope.

6.7 Lorenz curves

6.7.1 Introduction

A Lorenz curve is a graph designed to show the equality or otherwise of two
distributions. We are used to statements like 90% of the country is owned by 3% of the
people, a very inequitable split. This curve shows how near to an equal split we are. It is
based on plotting the cumulative figures of one measurement against the cumulative for
the other measurement. Suppose we have a breakdown of salaries and tax paid:

PRE-TAX INCOME	PERCENT OF TOTAL INCOME	PERCENT OF TAX PAID	CUMULATIVE INCOME	CUMULATIVE TAX
Less than £3,000	14.6	0.1	14.6	0.1
£3,000 - £5,000	17.6	7.9	32.2	8.0
£5,000 - £7,000	12.8	9.1	45.0	17.1
£7,000 - £9,000	12.6	10.8	57.6	27.9
£9,000 - £10,000	10.0	12.8	67.6	40.7
£10,000 - £11,000	9.7	15.5	77.3	56.2
£11,000 - £13,000	9.3	13.6	86.6	69.8
£13,000 - £15,000	6.0	12.9	92.6	82.7
£15,000 - £20,000	5.3	8.8	97.9	91.5
£20,000 - £30,000	1.9	6.5	99.8	98.0
£30,000 or over	0.2	2.0	100	100

We then plot the cumulative figures against each other:

LORENZ CURVE OF INCOME AGAINST TAX PAID

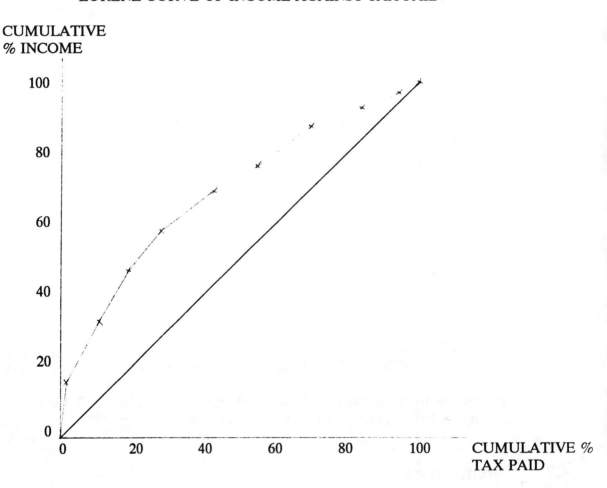

A line is drawn in at an angle of 45° to show what would happen if the cumulative percentages matched, ie, an equitable distribution. We can see from our graph that the actual figures are well away from this and illustrate that the total tax bill is not paid equally from each income band but rather that high income bands pay proportionally more tax than low income bands reflecting our tax system.

Example 6.5

A manufacturing industry consists of firms of varying sizes as given by the table below. Draw a Lorenz curve to illustrate the relationship between size of firm and output. Comment on the curve you obtain:

NUMBER OF EMPLOYEES	NUMBER OF FIRMS	NET OUTPUT (% OF INDUSTRY TOTAL)
Under 25	20	8
25 but less than 100	85	30
100 but less than 200	50	10
200 but less than 400	20	14
400 but less than 600	15	13
600 but less than 800	8	18
800 or over	2	7
	200	100

Solution

Before we can draw the Lorenz curve we need cumulative percentages. In this example we need a percentage figure for number of firms before this can be obtained. The figures are:

PERCENTAGE OF FIRMS	CUMULATIVE PERCENTAGE OF FIRMS	NET OUTPUT (%)	CUMULATIVE OUTPUT (%)
10.0	10.0	8	8
42.5	52.5	30	38
25.0	77.5	10	48
10.0	87.5	14	62
7.5	95.0	13	75
4.0	99.0	18	93
1.0	100.0	7	100
100		100	

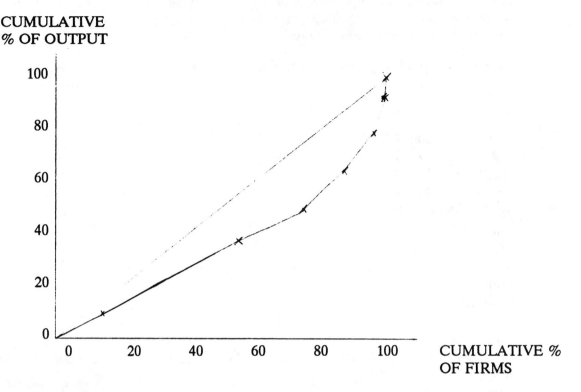

LORENZ CURVE OF OUTPUT AND
FIRMS IN AN INDUSTRY

We can see in this example that whilst the smaller firms seem to be more or less as efficient as each other (generate equal outputs) the larger firms generate proportionately more output.

6.8   Gantt charts

These are a special type of bar chart where the bars are drawn horizontally and scaled in units of time. They are particularly popular as progress charts in manufacturing organisations and are often drawn to a scale large enough to occupy a wall of the office of, for example, the works manager or chief cost accountant.

To construct a Gantt chart for use as a progress chart, actual performance is compared with planned performance. Suppose we have the following monthly production figures for a particular product, together with the monthly forecasted production.

MONTH	FORECAST	ACTUAL	ACTUAL AS A % OF FORECAST
1	600	480	80
2	500	500	100
3	700	910	130
4	400	270	67.5

To draw a Gantt chart for this data we also need to express the actual figures as a percentage of the forecasted figures. These are shown above. The Gantt chart for these production figures is shown below and explanation of its construction follows the chart.

MONTH 1		MONTH 2		MONTH 3		MONTH 4	
Monthly Forecast 600	Cum Forecast 600	Monthly Forecast 500	Cum Forecast 1,100	Monthly Forecast 700	Cum Forecast 1,800	Monthly Forecast 400	Cum Forecast 2,200

████████ ACTUAL   ▨▨▨▨▨▨▨ CUMULATIVE

For each period the actual production figures are plotted as a solid line on the chart as a percentage of the forecast figure. The forecast is represented by the full width of the columns, consequently the actual performance line will occupy the available width only if the actual performance is 100% of the forecasted performance. In other cases the line will either be shorter than the target line (for performance less than 100%) or it will be necessary to draw an additional actual line to account for the excess (see month 3).

In addition the chart contains a shaded line showing cumulative actual performance. This line illustrates very vividly to what extent a business is keeping up to, beating or failing to achieve its target as the year progresses. It should be noted that the individual columns are not separate charts drawn each month. They are the same chart which is gradually built up over the months as the figures become available.

6.9   Conclusion

You have been shown some very useful charts in this session. It is important that for each of them you are able to:

● construct the chart from raw data

● interpret a given chart

● comment on their appropriatness to a given situation.

6.10 Questions

6.10.1 Objective test questions

(1) Which of the following methods is unlikely to be suitable for presenting data concerning the numbers of audit, tax, investigation and other clients of a firm of accountants for each of the last five years?

    A   A series of pie charts
    B   Percentage component bar chart
    C   Compound bar chart
    D   Gantt chart

(2) Which of the following does not appear on a 'Z Chart'?

    A   Cumulative figures
    B   Line of equal distribution
    C   Moving Annual Total
    D   Budgeted cumulatives

Use the diagram below to answer the following two questions

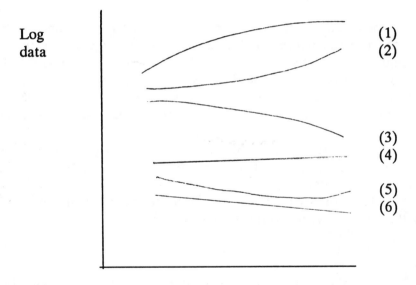

            19X4   19X5   19X6   19X7   19X8

(3) Which of the lines in the diagram could represent the following data concerning the population on the Isle of Barynia?

Year	19X4	19X5	19X6	19X7	19X8
Pop'n ('000)	342	376	410	444	478

    A   Line 1
    B   Line 2
    C   Line 4
    D   Line 5

(4)   Which of the lines in the diagram could represent the following data concerning the number of cigarette smokers in a company?

Year	19X4	19X5	19X6	19X7	19X8
No of smokers	64	51	38	27	16

A   Line 1
B   Line 2
C   Line 3
D   Line 6

6.10.2   Written test questions

6.1   Smith and Brown

A sample of 100 employees was selected from each of two different manufacturing companies, Smith Limited and Brown Limited. The annual salary of each employee in 1984 was recorded with the following results:

SALARY (£)	NUMBER OF EMPLOYEES Smith Limited	Brown Limited
2,500 but less than 5,000	18	16
5,000 but less than 7,500	26	23
7,500 but less than 10,000	27	23
10,000 but less than 15,000	14	18
15,000 but less than 20,000	9	12
20,000 and over	6	8
	100	100

Compare the salaries of the two companies diagrammatically and comment on the shape of the distributions.

6.2   Bakery shop

At a certain bakery shop it has been observed that the time between the arrival of customers has the following distribution.

TIME BETWEEN CUSTOMER ARRIVALS (minutes)	PERCENTAGE OF CUSTOMERS
less than $1/2$	15
$1/2$ but less than 1	28
1 but less than 2	23
2 but less than 3	18
3 but less than 4	8
4 but less than 5	4
5 but less than 7	2
7 but less than 10	1
10 and over	1

Illustrate this distribution using a histogram and comment upon its shape.

6.3 Bakery ogive

For the frequency distribution given in question 6.2, construct an ogive of the data and hence estimate the percentage of customers having inter-arrival times of:

(i)   less than $2^1/2$ minutes;

(ii) between $1^1/4$ and 5 minutes.

6.4 Z-chart

Construct a Z-chart for the following data and briefly explain what your chart shows:

SALES OF BENDYBIKES PLC (£10,000s)

Month	19X3	19X4
January	32	37
February	29	31
March	38	45
April	49	58
May	57	62
June	75	79
July	88	102
August	79	88
September	49	61
October	43	57
November	39	50
December	46	53

6.5 In Great Britain

Construct a semi-log graph and plot the following data:

IN GREAT BRITAIN

YEAR	TOTAL NO CARS LICENSED (thousands)	TOTAL NO GOODS VEHICLES LICENSED (thousands)	TOTAL CASUALTIES IN ROAD ACCIDENTS (thousands)
19X0	4,972	1,378	333
19X1	5,532	1,448	348
19X2	5,983	1,503	350
19X3	6,560	1,522	342
19X4	7,380	1,582	356
19X5	8,252	1,633	385
19X6	8,922	1,661	397
19X7	9,522	1,639	392
19X8	10,312	1,692	370
19X9	10,825	1,640	349

(Source: *Annual Abstract of Statistics*)

Interpret the graphs you have drawn.

6.6   Business Monitor II

In question 3.3 of session 3 an extract from a Business Monitor showing details of the motor vehicle manufacturing industry was presented. From that table the following frequency distribution can be formed.

NUMBER OF EMPLOYEES	NUMBER OF ESTABLISHMENTS	NET OUTPUT
Less than 100	1,658	99,358
100 but less than 400	164	122,887
400 but less than 1,000	66	213,681
1,000 but less than 2,000	34	206,403
2,000 but less than 4,000	13	137,449
4,000 and over	11	1,259,810
	1,946	2,039,588

Draw a Lorenz curve to illustrate the relationship between size of motor vehicle manufacturing establishments and output. Comment on the curve you obtain.

6.7   Bigga Engines

The following data is the weekly production figures for Bigga Engines Limited over a five week period. The estimated production figures are also shown.

WEEK	ACTUAL NUMBER PRODUCED	FORECASTED PRODUCTION
1	60	100
2	96	120
3	125	150
4	150	150
5	175	140

Construct the Gantt chart for Bigga Engines production.

SESSION 7

Measures of location and dispersion

So far we have only been looking at ways of summarising data into frequency distributions and representing those distributions diagrammatically. It is easy to look at such diagrams and decide whether the data is symmetrical or top-sided, what the range of values is and where the highest frequency occurs. However, the way we interpret a diagram is bound to be influenced, at least in part, by our own view of the diagram. This may well vary from person to person, so introducing a subjective element. In this session we shall consider statistical measures which can characterise a distribution.

7.1   Statistical measures

Our aim so far has been to summarise raw data into a more manageable form. We now take this one step further and summarise the original numbers by other numbers, called statistics. To give us a balanced view of the original data there are three qualities of its distribution that must be considered. These are:

(a)   *Central tendency*

Any summary of a set of numbers should tell us what size those numbers are. This session concentrates on measures (or averages) which tell us about central tendency - mode, median and mean.

(b)   *Dispersion or spread*

Having established an average size for our numbers the next concern is whether they are widely spread or closely grouped around the average. Measures of dispersion or spread are used to summarise the variation about a particular average and will be covered in a later session.

(c)   *Skewness*

Once we have established an average and measure of dispersion we then consider how symmetrical our raw data is. The lack of symmetry is called skewness. Skewness will be described in a later session but we shall not calculate measures of skewness.

7.2   Mode

7.2.1   Definition

If we have a list of values for a discrete variable (ungrouped data) then the mode is **that value which occurs most frequently**. If we have a list of figures:

1, 2, 2, 2, 3, 4, 4

then the mode is 2 since it occurs more frequently than any other individual value. The first problem we encounter with the mode is that it is not necessarily unique. Consider a set of values:

1, 2, 2, 2, 3, 3, 4, 4, 4

then 2 and 4 occur with equal and highest frequency so there are two modes: 2 and 4. For a list of values from a continuous variable it is quite possible that no two values will be the same. In this case we do not attempt to find the mode until our data has been grouped into a frequency table or distribution.

7.2.2   Mode for grouped, discrete data

If we have a frequency table for a discrete variable where the table has frequencies for individual values, then we simply look for the value with the highest frequency. If we have the following table:

Number of cars purchased per day

Number of cars	Frequency (number of days)
0	3
1	8
2	20
3	14
4	6
5	3
6 or more	1
	—
	55
	—

the mode is 2 cars purchased per day, since 2 has the highest frequency (on 20 of the days recorded 2 cars were purchased which is more days than for any of the other purchase levels).

7.2.3 Mode for grouped, discrete data with class intervals

Now consider the situation where we have discrete data but class intervals are used in the frequency distribution. In the previous example of transactions we had the following frequency distribution:

Number of transactions	Frequency
1-5	1
6-10	9
11-15	12
16-20	13
21-25	16
26-30	11
31-35	6
36-40	2
41-45	2
	—
	72
	—

To find a value for the mode we must first determine which interval has the highest frequency. This is called the **modal interval**. In this case it is the interval given as '21-25'. If we now wish to go on and find a value for the mode itself within the interval we can use either of two approaches. Both involve treating intervals as if they were continuous so this interval will be treated as being from 20.5-25.5.

(a)   *Graphical method*

Draw a histogram for the frequency distribution and find the modal interval. For the interval before the modal interval find where its column top meets the column for the modal interval (point B on diagram). Join it to the opposite top corner of the modal interval (point C on diagram). Next, for the interval following the modal interval find where its column top meets the column for the modal interval (point D on diagram). Join it to the opposite top corner of the modal interval (point A on diagram). The value on the horizontal scale where these two lines cross is the mode.

Frequency

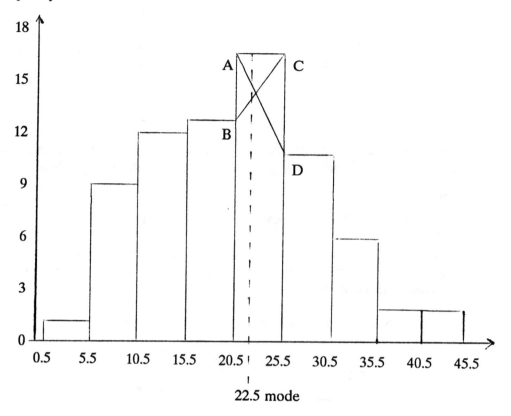

22.5 mode

In this example the mode is approximately 22.5 transactions, not the mid-point of the interval, which is 23.0.

(b)   *Calculation method*

To calculate the mode we must still find the modal interval first (20.5 to 25.5). The mode is then calculated in two stages:

(i)   Calculate:

$$\frac{\text{modal interval frequency - frequency for interval before modal interval}}{\text{twice modal interval frequency - sum of frequencies for intervals either side of modal interval}}$$

(ii)   Multiply this result by the width of the modal interval and add the result to the lower limit of the modal interval.

As a formula this set of calculations can be written as:

$$\text{Mode} = L_M + W_M \left[\frac{f_M - f_{M-1}}{2f_M - (f_{M+1} + f_{M-1})} \right]$$

where

L_M = Lower limit of modal interval

W_M = Width of modal interval

f_M = Frequency of modal interval

f_{M-1} = Frequency of interval before modal interval

f_{M+1} = Frequency of interval after modal interval

For the transactions example the calculations use:

$L_M = 20.5$, $W_M = 5$, $f_M = 16$, $f_{M-1} = 13$, $f_{M+1} = 11$

so the mode is calculated as:

$$\text{Mode} = 20.5 + 5 \left[\frac{16 - 13}{2 \times 16 - (11 + 13)} \right]$$

$$= 20.5 + 5 \left[\frac{3}{32 - 24} \right]$$

$$= 20.5 + 1.875$$

$$= 22.375$$

Notice that the approximate answer from the graphical method agrees closely with this answer.

Example 7.1

Calculate the mode from the following frequency table obtained for the complaints data:

Number of complaints	Frequency
0-4	6
5-9	9
10-14	5
15-19	4
20-24	1
	25

Solution

The modal interval is '5-9' since it has the highest frequency. Treating this as '4.5-9.5' we have:

$$L_M \quad = \quad 4.5 \quad \text{(the lower limit of this interval)}$$

$$W_M \quad = \quad 5 \quad \text{(9.5-4.5} = 5\text{, the width of the modal interval)}$$

$$f_M \quad = \quad 9 \quad \text{(there are 9 values in the modal interval)}$$

$$f_{M-1} \quad = \quad 6 \quad \text{(there are 6 values in the interval before the modal interval)}$$

$$f_{M+1} \quad = \quad 5 \quad \text{(there are 5 values in the interval after the modal interval)}$$

$$\text{Mode} \quad = \quad 4.5 \quad + \quad 5 \left[\frac{9 - 6}{2 \times 9 - (6+5)} \right]$$

$$= \quad 4.5 \quad + \quad 5 \left[\frac{3}{18 - 11} \right]$$

$$= \quad 4.5 \quad + \quad 2.143$$

$$= \quad 6.643$$

7.2.4   Mode for grouped, discrete data with unequal class intervals

When calculating a mode in this way it is assumed the widths of the intervals next to the modal interval are the same as for the modal interval. If this is not the case, ie, we have unequal intervals, the frequencies in our formula are replaced by density of frequency (ie, the height the column has been drawn to). The new formula is:

For unequal class intervals:

$$\text{Mode} = L_M + W_M \left[\frac{(f_M/W_M) - (f_{M-1}/W_{M-1})}{2(f_M/W_M) - ((f_{M+1}/W_{M+1}) + (f_{M-1}/W_{M-1}))} \right]$$

where L_M, W_M, f_M, f_{M-1}, f_{M+1} are as before but

W_{M-1} is the width of the interval before the modal interval

W_{M+1} is the width of the interval after the modal interval.

Illustration

Suppose we have the results of a survey concerning the number of salesmen and saleswomen employed by firms. The results were:

Number of salespersons	Frequency
1-10	6
11-20	10
21-30	28
31-50	16
Over 50	4

The mode is calculated with modal interval '21-30' since it has the highest frequency.

This is treated as 20.5-30.5 so we have:

$L_M = 20.5$, $W_M = 10$, $f_M = 28$, $f_{M-1} = 10$, $f_{M+1} = 16$

and also:

$W_{M-1} = 10$, $W_{M+1} = 20$

Hence:

$$\text{Mode} = 20.5 + 10 \left[\frac{(28/10) - (10/10)}{2(28/10) - (16/20 + 10/10)} \right]$$

$$= 20.5 + 10 \left[\frac{2.8 - 1.0}{5.6 - (0.8 + 1.0)} \right]$$

$$= 20.5 + 10 \left[\frac{1.8}{3.8} \right]$$

$$= 20.5 + 4.737$$

$$= 25.237$$

If we had used the graphical method it would work whether the intervals have equal or unequal width.

7.2.5   Mode for grouped, continuous data with equal class intervals

If our data is for a continuous variable and is presented as a frequency distribution with class intervals the methods for finding the mode are exactly the same as for discrete variables except that it is unnecessary to adjust the limits of the intervals.

Consider the table of sweet box weights:

Weight of package (in grams)	Frequency
Under 490	1
490 but less than 495	3
495 but less than 500	12
500 but less than 505	22
505 but less than 510	8
510 or over	2
	48

The interval with the highest frequency is '500 to $<$ 505' so this is the modal interval.

(a)   *Graphical method*

Draw a histogram and superimpose the same lines as used in the discrete case.

Frequency

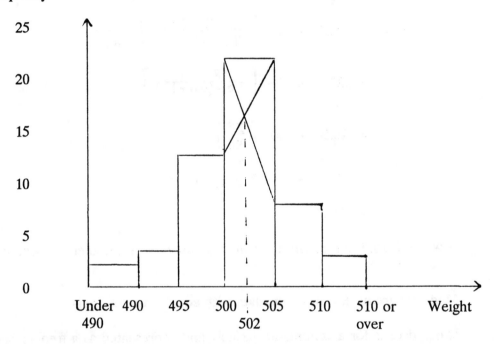

Reading from the horizontal scale the mode is approximately 502 grams. Remember this method will work whether or not we have equal width intervals.

(b)   *Calculation method*

We use the same formulae as in the discrete case.   As this table has equal width intervals we use:

$$\text{Mode} = L_M + W_M\left[\frac{f_M - f_{M-1}}{2f_M - (f_{M+1}+f_{M-1})}\right]$$

In this case the modal interval is 500   505 grams and we have:

$$L_M = 500,\ W_M = 5,\ f_M = 22,\ f_{M-1} = 12,\ f_{M+1} = 8$$

$$\text{Mode} = 500 + 5\left[\frac{22-12}{2\times22-(8+12)}\right]$$

$$= 500 + 5\left[\frac{10}{24}\right]$$

$$= 502.083 \text{ grams}$$

7.2.6 Mode for grouped, continuous data with unequal class intervals.

When we have unequal intervals we use the second formula as for the discrete case:

$$\text{Mode} = L_M + W_M\left[\frac{(f_M/W_M)-(f_{M-1}/W_{M-1})}{2(f_M/W_M) - ((f_{M+1}/W_{M+1})+(f_{M-1}/W_{M-1}))}\right]$$

Example 7.2

Suppose we have a table recording the distribution of annual salaries in a firm:

Annual salary	Frequency (number of employees)
Under £4,000	0
£4,000 but less than £6,000	6
£6,000 but less than £8,000	63
£8,000 but less than £10,000	67
£10,000 but less than £12,500	38
£12,500 but less than £15,000	15
£15,000 or over	3
	192

Solution

The modal interval is '£8,000 to $<$ £10,000'. We then have:

$$L_M = 8,000, \quad W_M = 2,000, \quad f_M = 67, \quad f_{M-1} = 63, \quad f_{M+1} = 38$$

and also

$$W_{M-1} = 2,000, \quad W_{M+1} = 2,500.$$

$$\text{Mode} = 8,000 + 2,000 \left[\frac{(67/2,000) - (63/2,000)}{2(67/2,000) - ((38/2,500)+(63/2,000))} \right]$$

$$= 8,000 + 2,000 \left[\frac{0.0335 - 0.0315}{0.0670 - (0.0152+0.0315)} \right]$$

$$= 8,000 + 2,000 \left[\frac{0.0020}{0.0203} \right]$$

$$= 8,000 + 197.04$$

$$= \text{£}8,197.04$$

7.2.7 Features of the mode

The mode has the following properties:

(a) It is easy to understand.

(b) Extreme items do not affect its value.

(c) For discrete data it is an actual single value.

(d) For continuous data it is the point of highest frequency density.

(e) It can be estimated even if data is missing.

(f) It cannot be used for further mathematical processing.

(g) It may not be unique or clearly defined.

(h) It requires arrangement of the data which may be time consuming.

Example 7.3

Determine the mode for the following sets of data:

(a) The number of new firms commencing trade, per month, in a metropolitan district were recorded for each month of a year as:

0, 3, 2, 2, 1, 0, 1, 1, 5, 2, 1, 6

(b) A firm has recorded the number of applicants for posts it advertises. The figures are given in the following table:

Applications	Frequency
1-5	17
6-10	38
11-15	19
16-20	13
21-25	5
Over 25	1
	93

(c) The lengths of steel bars produced at a mill gave the following frequency distribution:

Lengths (in metres)	Frequency
Under 1.95	4
1.95 but less than 2.00	12
2.00 but less than 2.05	27
2.05 but less than 2.10	28
2.10 but less than 2.20	61
2.20 but less than 2.50	25
2.50 or over	3
	160

Solution

(a)   Putting the numbers in numerical order we obtain:

0, 0, 1, 1, 1, 1, 2, 2, 2, 3, 5, 6

We can see that '1' occurs four times which is more frequently than any other of the values so 1 new firm per month is the modal value.

(b)   The modal interval is '6-10'. As we have a discrete variable treat this as 5.5-10.5. The table has equal width intervals so use:

L_M = 5.5, W_M = 5, f_M = 38, f_{M-1} = 17, f_{M+1} = 19

$$\text{Mode} = 5.5 + 5\left[\frac{38 - 17}{2 \times 38 - (17+19)}\right]$$

$$= 5.5 + 5\left[\frac{21}{40}\right]$$

$$= 5.5 + 2.625$$

$$= 8.125$$

(c)   The modal interval is '2.10 to < 2.20'. As we have unequal intervals around this we use:

7.11   0176z

$$L_M = 2.10, \quad W_M = 0.10, \quad f_M = 61, \quad f_{M-1} = 28, \quad f_{M+1} = 25$$

and

$$W_{M-1} = 0.05 \quad \text{(since the interval is 2.05 to} < 2.10)$$

$$W_{M+1} = 0.30 \quad \text{(since the interval is 2.20 to} < 2.50)$$

$$\text{Mode} = 2.10 + 0.10 \left[\frac{(61/0.1) - (28/0.05)}{2(61/0.1) - ((25/0.3) + (28/0.05))} \right]$$

$$= 2.10 + 0.10 \left[\frac{610 - 560}{1{,}220 - (83.333 + 560)} \right]$$

$$= 2.10 + 0.10 \left[\frac{50}{576.667} \right]$$

$$= 2.10 + 0.009$$

$$= 2.109 \text{ metres}$$

7.3 Median

7.3.1 Definition

If we have a list of figures for a discrete variable (ungrouped data) then the median is that value which falls in the middle after the data has been put in numerical order. It is literally the middle value. If we have a list of figures:

6, 3, 1, 1, 4, 5, 1, 5, 2

then we must first put them in numerical order, ie:

1, 1, 1, 2, 3, 4, 5, 5, 6

We now find which value is in the middle of the list. In this case it is the '3' so 3 is the median. Suppose we now have a list:

1, 3, 3, 4, 5, 5, 6, 9

For a list of values with an even number of items there is no middle item. The median is usually taken as the mid-point of the middle two items. Here the median would be half way between 4 and 5 (the middle two values), ie, the median is 4.5.

For a list of values for a continuous variable exactly the same approach is used. If the values are:

3.1, 5.6, 6.4, 7.1, 7.8, 8.3, 9.9

then the median value is the middle value, 7.1, and if the values are:

1.7, 2.3, 4.5, 4.7, 5.3, 6.8

then the median is mid-way between 4.5 and 4.7, ie, the median is 4.6.

7.3.2   Median for grouped, discrete data

If we have a frequency table for a discrete variable where the table has frequencies for individual values, then we work out a cumulative frequency. If the total number of values, n, is odd, the median value is the value for which cumulative frequency first exceeds or equals:

$$\frac{n + 1}{2}$$

For the table of cars purchased per day we have:

Number of cars	Frequency	Cumulative frequency
0	3	3
1	8	11
2	20	31
3	14	45
4	6	51
5	3	54
6 or more	1	55
	55	

In this example

$$\frac{n + 1}{2} = \frac{56}{2} = 28$$

and we see from the cumulative frequency column that this total is first exceeded by the figure for 2 cars. The median is therefore 2 cars per day.

If n is even, the median is the value for which cumulative frequency first exceeds $n/2$. If the cumulative frequency equals $n/2$ for a value, then the median is half-way between this value and the next value. For the table:

Number	Frequency	Cumulative frequency
0	3	3
1	8	11
2	12	23
3	15	38
4	10	48
5	2	50
	50	

we have n = 50 so $n/2$ = 25. Cumulative frequency first exceeds 25 for the value 3 so 3 is the median. For the table:

Number	Frequency	Cumulative frequency
0	1	1
1	3	4
2	16	20
3	11	31
4	5	36
5	4	40
	—	
	40	
	—	

we have $n = 40$ so $n/2 = 20$. Cumulative frequency equals 20 for the value 2. The next value is 3 so the median is half-way between these values, ie, the median is 2.5.

7.3.3 Median for grouped, discrete data with class intervals

Now consider the situation where we have discrete data but class intervals are used in the frequency distribution. There are two methods which can be used to determine the median.

(a) *Graphical method*

Draw a cumulative frequency curve, then look up half the total frequency, ie, $1/2$ n, on the vertical scale and read off the corresponding value. This value is the median. For the transactions frequency table:

Number of transactions	Frequency	Cumulative frequency
1-5	1	1
6-10	9	10
11-15	12	22
16-20	13	35
21-25	16	51
26-30	11	62
31-35	6	68
36-40	2	70
41-45	2	72
	—	
	72	
	—	

Remembering the intervals should be treated as 0.5-5.5, 5.5-10.5, etc, because the data is discrete, the cumulative frequency curve is:

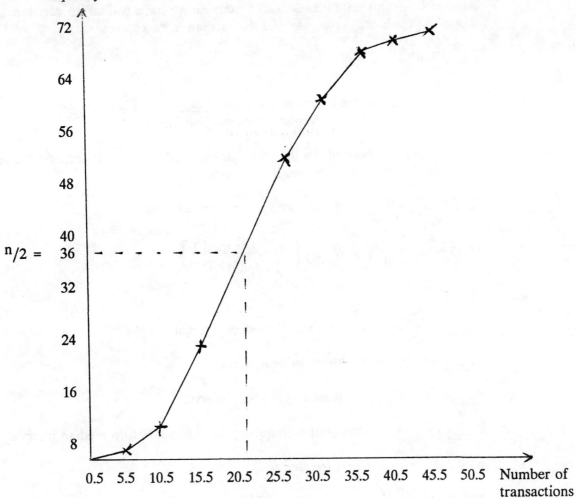

Reading across from 36 on the vertical scale (ie, $n/2$) the corresponding value is about 21 so the median is 21.

(b)   *Calculation method*

To calculate a value for the median we must first determine the interval which contains the median, called the median interval.   To do this work out the cumulative frequencies for each interval, then the following convention is used:

(i)   if n is odd the median interval is the one for which the cumulative frequency first equals or exceeds:

$$\frac{n + 1}{2}$$

(ii)   if n is even the median interval is the one for which the cumulative frequency first equals or exceeds:

$$\frac{n}{2}$$

0176z

Looking at the transactions example cumulative frequencies, as n is even and $n/2 = 36$, we see this figure is first exceeded for the '21-25' interval. This interval is again treated as 20.5-25.5 because we have a discrete variable. Having found the median interval, we find the median in two stages:

(i)   Find:

$$\frac{n/2 - \text{cumulative frequency of interval before median interval}}{\text{frequency for median interval}}$$

(ii) Multiply this result by the width of the median interval and add the result to the lower limit of the median interval.

As a formula this set of calculations can be written as:

$$\text{Median} = L_{med} + W_{med}\left[\frac{n/2 - C_{med-1}}{f_{med}}\right]$$

where

L_{med} = Lower limit of median interval

W_{med} = Width of median interval

f_{med} = Frequency of median interval

C_{med-1} = Cumulative frequency for interval before median interval

n = Total frequency

For the transactions example the calculations are:

$L_{med} = 20.5, \ W_{med} = 5, \ f_{med} = 16, \ C_{med-1} = 35$

so the median is calculated as:

$$\text{Median} = 20.5 + 5\left[\frac{36 - 35}{16}\right]$$

$$= 20.5 + 0.3125$$

$$= 20.81$$

The only reason this is different to the figure from the graphical method is the degree of accuracy obtainable from the graph. We do not have to concern ourselves with what type of intervals we have. Both methods above will work whether intervals are equal or unequal widths in the table.

7.3.4   Median for grouped, continuous data

If our data is for a continuous variable and is presented as a frequency distribution with class intervals, the methods for finding the median are exactly the same as for discrete variables except there is no need to adjust the limits of the intervals. Consider the sweet box weights example:

Weight of package (in grams)	Frequency	Cumulative frequency
Under 490	1	1
490 but less than 495	3	4
495 but less than 500	12	16
500 but less than 505	22	38
505 but less than 510	8	46
510 or over	2	48
	—	
	48	
	—	

The interval for which cumulative frequency first equals or exceeds $n/2$ (since n is even) is the interval '500 to $<$ 505 grams' since the cumulative frequency total is the first to exceed 24 (ie, $n/2$).

(a) *Graphical method*

Draw a cumulative frequency curve and see which value corresponds to a cumulative frequency of $n/2$, 24 in this example:

Cumulative
frequency

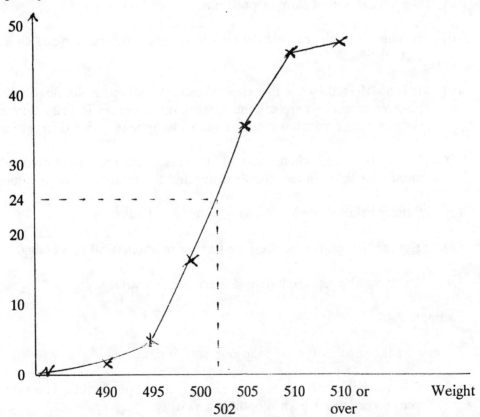

Reading from the horizontal scale the median is approximately 502 grams.

(b) *Calculation method*

We use the same formula as in the discrete case. We have:

$$\text{Median} = L_{med} + W_{med} \left[\frac{n/2 - C_{med-1}}{f_{med}} \right]$$

and in this example

$$L_{med} = 500, \ W_{med} = 5, \ f_{med} = 22, \ C_{med-1} = 16, \ n = 48.$$

$$\text{Median} = 500 + 5 \left[\frac{24 - 16}{22} \right]$$

$$= 500 + 1.82$$

$$= 501.82 \text{ grams}$$

7.3.5 Features of the median

The median has the following properties:

(a)   It is easy to understand.

(b)   Half the values in the set of data will have a value greater than or equal to the median and half less than or equal to the median.

(c)   It is a measure of rank or position.

(d)   If found from ungrouped data it will generally be the same as an actual value in the distribution.

(e)   It is unaffected by the presence of extreme values in the distribution (this can be a positive advantage since human error often occurs in collection and tabulation of data causing erroneous extreme values to appear in our distribution).

(f)   It may be found when some of the values are unknown provided that values are known for those in the middle order and the total number of values is known.

(g)   Putting values in order (ranking) can be tedious.

(h)   The median cannot be used for further mathematical processing.

(i)   It may not be representative if there are few values.

Example 7.4

Determine the median for the following sets of data:

(a)   The number of new firms commencing trade, per month, in a metropolitan district were recorded for each month of a year as:

0, 3, 2, 2, 1, 0, 1, 1, 5, 2, 1, 6

(b)   A firm has recorded the number of applicants for posts it had advertised. The figures are given in the following table:

Applications	Frequency
1-5	17
6-10	38
11-15	19
16-20	13
21-25	5
over 25	1
	93

(c)   The lengths of steel bars produced at a mill gave the following frequency distribution:

Lengths (in metres)	Frequency
Under 1.95	4
1.95 but less than 2.00	12
2.00 but less than 2.05	27
2.05 but less than 2.10	28
2.10 but less than 2.20	61
2.20 but less than 2.50	25
2.50 or over	3
	160

Solution

(a)   The data, in order is:

$$0, 0, 1, 1, 1, 1, 2, 2, 2, 3, 5, 6$$

As n is even (= 12), we must find half-way between the middle two values, the 6th and 7th. These are 1 and 2 respectively so the median is:

$$\text{Median} = \frac{1 + 2}{2} = 1.5$$

(b)

Applicants	Frequency	Cumulative frequency
1-5	17	17
6-10	38	55
11-15	19	74
16-20	13	87
21-25	5	92
Over 25	1	93
	93	

As cumulative frequency first exceeds

7.19

$$\frac{93 + 1}{2} \quad = \quad 47 \text{ (since n is odd)}$$

for the interval 6-10 this is the median interval. Treating this as 5.5-10.5 we have:

$$L_{med} = 5.5, \quad W_{med} = 5, \quad f_{med} = 38, \quad C_{med-1} = 17$$

Finding the median by calculation we have:

$$\text{Median} \quad = \quad 5.5 \quad + \quad 5\left[\frac{46.5 - 17}{38}\right]$$

$$= \quad 5.5 \quad + \quad 3.882$$

$$= \quad 9.382$$

(c) Working out the cumulative frequencies we obtain:

Lengths (in metres)	Frequency	Cumulative frequency
Under 1.95	4	4
1.95 but less than 2.00	12	16
2.00 but less than 2.05	27	43
2.05 but less than 2.10	28	71
2.10 but less than 2.20	61	132
2.20 but less than 2.50	25	157
2.50 or over	3	160
	160	

As cumulative frequency first exceeds

$$\frac{160}{2} \quad = \quad 80$$

for the interval '2.10 to $<$ 2.20', this is the median interval.

$$L_{med} = 2.10, \quad W_{med} = 0.10, \quad f_{med} = 61, \quad C_{med-1} = 71$$

and the median is calculated as:

$$\text{Median} \quad = \quad 2.10 \quad + \quad 0.10\left[\frac{80 - 71}{61}\right]$$

$$= \quad 2.10 \quad + \quad 0.015$$

$$= \quad 2.115$$

7.4   Arithmetic mean

7.4.1   Definition

If we have a list of values for a discrete variable (ungrouped data) then the arithmetic mean, usually shortened to the mean, is the simple average of the values. It is calculated by adding all the values together and dividing by the total number of values in our list. If we have the values:

3, 7, 1, 8, 2, 9, 9, 3, 5, 4

the arithmetic mean is:

$$\bar{x} = \frac{3 + 7 + 1 + 8 + 2 + 9 + 9 + 3 + 5 + 4}{10} = \frac{51}{10} = 5.1$$

(The symbol $\bar{x}$ (pronounced 'x-bar') is conventionally used for the arithmetic mean.)

7.4.2   Summation notation

So that we can develop formulae commonly used in statistics we must now introduce a mathematical shorthand. We have just seen that when we find the arithmetic mean it involves adding values together. This can be rather tedious to write down for a large series of values, instead we use an abbreviation. The abbreviation is a Greek letter - $\sum$ (pronounced sigma) - which stands for 'the sum of'. Another shorthand used in statistics is that we denote variables by a letter rather than quoting its name every time and the most commonly used is x. For our list of values above we could call them measurements of a variable x. We can then give each a subscript to show which one it is in order. We finish up with:

3	7	1	8	2	9	9	3	5	4
x_1	x_2	x_3	x_4	x_5	x_6	x_7	x_8	x_9	x_{10}

The sum of a set of values, if there are n values altogether, is written as:

$$\sum_{i=1}^{n} x_i$$

This tells us to sum all the values x_i (with i representing the different subscripts) from a subscript of 1 to a subscript of n inclusive. In our example we might write:

$$\sum_{i=1}^{10} x_i$$

to represent the total of the values. To simplify this expression it is often written as $\sum x$, meaning the sum of the values since it is usually known how many values there are and what values they take. The notation is not limited to $\sum x$. Let us look at a few common examples which we will come across again in statistical work. Suppose we have the following values:

$$x: \quad 3, 5, 6, 7, 10$$
$$y: \quad -1, 0, 3, 4, 6$$

then $x_3 = 6$, $y_4 = 4$, etc.

(a)　$\sum x = 3 + 5 + 6 + 7 + 10 = 31$

(b)　$\sum y = -1 + 0 + 3 + 4 + 6 = 12$

(c)　$\sum x^2 \quad = 3^2 + 5^2 + 6^2 + 7^2 + 10^2$
$$= 9 + 25 + 36 + 49 + 100$$
$$= 219$$

since the formula says 'add up x^2 values'. However, if we have:

(d)　$(\sum x)^2 = 31 \times 31 = 961$

since this formula says 'add up x values and square the result'

(e)　$(\sum x)(\sum y) = 31 \times 12 = 372$

(f)　If we have $\sum xy$ this says multiply corresponding x and y values and then add the results, so:

$$\sum xy \quad = 3 \times (-1) + 5 \times 0 + 6 \times 3 + 7 \times 4 + 10 \times 6$$
$$= -3 + 0 + 18 + 28 + 60$$
$$= 103$$

Other variations are:

(g)　$\sum(x-2) \quad = (3-2) + (5-2) + (6-2) + (7-2) + (10-2)$
$$= 1 + 3 + 4 + 5 + 8$$
$$= 21$$

but if we have:

(h)　$(\sum x)-2 \quad = 31-2 = 29$

Notice how important the brackets are in the expressions and how they are interpreted.

7.4.3　Formula for the mean

Using the Σ notation the formula for the arithmetic mean is:

$$\bar{x} = \frac{1}{n} \Sigma x$$

where we have n values of x.

7.4.4 Short-cut method

Calculation of a mean can often be a tedious process. It is helpful to have and use an electronic calculator which has a facility for calculating the mean of a set of values. If you do not have such a calculator available then the following method may be used to simplify the calculations. For a list of ungrouped data this method will not make much difference but when we come on to grouped data it can be very helpful, especially as few calculators have a facility on them for calculating the mean of frequency data. The first step is to guess what the mean could be (it does not have to be a particularly good guess!!). This guess is to be used to make calculations easier so should be chosen as a simple number, usually a whole number. If we call the guess A (for assumed mean) then the new formula is:

$$\bar{x} = A + \frac{\Sigma d}{n}$$

where d represents the difference of each value from the assumed mean. Using the list of values:

3, 7, 1, 8, 2, 9, 9, 3, 5, 4

try an assumed mean of 7 so the differences are:

x	3	7	1	8	2	9	9	3	5	4
d(= x - A)	-4	0	-6	1	-5	2	2	-4	-2	-3

(Note the values of d are positive or negative depending on whether the value is above or below the assumed mean.) We have:

$$\Sigma d = -19, \ A = 7, \ n = 10$$

so the mean is calculated as:

$$\bar{x} = A + \frac{\Sigma d}{n} = 7 + \frac{-19}{10} = 7 - 1.9 = 5.1 \ (\text{as before})$$

In this example it only seems to have made things more complicated but if we had the figures:

11963, 11874, 11886, 11938, 11868, 11921

and we use an assumed mean of 11900 then we have:

x	11963	11874	11886	11938	11868	11921
d(= x - A)	63	-26	-14	38	-32	21

$$\Sigma d = 50, \ A = 11900, \ n = 6$$

so the mean is given by:

$$\bar{x} \;=\; A \;+\; \frac{\Sigma d}{n} \;=\; 11900 \;+\; \frac{50}{6} \;=\; 11908.33$$

which gives us easier numbers to deal with, so simplifying the calculations.

7.4.5 Mean for grouped, discrete data

When the data is given as a frequency table with frequencies for individual values we use an amended version of the formulae already given. It becomes:

$$\bar{x} \;=\; \frac{\Sigma fx}{\Sigma f}$$

or, if we have an assumed mean (A)

$$\bar{x} \;=\; A \;+\; \frac{\Sigma fd}{\Sigma f}$$

We use f to stand for frequency. Using the table for the number of cars purchased per day we work the mean out as follows:

Number of cars purchased		Frequency	
x	f	fx	
0	3	0 x 3	= 0
1	8	1 x 8	= 8
2	20	2 x 20	= 40
3	14	3 x 14	= 42
4	6	4 x 6	= 24
5	3	5 x 3	= 15
6 or more	1	6 x 1	= 6
	55	135	

$\Sigma f = n = 55$, $\Sigma fx = 135$ and was worked out by multiplying corresponding values of x and f, then adding.

The mean is:

$$\bar{x} \;=\; \frac{\Sigma fx}{\Sigma f} \;=\; \frac{135}{55} \;=\; 2.455$$

If we use the assumed mean approach with an assumed mean A = 2, then:

x	f	d(= x - A)	fd		
0	3	-2	3 x (-2)	=	-6
1	8	-1	8 x (-1)	=	-8
2	20	0	20 x 0	=	0
3	14	1	14 x 1	=	14
4	6	2	6 x 2	=	12
5	3	3	3 x 3	=	9
6 or more	1	4	1 x 4	=	4
	55				25

and the mean is:

$$\bar{x} = A + \frac{\Sigma fd}{\Sigma f} = 2 + \frac{25}{55} = 2.455 \text{ (as before)}$$

In this example we had an open-ended interval. It is treated as having the same width as its adjacent interval, here a single unit. That means '6 or over' is taken to be 6.

7.4.6 Mean for grouped discrete data with class intervals

Next consider the situation where we have discrete data but class intervals are used in the frequency distribution. To calculate the mean we again start by adjusting the intervals so that they are the equivalent of continuous intervals. Having done this we encounter the problem which always arises with grouped data, we do not know the exact value for each result in an interval. This makes it necessary to approximate and what we do is assume all values in an interval are at the mid-point of that interval. Returning to the transactions examples, the x-values will be the mid-points of each interval and then we use the previous formulae:

Number of transactions	Mid-points	Frequency	
	x	f	fx
0.5- 5.5	3	1	3
5.5-10.5	8	9	72
10.5-15.5	13	12	156
15.5-20.5	18	13	234
20.5-25.5	23	16	368
25.5-30.5	28	11	308
30.5-35.5	33	6	198
35.5-40.5	38	2	76
40.5-45.5	43	2	86
		72	1501

and after adjusting the intervals as shown, the mean is:

$$\bar{x} = \frac{\sum fx}{\sum f} = \frac{1501}{72} = 20.847$$

If an assumed mean of 18 is used (this makes the mid-points easy) then the calculations are:

Mid-points		Frequency	
x	d = (x - 18)	f	fd
3	-15	1	-15
8	-10	9	-90
13	-5	12	-60
18	0	13	0
23	5	16	80
28	10	11	110
33	15	6	90
38	20	2	40
43	25	2	50
		72	205

and the mean is:

$$\bar{x} = A + \frac{\sum fd}{\sum f} = 18 + \frac{205}{72} = 18 + 2.847 = 20.847 \text{ (as before)}$$

7.4.7 Mean for grouped, continuous data

If our data is for a continuous variable and is presented as a frequency distribution with class intervals the method for finding the mean is exactly the same as for the discrete examples except that no adjustment of the class interval limits is necessary. Consider the sweet box weights table, then the calculations are:

Weight of package (in grams)	Mid-point x	Frequency f	fx
Under 490	487.5	1	487.5
490 but less than 495	492.5	3	1,477.5
495 but less than 500	497.5	12	5,970.0
500 but less than 505	502.5	22	11,055.0
505 buy less than 510	507.5	8	4,060.0
510 or over	512.5	2	1,025.0
		48	24,075.0

$$\bar{x} = \frac{\Sigma fx}{\Sigma f} = \frac{24,075.0}{48} = 501.56 \text{ grams (to 2 decimal places)}$$

(Each of the open-ended intervals has been treated as if it had the same width as its adjacent interval, ie, both 5 grams wide.)

In this example we can see the advantage of using an assumed mean. Suppose we use an assumed mean of 502.5 grams, the calculations are:

x	d (= x - 502.5)	f	fx
487.5	-15	1	-15
492.5	-10	3	-30
497.5	-5	12	-60
502.5	0	22	0
507.5	5	8	40
512.5	10	2	20
		48	-45

and the mean is:

$$\bar{x} = A + \frac{\Sigma fd}{\Sigma f} = 502.5 + \frac{(-45)}{48} = 502.5 - 0.9375$$

$$= 501.56 \text{ grams (to 2 decimal places)}$$

7.4.8 Features of the mean

The mean has the following properties:

(a)   It is easy to understand.

(b)   It is easy to calculate.

(c)   It makes use of every value in the distribution, leading to a mathematical exactness which is useful for further mathematical processing.

(d)   It can be determined if only the total of the values and number of values are known, without having individual values.

(e)   It can be distorted by extreme values in the distribution.

(f)   For a discrete distribution the mean will usually be an 'impossible' figure, eg, 20.847 transactions per day when only whole numbers of transactions can actually occur.

Example 7.5

Find the mean for the following sets of data:

(a)   The number of new firms commencing trade, per month, in a metropolitan district were recorded for each month of a year as:

0, 3, 2, 2, 1, 0, 1, 1, 5, 2, 1, 6

(b)   A firm has recorded the number of applicants for posts it advertises. The figures are given in the following table:

Applications	Frequency
1-5	17
6-10	38
11-15	19
16-20	13
21-25	5
over 25	1
	93

(c)   The lengths of steel bars produced at a mill gave the following frequency distribution:

Lengths (in metres)	Frequency
Under 1.95	4
1.95 but less than 2.00	12
2.00 but less than 2.05	27
2.05 but less than 2.10	28
2.10 but less than 2.20	61
2.20 but less than 2.50	25
2.50 or over	3
	160

Solution

(a)   Adding the figures we obtain $\sum x = 24$. There are 12 figures so the mean is:

$$\bar{x} = \frac{\sum x}{n} = \frac{24}{12} = 2.00 \text{ new firms}$$

(b)   As we have discrete data with class intervals adjust the intervals before finding their mid-points. The calculations are:

Applications	Mid-points	Frequency	
	x	f	fx
0.5- 5.5	3	17	51
5.5-10.5	8	38	304
10.5-15.5	13	19	247
15.5-20.5	18	13	234
20.5-25.5	23	5	115
25.5-30.5	28	1	28
		93	979

and the mean is:

$$\bar{x} = \frac{\Sigma fx}{\Sigma f} = \frac{979}{93} = 10.53 \text{ applications}$$

The open-ended interval has been assumed to have width 5, the same as its adjacent interval. If the assumed mean approach is used, an assumed mean of A = 8 or A = 13, would make the calculations easier.

(c)   As we have class interval data for a continuous variable we need the mid-points of the intervals. We will treat the lower open-ended interval as if it had width 0.05 whereas the upper open-ended interval is treated as having width 0.30 (same as their adjacent intervals). The calculations are:

Mid-points	Frequency	
x	f	fx
1.925	4	7.700
1.975	12	23.700
2.025	27	54.675
2.075	28	58.100
2.15	61	131.150
2.35	25	58.750
2.65	3	7.950
	160	342.025

and the mean is:

$$\bar{x} = \frac{\Sigma fx}{\Sigma f} = \frac{342.025}{160} = 2.138 \text{ metres}$$

This is an example where an assumed mean of 2.025 or 2.075 would make the calculations more manageable.

7.5   Comparison of mean, median and mode

These three measures are the most important and commonly used measures of location or central tendency. Three descriptions can be used for the 'ideal' average. It should be typical of the data, it should be a central value and it should be representative of all the data. Each measure meets one of these descriptions, the most typical value is the mode, the middle value is the median and the measure which represents (makes use of) all the data is the mean. Other measures will be covered later but each of them will have a special rather than general use. Of these three measures none is ideal for every problem but some are more useful than others in certain situations. Here are some guidelines to assist in the choice of an average to use.

(a)   To determine what would result from an equal distribution use the mean (eg, to determine per capita consumption of a commodity).

(b)   If order or ranking is important then the median is used (eg, a company may wish to know whether it is in the upper or lower half of its industry as regards turnover. A comparison with the median is necessary.)

(c)   Where we are interested in the most common value then the mode should be used (eg, a clothes manufacturer may wish to know, for production planning, the most common dress size).

Remember that the arithmetic mean is the measure most commonly used because it is the one people naturally calculate. However, also remember that the answer obtained is often awkward to relate to practice easily. How do you explain 1.78 people absent?

These measures are not intended to be repeats of each other and do not generally given the same results. Check through the work you have just done and see how, for the same examples, the mean, median and mode differ in value. We will use this differing information later.

7.6   Measures of dispersion

We have already seen how to calculate the various measures of the central tendency of a population. It is clearly very important to know whether the mean or median etc of the population has a high or low value. A second important feature of a population is the spread or dispersion of all the values of the population around the central measure.

Consider the output of two machines that both produce valves whose diameters have to be between 1.95 and 2.05 cm. The output of machines A and B on a typical day are as shown below:

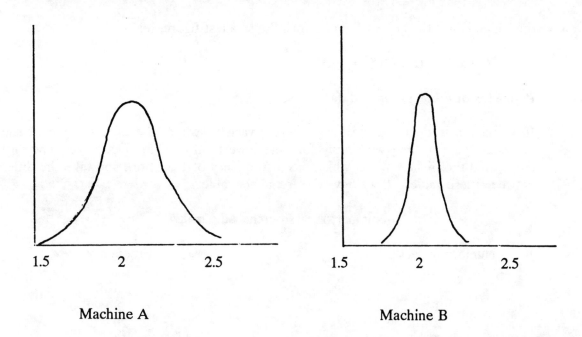

Machine A   Machine B

Although they both have a mean of 2.0 cm, machine A will produce far more values that are outside the tolerance limits and therefore are useless than machine B because its population is far more widely spread.

In this session we examine a few of the most common measures of dispersion:

(a)   Range;

(b)   Quartile deviation;

(c)   Mean deviation; and

(d)   Standard deviation.

7.7   Range

7.7.1   Definition

The range of a set of results is the difference between the smallest and the largest figure in the data. It is literally the 'spread' or 'width' of our data. If we have the figures:

        7, 1, 6, 3, 8, 8, 15, 4, 7

then the range is the largest figure minus the smallest figure, in other words:

$$\text{Range} = 15 - 1 = 14$$

Similarly, if our measurement is continuous, for the figures:

7.4, 12.2, 8.6, 7.7, 9.3, 5.8, 11.6, 8.8, 9.0

the range is still the largest figure minus the smallest figure, ie:

$$\text{Range} = 12.2 - 5.8 = 6.4$$

7.7.2 Range for discrete, grouped data

If we have a frequency table for a discrete variable where the table has frequencies for individual values, then we simply find the lowest value which has a frequency of 1 or more, find the highest value, which has a frequency of 1 or more and take the difference between these values. If we have the frequency table:

Number of cars purchased per day

Number of cars	Frequency
0	3
1	8
2	20
3	14
4	6
5	3
6	0

then the lowest value with any observations is zero, the largest with any observations is 5, so the range is:

$$\text{Range} = 5 - 0 = 5$$

7.7.3 Range for discrete, grouped data with class intervals

If the grouped table uses class intervals we take the bottom limit of the lowest interval with a frequency of 1 or more, this is then subtracted from the top limit of the highest interval with a frequency of 1 or more. For the table with number of transactions:

Number of transactions	Frequency
1-5	1
6-10	9
11-15	12
16-20	13
21-25	16
26-30	11
31-35	6
36-40	2
41-45	2
46-50	0

the lowest interval with values in that interval is 1-5. Choosing the bottom limit we have 1. The highest interval with values in that interval is 41-45. The top limit of this interval is 45 so the range is:

Range = 45 - 1 = 44

7.7.4 Range with open-ended intervals

If we have open-ended intervals we use the same approach we have used throughout. Treat the open-ended interval as if it had the same width as its adjacent interval. For the table:

Number of videos purchased (per week)	Frequency
Under 20	1
20-29	17
30-39	31
40-49	12
50 or over	2
	—
	63
	—

we would have a lowest interval with frequency 'under 20'. Treating this as having the same width as the interval next to it, the interval is assumed to be '10-19', so the bottom limit is 10. Similarly, the highest interval with frequency is '50 or over'. This is treated as '50-59' since the interval adjacent to it has this width. The top limit is 59 so we have a range of:

Range = 59 - 10 = 49

7.7.5 Range with class intervals of unequal width

It does not make any difference whether we have equal or unequal width intervals, the approach is the same. For the following table giving numbers of salespersons employed by firms:

Number of sales persons	Frequency
1-10	6
11-20	10
21-30	28
31-50	16
over 50	4
	—
	64
	—

then the bottom limit of the lower interval is 1 and the upper interval is 'over 50'. This is taken to be 51-70 (same width as adjacent interval) so top limit is 70. The range is then:

Range = 70 - 1 = 69

Whenever interval data is used, the range is not exact but an approximation. The range can only be found exactly from the original or raw data.

7.7.6   Range for continuous, grouped data

If our data is of a continuous variable and is presented as a frequency distribution with class intervals, the methods for finding the range are exactly the same as for discrete variables except the top point of an interval '20 but less than 30' is taken as 30. For the sweet box weights table we have:

Weight of package (grams)	Frequency
Under 490	1
490 but less than 495	3
495 but less than 500	12
500 but less than 505	22
505 but less than 510	8
510 or over	2
	48

The lowest interval with figures in it is 'under 490'. We treat this as having the same width as the interval next to it so '485   490'. The bottom limit is then 485. The highest interval with figures in it is '510 or over'. We treat this as '510   515', again the same width as the adjacent interval. The top limit is then 515. The range is:

Range = 515 - 485 = 30 grams

7.7.7   Features of the range

The range has the following properties:

(a)   It is easy to understand.

(b)   It is easy to calculate.

(c)   It depends on extreme values so is susceptible to 'odd' results.

(d)   It only uses two values - the remaining data is ignored.

(e)   It is only rarely used for further statistical work.

Example 7.6

Determine the range for the following sets of data:

(a)   The number of new firms commencing trade, per month, in a metropolitan district were recorded each month for a year as:

0, 3, 2, 2, 1, 0, 1, 1, 5, 2, 1, 6

(b)   A firm has recorded the number of applicants for posts it advertises. The figures are given in the following table:

Applicants	Frequency
1-5	17
6-10	38
11-15	19
16-20	13
21-25	5
over 25	1
	—
	93
	—

(c)   The lengths of steel bars gave the following frequency distribution:

Length (in metres)	Frequency
Under 1.95	4
1.95 but less than 2.00	12
2.00 but less than 2.05	27
2.05 but less than 2.10	28
2.10 but less than 2.20	61
2.20 but less than 2.50	25
2.50 or over	3
	—
	160
	—

Solution

(a)   The lowest value is zero, the highest value is 6, so the range is:

$$\text{Range} = 6 - 0 = 6$$

(b)   The lowest interval with frequency is 1-5 so the bottom limit is 1. The highest interval with frequency is 'over 25'. Treating this as '26-30' so that it has the same width as the adjacent interval, the top limit is 30 so the range is:

$$\text{Range} = 30 - 1 = 29$$

(c)   The lowest interval with frequency is 'under 1.95'. If this has same width as its adjacent interval it is treated as '1.90 to $<$ 1.95' so the bottom limit is 1.90. The highest interval with frequency is '2.50 or over'. If this has same width as its adjacent interval it is treated as '2.50 to $<$ 2.80' so the top limit is 2.80. The range is:

$$\text{Range} = 2.80 - 1.90 = 0.90 \text{ metres}$$

7.8 Quartile deviation

7.8.1 Definition

We have seen that quartiles split a set of data into four equal parts. The difference between the first and third quartiles is called the inter-quartile range. Half of this inter-quartile range is called the quartile deviation (often shortened to QD), so:

$$QD = \frac{Q3 - Q1}{2}$$

It is a measure of dispersion which is often related to or quoted with the median. It is sometimes called the semi-interquartile range.

7.8.2 Quartile deviation for discrete, grouped data

If we have a frequency table for a discrete variable where the table has frequencies for individual values, then we work out a cumulative frequency table. If we have n values altogether we work out $n/4$ and $3n/4$. Find the value for which cumulative frequency first equals or exceeds $n/4$. This is the first quartile, Q1. Then find the value for which cumulative frequency first equals or exceeds $3n/4$. This is the third quartile, Q3. For the table giving the number of cars purchased per day we have:

Number of cars	Frequency	Cumulative Frequency	
0	3	3	
1	8	11	
2	20	31	Q1
3	14	45	Q3
4	6	51	
5	3	54	
6 or more	1	55	
	55		

$$n = 55, \quad \frac{n}{4} = \frac{55}{4} = 13.75, \quad \frac{3n}{4} = \frac{3 \times 55}{4} = 41.25$$

Cumulative frequency first exceeds 13.75 for 2 cars so the first quartile is:

$$Q1 = 2$$

Cumulative frequency first exceeds 41.25 for 3 cars so the third quartile is:

$$Q3 = 3$$

We can then find the quartile deviation as:

$$QD = \frac{Q3 - Q1}{2} = \frac{3 - 2}{2} = 0.5$$

Example 7.7

Find the quartile deviation for the number of absentees from work, as given by the table:

Number of absentees	Frequency
0	27
1	41
2	17
3	11
4	3
5 or more	1
	100

Solution

The cumulative frequencies are:

Number of absentees	Cumulative Frequency
0	27
1	68
2	85
3	96
4	99
5 or more	100

so $n = 100$, $n/4 = 25$ and $3n/4 = 75$.

Since cumulative frequency first exceeds 25 for no absentees we have $Q1 = 0$ and as cumulative frequency first exceeds 75 for 2 absentees we have $Q3 = 2$. This gives us a quartile deviation of:

$$QD = \frac{2 - 0}{2} = 1$$

7.8.3 Quartile deviation for discrete, grouped data with class intervals

Now consider the situation where we have discrete data but class intervals are used in the frequency distribution. There are two methods that can be used to find the quartile deviation just as there were for the median.

(a)   Graphical method

Draw a cumulative frequency curve, remembering to extend the class intervals by half a unit at each end, then look up $n/4$ and $3n/4$ on the vertical scale. The corresponding values are, respectively, the first and third quartiles. For the transactions example the table is:

Number of transactions	Frequency	Cumulative Frequency
1-5	1	1
6-10	9	10
11-15	12	22
16-20	13	35
21-25	16	51
26-30	11	62
31-35	6	68
36-40	2	70
41-45	2	72
	$\overline{72}$	

Drawing the cumulative frequency curve we obtain:

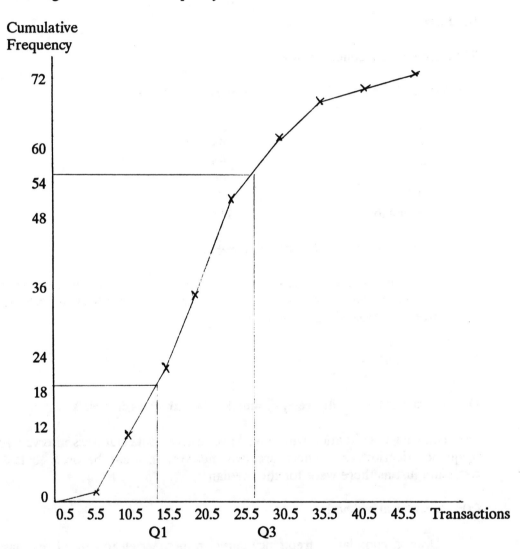

Reading across from $n/4$ (= 18) on the vertical axis we find the first quartile as:

    Q1 = 14 (approximately)

Then reading across from $3n/4$ (= 54) we find the third quartile as:

    Q3 = 27 (approximately)

7.38

The quartile deviation is then:

$$QD = \frac{Q3 - Q1}{2} = \frac{27 - 14}{2} = 6.5$$

(b) Calculation method

Using this method the first and third quartiles are found in the same way that the median was. For the first quartile find the interval for which cumulative frequency first equals or exceeds $n/4$. For this example the appropriate interval when cumulative frequency first equals or exceeds $n/4$ is the interval '11-15'. This is the first quartile interval and because it is a discrete variable would be treated as 10.5-15.5. The first quartile is then calculated in two steps:

(i) Find

$$\frac{n/4 - \text{cumulative frequency of interval before Q1 interval}}{\text{frequency for Q1 interval}}$$

(ii) Multiply this by the width of the first quartile interval and add the result to the lower limit of the Q1 interval.

As a formula this set of calculations can be written as:

$$Q1 = L_{Q1} + W_{Q1} \left[\frac{n/4 - C_{Q1-1}}{f_{Q1}} \right]$$

where

L_{Q1} = Lower limit of Q1 interval

W_{Q1} = Width of Q1 interval

f_{Q1} = Frequency of Q1 interval

C_{Q1-1} = Cumulative frequency for interval before Q1 interval

n = Total frequency

For the transactions data the first quartile calculations are based on:

$L_{Q1} = 10.5, W_{Q1} = 5, f_{Q1} = 12, C_{Q1-1} = 10$

so the first quartile is calculated as:

$$Q1 = 10.5 + 5 \left[\frac{18 - 10}{12} \right]$$

$$= 10.5 + 3.333$$

$$= 13.833$$

We must now go on and calculate the third quartile. For the third quartile find the interval for which cumulative frequency first equals or exceeds $3n/4$. For this example the appropriate interval when cumulative frequency first equals or exceeds 54 is the interval '26-30' which should be treated as '25.5-30.5'. This is the third quartile interval. The third quartile itself is then calculated in two steps:

(iii)   Find:

$$\frac{3n/4 - \text{cumulative frequency of interval before Q3 interval}}{\text{frequency for Q3 interval}}$$

(iv)   Multiply this result by the width of the third quartile interval and add the result to the lower limit of the third quartile interval.

As a formula this set of calculations can be written as:

$$Q3 = L_{Q3} + W_{Q3} \left[\frac{3n/4 - C_{Q3-1}}{f_{Q3}} \right]$$

where

L_{Q3} = Lower limit of Q3 interval

W_{Q3} = Width of Q3 interval

f_{Q3} = Frequency of Q3 interval

C_{Q3-1} = Cumulative frequency of interval before Q3 interval

n = Total frequency

Continuing the transactions example, the third quartile calculations are based on:

L_{Q3} = 25.5, W_{Q3} = 5, f_{Q3} = 11, C_{Q3-1} = 51

so the third quartile is calculated as:

$$Q3 = 25.5 + 5 \left[\frac{54 - 51}{11} \right]$$

$$= 25.5 + 1.364$$

$$= 26.864$$

The quartile deviation is then:

$$QD = \frac{Q3 - Q1}{2} = \frac{26.864 - 13.833}{2}$$

$$= \frac{13.031}{2}$$

$$= 6.52 \text{ (to 2 decimal places)}$$

The difference between the graphical and the calculation method answers is again due to the accuracy that can be obtained from the graph.

We do not have to worry about the type of intervals we have. Both methods will work whether we have equal or unequal width intervals in the table.

Example 7.8

Calculate the quartile deviation for the table of complaints:

Number of complaints	Frequency
0-4	6
5-9	9
10-14	5
15-19	4
20-24	1
	—
	25
	—

Solution

We must first work out a cumulative frequency table and adjust the intervals:

Number of complaints	Cumulative frequency
0.5-4.5	6
4.5-9.5	15
9.5-14.5	20
14.5-19.5	24
19.5-24.5	25

$n = 25$, so we have $n/4 = 6.25$, $3n/4 = 18.75$

The first quartile interval is '4.5-9.5'. The calculations for Q1 are then based on :

$$L_{Q1} = 4.5, \quad W_{Q1} = 5, \quad f_{Q1} = 9, \quad C_{Q1-1} = 6$$

and give:

$$Q1 = 4.5 + 5 \left[\frac{6.25 - 6}{9} \right]$$

$$= 4.5 + 5 \left[\frac{0.25}{9} \right]$$

$$= 4.5 + 0.139$$

$$= 4.639 \text{ (to 3 decimal places)}$$

The third quartile interval is '9.5-14.5'. The calculations for Q3 are then based on:

$$L_{Q3} = 9.5, \ W_{Q3} = 5, \ f_{Q3} = 5, \ C_{Q3-1} = 15$$

and give:

$$Q3 \ = \ 9.5 \ + \ 5 \ \frac{18.75 - 15}{5}$$

$$= \ 9.5 \ + \ 5 \ \frac{3.75}{5}$$

$$= \ 9.5 \ + \ 3.75$$

$$= \ 13.25$$

The quartile deviation is then:

$$QD \ = \ \frac{Q3 - Q1}{2} \ = \ \frac{13.25 - 4.639}{2}$$

$$= \ \frac{8.611}{2}$$

$$= \ 4.31 \text{ (to 2 decimal places)}$$

7.8.4 Quartile deviation for grouped, continuous data

If we have a frequency distribution for a continuous variable with class intervals then the methods for finding the quartile deviation are the same as for discrete variables except there is no need to adjust limits of the intervals. Considering the sweet box weight table:

Weight of package (in grams)	Frequency	Cumulative Frequency
Under 490	1	1
490 but less than 495	3	4
495 but less than 500	12	16
500 but less than 505	22	38
505 but less than 510	8	46
510 or over	2	48
	48	

(a) *Graphical method*

We draw a cumulative frequency curve and see which value corresponds to a cumulative frequency of $n/4$ (ie, 12). This is the first quartile. Then see which value corresponds to a cumulative frequency of $3n/4$ (ie, 36). This is the third quartile.

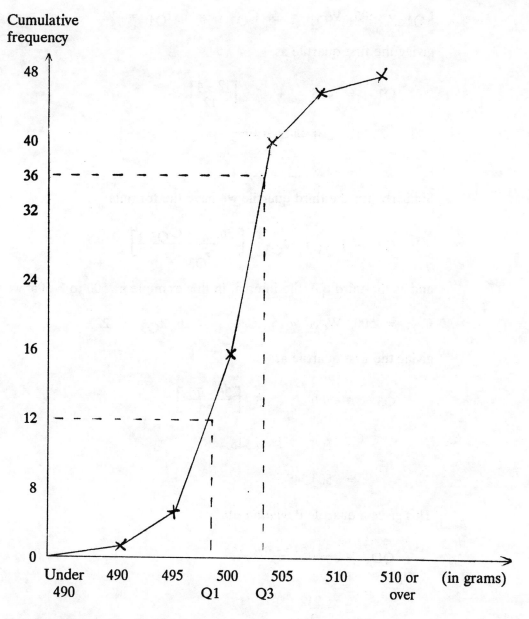

Reading from the horizontal scale we have that Q1 = 498.5 and Q3 = 504.5 approximately. The quartile deviation is then calculated as:

$$QD = \frac{Q3 - Q1}{2} = \frac{504.5 - 498.5}{2} = \frac{6}{2}$$

$$= 3$$

(b)   *Calculation method*

We use the same formulae as we had in the discrete case, so:

$$Q1 = L_{Q1} + W_{Q1} \; \frac{n/4 - C_{Q1-1}}{f_{Q1}}$$

and in this example, as the first quartile interval is '495 to $<$ 500', we have:

7.43

0176z

$$L_{Q1} = 495, \ W_{Q1} = 5, \ C_{Q1-1} = 4, \ f_{Q1} = 12$$

giving the first quartile as:

$$Q1 = 495 + 5 \left[\frac{12 - 4}{12} \right]$$

$$= 495 + 3.333$$

$$= 498.333$$

Similarly, for the third quartile we have the formula:

$$Q3 = L_{Q3} + W_{Q3} \left[\frac{3n/4 - C_{Q3-1}}{f_{Q3}} \right]$$

and as the third quartile interval in this example is '500 to $<$ 505' we use:

$$L_{Q3} = 500, \ W_{Q3} = 5, \ C_{Q3-1} = 16, \ f_{Q3} = 22$$

giving the first quartile as:

$$Q3 = 500 + 5 \left[\frac{36 - 16}{22} \right]$$

$$= 500 + 4.545$$

$$= 504.545$$

This gives a quartile deviation of:

$$QD = \frac{504.545 - 498.333}{2}$$

$$= \frac{6.212}{2}$$

$$= 3.11 \text{ (to 2 decimal places)}$$

Example 7.9

For the following table of service times find the quartile deviation by graphical and by calculation methods.

Service time (in minutes)	Frequency
Under 5	1
5 but less than 10	15
10 but less than 15	18
15 but less than 20	12
20 but less than 30	7
30 or over	2
	55

Solution

Using the graphical method we draw a graph for the cumulative frequency table.

Service time (in minutes)	Cumulative frequency
Under 5	1
5 $<$ 10	16
10 $<$ 15	34
15 $<$ 20	46
20 $<$ 30	53
30 or over	55

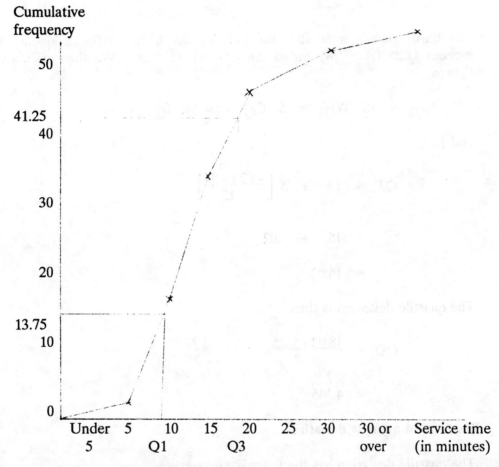

As n = 55, $n/4$ = 13.75, $3n/4$ = 41/25.

From the graph we obtain Q1 = 9 and Q3 = 18 approximately. The quartile deviation is:

$$QD = \frac{18 - 9}{2} = 4.5$$

Using the calculation method the first quartile interval is the one for which cumulative frequency first equals or exceeds 13.75 (ie, $n/4$) and is the interval '5 to $<$ 10'. We then calculate Q1 using the figures:

$$L_{Q1} = 5, \ W_{Q1} = 5, \ C_{Q1-1} = 1, \ f_{Q1} = 15$$

and so:

$$Q1 = 5 + 5 \left[\frac{13.75 - 1}{15} \right]$$

$$= 5 + 5 \left[\frac{12.75}{15} \right]$$

$$= 5 + 4.25$$

$$= 9.25$$

The third quartile interval is the one for which cumulative frequency first equals or exceeds 41.25 (ie, $3n/4$) and is the interval '15   20'. We then calculate Q3 using the figures:

$$L_{Q3} = 15, \ W_{Q3} = 5, \ C_{Q3-1} = 34, \ f_{Q3} = 12$$

and so:

$$Q3 = 15 + 5 \left[\frac{41.25 - 34}{12} \right]$$

$$= 15 + 3.02$$

$$= 18.02$$

The quartile deviation is then:

$$QD = \frac{18.02 - 9.25}{2} = \frac{8.77}{2}$$

$$= 4.385$$

7.8.5   Features of quartile deviation

The quartile deviation has the following properties:

(a)   It is easy to understand.

(b)   It is half the range of the middle 50% of values so tells us about the spread of the middle values.

(c)   It is unaffected by the presence of extremes values in the distribution.

(d)   It is rather awkward to calculate.

(e)   It cannot be used for further mathematical processing.

(f)   It may not be representative if there are few values.

Example 7.10

Find the quartile deviation for the following sets of data:

(a)   A firm has recorded the number of applicants for posts it advertises. The figures are given in the following table:

Applicants	Frequency
1-5	17
6-10	38
11-15	19
16-20	13
21-25	5
over 25	1
	93

(b)   The lengths of steel bars gave the following frequency distribution:

Length (in metres)	Frequency
Under 1.95	4
1.95 but less than 2.00	12
2.00 but less than 2.05	27
2.05 but less than 2.10	28
2.10 but less than 2.20	61
2.30 but less than 2.50	25
2.50 or over	3
	160

Solution

(a)   The cumulative frequencies are:

Applicants	Frequency	Cumulative frequency
1-5	17	17
6-10	38	55
11-15	19	74
16-20	13	87
21-25	5	92
over 25	1	93
	93	

The interval for which cumulative frequency first equals or exceeds 23.25 (ie, $n/4$) is '6-10'. Treating this as '5.5-10.5' the first quartile interval gives us:

$$L_{Q1} = 5.5, \ W_{Q1} = 5, \ C_{Q1-1} = 17, \ f_{Q1} = 38$$

so that:

$$Q1 = 5.5 + 5\left[\frac{23.25 - 17}{38}\right]$$

$$= 5.5 + 0.822$$

$$= 6.322$$

The interval for which cumulative frequency first equals or exceeds 69.75 (ie, $3n/4$) is '11-15'. Treating this as '10.5-15.5' the third quartile interval gives us:

$$L_{Q3} = 10.5, \ W_{Q3} = 5, \ C_{Q3-1} = 55, \ f_{Q3} = 19$$

so that:

$$Q3 = 10.5 + 5\left[\frac{69.75 - 55}{19}\right]$$

$$= 10.5 + 3.882$$

$$= 14.382$$

The quartile deviation is then:

$$QD = \frac{14.382 - 6.322}{2} = \frac{8.060}{2}$$

$$= 4.03 \ \text{(to 2 decimal places)}$$

(b)   The cumulative frequencies are:

Lengths (in metres)	Frequency	Cumulative frequency
Under 1.95	4	4
1.95 but less than 2.00	12	16
2.00 but less than 2.05	27	43
2.05 but less than 2.10	28	71
2.10 but less than 2.20	61	132
2.20 but less than 2.50	25	157
2.50 or over	3	160
	160	

The interval for which cumulative frequency first equals or exceeds 40 (ie, $n/4$) is '2.00 to $<$ 2.05' so this is the first quartile interval. We use the following figures in the calculations:

$$L_{Q1} = 2.00, \ W_{Q1} = 0.05, \ C_{Q1-1} = 16, \ f_{Q1} = 27$$

which give:

$$Q1 = 2.00 + 0.05 \left[\frac{40 - 16}{27} \right]$$

$$= 2.00 + 0.05 \left[\frac{24}{27} \right]$$

$$= 2.00 + 0.044$$

$$= 2.044$$

The interval for which cumulative frequency first equals or exceeds 120 (ie, $3n/4$) is '2.10 to $<$ 2.20' so this is the the third quartile interval. The figures we require for the calculations are:

$$L_{Q3} = 2.10, \ W_{Q3} = 0.10, \ C_{Q3-1} = 71, \ f_{Q3} = 61$$

which give:

$$Q3 = 2.10 + 0.10 \left[\frac{120 - 71}{61} \right]$$

$$= 2.10 + 0.10 \left[\frac{49}{61} \right]$$

$$= 2.10 + 0.080$$

$$= 2.180$$

The quartile deviation is then:

$$QD = \frac{2.180 - 2.044}{2} = \frac{0.136}{2}$$

$$= 0.068 \text{ metres}$$

7.9 Mean deviation

7.9.1 Definition

The mean deviation measures the average spread of values from the arithmetic mean. It averages the differences of the values from the arithmetic mean, ignoring negative signs of differences. For the figures 2, 3, 5, 6, the arithmetic mean is:

$$\bar{x} = \frac{2 + 3 + 5 + 6}{4} = 4$$

The differences from the arithmetic mean are:

2 - 4, 3 - 4, 5 - 4, 6 - 4

which are

-2, -1, 1, 2

Ignoring negative signs these are:

2, 1, 1, 2

which average

$$\frac{2+1+1+2}{4} = 1.5$$

This is the mean deviation (MD), the average difference from the mean. More formally we can write:

$$MD = \frac{\sum |x - \bar{x}|}{n}$$

where $|x - \bar{x}|$ means 'find the differences between x and $\bar{x}$, then ignore negative signs'. It is called the 'modulus' and is signified by$|\quad|$, two vertical, parallel lines.

7.9.2   Mean deviation for ungrouped data

Whether we have a list of discrete values (as we had in the previous section) or a list of continuous values we calculate the mean deviation in the same way. Firstly, work out the arithmetic mean, the use the formula:

$$MD = \frac{\sum |x - \bar{x}|}{n}$$

Suppose we have recorded the volumes of eight bottles produced on a new machine as:

496.8, 502.7, 500.6, 501.2, 497.3, 499.2, 502.0, 500.2 (in cc)

then the calculations can be set out as follows:

x	$x - \bar{x}$	$|x - \bar{x}|$
496.8	-3.2	3.2
502.7	2.7	2.7
500.6	0.6	0.6
501.2	1.2	1.2
497.3	-2.7	2.7
499.2	-0.8	0.8
502.0	2.0	2.0
500.2	0.2	0.2
4,000.0		13.4

$$\bar{x} = \frac{4,000}{8} = 500.00$$

Where a column of the values minus the mean $(x - \bar{x})$ is worked out, then a column with all negative values changed to positive values, $x - x$, is written down. To find the mean deviation work out the average of this last column

$$MD = \frac{13.4}{8} = 1.675$$

7.9.3 Mean deviation for discrete, grouped data

When data is given as a frequency table with frequencies for individual values we use a modified version of the formula already given. It is:

$$MD = \frac{\sum f|x - \bar{x}|}{\sum f}$$

which says we need to find the arithmetic mean first, then take differences as before and ignore negative signs. Multiply these differences by the corresponding frequency, add them and finally divide by total frequency. Suppose we have the table of cars purchased per day:

Number of cars purchased	Frequency
0	3
1	8
2	20
3	14
4	6
5	3
6 or more	1
	55

the calculations can be set out like this:

x	f	fx	x - x	|x - x|		f |x - x|		
0	3	0	-2.455	2.455	3	x	2.455	= 7.365
1	8	8	-1.455	1.455	8	x	1.455	= 11.640
2	20	40	-0.455	0.455	20	x	0.455	= 9.100
3	14	42	0.545	0.545	14	x	0.545	= 7.630
4	6	24	1.545	1.545	6	x	1.545	= 9.270
5	3	15	2.545	2.545	3	x	2.545	= 7.635
6	1	6	3.545	3.545	1	x	3.545	= 3.545
	55	135						56.185

where, the mean, using the frequency formula, is:

$$\bar{x} = \frac{\sum fx}{\sum f} = \frac{135}{55} = 2.455$$

We then take the mean away from the x-values, draw up a further column with the negative signs of these differences ignored and finally calculate a column of these figures multiplied by the corresponding frequency. We can now find the mean deviation as:

$$MD = \frac{\sum f |x - \bar{x}|}{\sum f} = \frac{56.185}{55}$$

$$= 1.022$$

In this example we had an open-ended interval '6 or over'. As we have done before, it was treated as a single unit '6'.

7.9.4   Mean deviation for discrete data with class intervals

Now consider the situation where we have class intervals for discrete data. To calculate the mean deviation we begin by adjusting class intervals so that they are the equivalent of continuous intervals (as we have done before). Having done this we then use the mid-points of each interval as the x-value for that interval. This allows us to use the frequency formula for mean deviation. This approach can be used whether we have equal or unequal width intervals. For the table of transactions:

Number of transactions	Frequency
1-5	1
6-10	9
11-15	12
16-20	13
21-25	16
26-30	11
31-35	6
36-40	2
41-45	2
	72

the calculations are as follows:

Mid-Points						
x	f	fx	x - x̄	|x - x̄|		f |x - x̄|
3	1	3	-17.847	17.847	1 x 17.847	= 17.847
8	9	72	-12.847	12.847	9 x 12.847	= 115.623
13	12	156	-7.847	7.847	12 x 7.847	= 94.164
18	13	234	-2.847	2.847	13 x 2.847	= 37.011
23	16	368	2.153	2.153	16 x 2.153	= 34.448
28	11	308	7.153	7.153	11 x 7.153	= 78.683
33	6	198	12.153	12.153	6 x 12.153	= 72.918
38	2	76	17.153	17.153	2 x 17.153	= 34.306
43	2	86	22.153	22.153	2 x 22.153	= 44.306
	72	1,501				529.306

The mean is:

$$\bar{x} = \frac{\sum fx}{\sum f} = \frac{1,501}{72} = 20.847$$

and the mean deviation is calculated as:

$$MD = \frac{\sum f |x - \bar{x}|}{\sum f} = \frac{529.306}{72} = 7.351$$

7.9.5 Mean deviation for continuous, grouped data

When we have a frequency table for a continuous variable we use the same approach and formula as for the discrete case. The only alteration is that no adjustment is necessary for the limits of the class intervals. Considering the sweet box weights given in the table:

Weight of package (in grams)	Frequency
Under 490	1
490 but less than 495	3
495 but less than 500	12
500 but less than 505	22
505 but less than 510	8
510 or over	2
	48

then we set the calculations out as follows, remembering to treat the open-ended intervals as if they had the same width as their adjacent interval.

Intervals	Mid-points (x)	f	$\dot{\imath}x$	$x - \bar{x}$	$|x - \bar{x}|$	$f|x - \bar{x}|$
485 490	487.5	1	487.5	-14.06	14.06	14.06
490 495	492.5	3	1,477.5	-9.06	9.06	27.18
495 500	497.5	12	5,970.0	-4.06	4.06	48.72
500 505	502.5	22	11,055.0	0.94	0.94	20.68
505 510	507.5	8	4,060.0	5.94	5.94	47.52
510 515	512.5	2	1,025.0	10.94	10.94	21.88
		48	24,075.0			180.04

The mean is:

$$\bar{x} = \frac{\Sigma fx}{\Sigma f} = \frac{24,075.0}{48} = 501.56 \text{ grams}$$

and the mean deviation is found as:

$$MD = \frac{\Sigma f|x - \bar{x}|}{\Sigma f} = \frac{180.04}{48}$$

$$= 3.75$$

7.9.6 Features of the mean deviation

The mean deviation has the following properties:

(a) It is easy to understand.

(b) It is fairly straightforward to calculate.

(c) It can be distorted by extreme values.

(d) It makes use of every value in the distribution.

(e) It has not been developed for mathematical processing.

Example 4.11

Determine the mean deviation for the following sets of data:

(a) The number of firms commencing trade, per month, in a metropolitan district were recorded each month for a year as:

0, 3, 2, 2, 1, 0, 1, 1, 5, 2, 1, 6

(b) A firm has recorded the number of applicants for posts it advertises. The figures are given in the following table:

Applicants	Frequency
1-5	17
6-10	38
11-15	19
16-20	13
21-25	5
over 25	1
	93

(c)   The lengths of steel bars gave the following frequency distribution:

Length (in metres)	Frequency
Under 1.95	4
1.95 but less than 2.00	12
2.00 but less than 2.05	27
2.05 but less than 2.10	28
2.10 but less than 2.20	61
2.20 but less than 2.50	25
2.50 or over	3
	160

Solution

(a)   As we have a list of figures the calculations are:

x	$x - \bar{x}$	$|x - \bar{x}|$
0	-2	2
3	1	1
2	0	0
2	0	0
1	-1	1
0	-2	2
1	-1	1
1	-1	1
5	3	3
2	0	0
1	-1	1
6	4	4
24		16

The mean is:

$$\bar{x} \quad = \frac{\sum x}{n} \quad = \frac{24}{12} = 2$$

7.55

and the mean deviation is given by:

$$\text{MD} = \frac{\sum |x - \bar{x}|}{n} = \frac{16}{12} = 1.333$$

(b) As we have a discrete variable, categorised in class intervals, the calculations are:

Mid-points (x)	f	fx	x - $\bar{x}$	|x - $\bar{x}$|	f |x - $\bar{x}$|
3	17	51	-7.527	7.527	127.959
8	38	304	-2.527	2.527	96.026
13	19	247	2.473	2.473	46.987
18	13	234	7.473	7.473	97.149
23	5	115	12.473	12.473	62.365
28	1	28	17.473	17.473	17.473
	93	979			447.959

The mean is:

$$\bar{x} = \frac{\sum fx}{\sum f} = \frac{979}{93} = 10.527$$

The mean deviation is given by:

$$\text{MD} = \frac{\sum f |x - \bar{x}|}{\sum f} = \frac{447.959}{93} = 4.817$$

(c) We have an interval table for a continuous variable so the calculations are:

Mid-points (x)	Frequency (f)	fx	x - $\bar{x}$	|x - $\bar{x}$|	f |x - $\bar{x}$|
1.925	4	7.700	-0.213	0.213	0.852
1.975	12	23.700	-0.163	0.163	1.956
2.025	27	54.675	-0.113	0.113	3.051
2.075	28	58.100	-0.063	0.063	1.764
2.150	61	131.150	0.012	0.012	0.732
2.350	25	58.750	0.212	0.212	5.300
2.650	3	7.950	0.512	0.512	1.536
	160	342.025			15.191

The mean is:

$$\bar{x} = \frac{\sum fx}{\sum f} = \frac{342.025}{160} = 2.138$$

7.56

and the mean deviation is given by:

$$\text{MD} = \frac{15.191}{160} = 0.095$$

7.10 Standard deviation

7.10.1 Definition

The standard deviation is the square root of the average squared difference from the mean. It is used widely in statistics as a measure of spread since it is easy to develop mathematically. It is much like the mean deviation but instead of ignoring the negative signs of differences from the mean, these differences are squared. The squaring process automatically eliminates the negative sign. When the squared differences have been averaged we have a measure called **variance**. The square root of variance is then taken to give standard deviation. This is to ensure standard deviation is in the same units as the original data. Variance is always the square of standard deviation, standard deviation is always the positive square root of variance.

7.10.2 Standard deviation for ungrouped data

When we have a set of raw data, either for a discrete variable or for a continuous variable, standard deviation is calculated using the formula:

$$\text{SD} = s = \sqrt{\frac{\Sigma(x - \bar{x})^2}{n}}$$

For calculation purposes, though, this formula is often rearranged as:

$$s = \sqrt{\frac{\Sigma x^2}{n} - \bar{x}^2}$$

Illustration

Suppose we have the following results for the volumes of bottles produced by a process (measured in cm^3):

496.8, 502.7, 500.6, 501.2, 497.3, 499.2, 502.0, 500.2

We we can set out the calculations using the definition formula as:

x	$x - \bar{x}$	$(x - \bar{x})^2$
496.8	-3.2	10.24
502.7	2.7	7.29
500.6	0.6	0.36
501.2	1.2	1.44
497.3	-2.7	7.29
499.2	-0.8	0.64
502.0	2.0	4.00
500.2	0.2	0.04
4,000.0		31.30

The mean is:

$$\bar{x} = \frac{\Sigma x}{n} = \frac{4,000}{8} = 500.00 \text{ cm}^3$$

and we calculate a column of values minus the mean, then a column of these differences squared. The standard deviation is given by:

$$s = \sqrt{\frac{\Sigma(x - \bar{x})^2}{n}} = \sqrt{\frac{31.30}{8}} = \sqrt{3.9125}$$

$$= 1.978 \text{ cm}^3$$

(Remember to take the square root!!)

If we use the calculation formula, the workings can be set out like this:

x	x^2
496.8	246,810.24
502.7	252,707.29
500.6	250,600.36
501.2	251,201.44
497.3	247,307.29
499.2	249,200.64
502.0	252,004.00
500.2	250,200.04
4,000.0	2,000,031.30

then the mean is:

7.58

$$\bar{x} = \frac{4,000.0}{8} = 500.00 \text{ cm}^3$$

and

$$s = \sqrt{\frac{\Sigma x^2}{n} - \bar{x}^2} = \sqrt{\frac{2,000,031.3}{8} - (500.0)^2}$$

$$= \sqrt{250,003.9125 - 250,000}$$

$$= \sqrt{3.9125}$$

$$= 1.978 \text{ cm}^3 \text{ (as before)}$$

The formulae are equivalent and so will always give the same answers providing no rounding is carried out. The calculation formula involves working out one less column of figures and there is less opportunity for rounding errors to occur. Some calculators work out the standard deviation of a list of figures directly for you. Remember that the standard deviation (1.978 cm^3) is a measure of the spread or dispersion of the population around the mean.

Example 7.12

Find the standard deviation of the following five daily output figures for a product:

3,750; 3,290; 3,360; 3,550; 3,600

Solution

Using the definition formula the calculations are:

x	x - $\bar{x}$	$(x - \bar{x})^2$
3,750	240	57,600
3,290	-220	48,400
3,360	-150	22,500
3,550	40	1,600
3,600	90	8,100
17,550		138,200

then the mean is:

$$\bar{x} = \frac{17,550}{5} = 3,510$$

and the standard deviation is given by:

$$s = \sqrt{\frac{\sum(x - \bar{x})^2}{n}} \qquad = \sqrt{\frac{138,200}{5}} \qquad = \sqrt{27,640}$$

$$= 166.25$$

Using the calculation formula we have:

x	x^2
3,750	14,062,500
3,290	10,824,100
3,360	11,289,600
3,550	12,602,500
3,600	12,960,000
17,550	61,738,700

then the mean is:

$$\bar{x} = \frac{17,550}{5} = 3,510$$

and the standard deviation is given by:

$$s = \sqrt{\frac{\sum x^2}{n} - \bar{x}^2} \qquad = \sqrt{\frac{61,738,700}{5} - (3,510)^2}$$

$$= \sqrt{12,347,740 - 12,320,100}$$

$$= \sqrt{27,460}$$

$$= 166.25 \text{ (as before)}$$

7.10.3 Short-cut method

Calculation of the standard deviation can often be a tedious process and, as we have already seen, can lead to us having to deal with pretty large numbers. The following method can be used to simplify some of the calculations whether we are using a calculator or not. It will be especially helpful when we deal with frequency data. It is the same method we saw when calculating the mean.

The first step is to guess what the mean might be (the guess does not have to be a particularly good one). This guess is to be used to make the calculations easier so should be chosen as a simple number, usually a whole number or one which leads to our dealing with whole numbers. If we call the guess 'A' (for assumed mean) and if the differences x - A are called 'd', the standard deviation is given by:

$$s = \sqrt{\frac{\sum(d - \bar{d})^2}{n}} \qquad \text{the definition formula}$$

or by

$$s = \sqrt{\frac{\Sigma d^2}{n} - d^2}$$ the calculation formula

This means we must calculate the average of the differences, d, but that no adjustment for the assumed mean, A, is necessary at the end of our calculations of standard deviation.

If we look back at the bottle volume example, suppose we guess a mean of 495, then A = 495 and the workings for the calculation formula are:

x	d (= x - 495)	d^2
496.8	1.8	3.24
502.7	7.7	59.29
500.6	5.6	31.36
501.2	6.2	38.44
497.3	2.3	5.29
499.2	4.2	17.64
502.0	7.0	49.00
500.2	5.2	27.04
	40.0	231.30

then we have:

$$\bar{d} = \frac{40.0}{8} = 5$$

and standard deviation is given by:

$$s = \sqrt{\frac{\Sigma d^2}{n} - \bar{d}^2} = \sqrt{\frac{231.30}{8} - 5^2}$$

$$= \sqrt{28.9125 - 25}$$

$$= \sqrt{3.9125}$$

$$= 1.978 \text{ (as before)}$$

7.10.4 Standard deviation for discrete, grouped data

For a frequency table giving frequencies for individual values we use modified versions of the formulae already given. The definition formula, for frequency data, is:

$$s = \sqrt{\frac{\Sigma f(x - \bar{x})^2}{f}}$$

and the calculation formula is:

$$s = \sqrt{\frac{\Sigma fx^2}{\Sigma f} - \bar{x}^2}$$

If we use the table giving number of cars purchased per day:

Number of cars purchased	Frequency
0	3
1	8
2	20
3	14
4	6
5	3
6 or more	1
	——
	55
	——

then the calculations for the standard deviation, using the definition formula, are:

x	f	fx	$(x - \bar{x})$	$(x - \bar{x})^2$	$f(x - \bar{x})^2$
0	3	0	-2.455	6.027025	18.081075
1	8	8	-1.455	2.117025	16.936200
2	20	40	-0.455	0.207025	4.140500
3	14	42	0.545	0.297025	4.158350
4	6	24	1.545	2.387025	14.322150
5	3	15	2.545	6.477025	19.431075
6	1	6	3.545	12.567025	12.567025
	——	——			——————
	55	135			89.636375
	——	——			——————

where the mean is:

$$\bar{x} = \frac{135}{55} = 2.455$$

and the standard deviation is given by:

$$s = \sqrt{\frac{\Sigma f(x - \bar{x})^2}{\Sigma f}} = \sqrt{\frac{89.636375}{55}}$$

$$= \sqrt{1.62975}$$

$$= 1.277$$

Using the calculation formula the working is:

x	f	fx	fx^2					
0	3	0	0	x	0	=	0	
1	8	8	1	x	8	=	8	
2	20	40	2	x	40	=	80	
3	14	42	3	x	42	=	126	
4	6	24	4	x	24	=	96	
5	3	15	5	x	15	=	75	
6	1	6	6	x	6	=	36	
	55	135					421	

The fx^2 column is worked out by taking the product of the x-column and the fx-column. The mean is 2.455 as we have already calculated, and standard deviation is:

$$s = \sqrt{\frac{\Sigma fx^2}{\Sigma f} - \bar{x}^2} = \sqrt{\frac{421}{55} - (2.455)^2}$$

$$= \sqrt{7.654545 - 6.027025}$$

$$= \sqrt{1.62752}$$

$$= 1.276$$

The slight difference in these results is due to the rounding of the mean used in the definition formula calculations.

If we use an assumed mean (= A) then the frequency formulae are:

$$s = \sqrt{\frac{\Sigma f(d - \bar{d})^2}{\Sigma f}} \qquad \text{the definition formula}$$

$$s = \sqrt{\frac{\Sigma fd^2}{\Sigma f} - \bar{d}^2} \qquad \text{the calculation formula}$$

If we assume a mean of 2 (A = 2) the calculations in this example are:

x	f	d (= x - 2)	fd	fd^2
0	3	-2	-6	12
1	8	-1	-8	8
2	20	0	0	0
3	14	1	14	14
4	6	2	12	24
5	3	3	9	27
6	1	4	4	16
	55		25	101

7.63

then we have that:

$$\bar{d} = \frac{\Sigma d}{n} = \frac{25}{55} = 0.455$$

and the standard deviation is:

$$s = \sqrt{\frac{\Sigma fd^2}{\Sigma f} - \bar{d}^2} = \sqrt{\frac{101}{55} - (0.455)^2}$$

$$= \sqrt{1.836364 - 0.207025}$$

$$= \sqrt{1.62934}$$

$$= 1.276$$

Again, the figure varies slightly because of rounding at different stages. Note that the interval '6 or over' has been treated as '6'.

7.10.5 Standard deviation of grouped, discrete data with class intervals

Next, we consider the situation where we have class intervals for the discrete data. To calculate the standard deviation we again adjust the limits of the class intervals so that they are equivalent to continuous intervals. Having done this we then use the mid-points of each interval as the x-value for the interval just as we have done previously. This allows us to use the frequency formulae already introduced. We can use this method whether intervals have equal or unequal widths. For the transactions example:

Number of transactions	Frequency
1-5	1
6-10	9
11-15	12
16-20	13
21-25	16
26-30	11
31-35	6
36-40	2
41-45	2
	72

The calculations, using the definition formula, are:

Mid-points

(x)	f	fx	x - x̄	$(x - \bar{x})^2$	$f(x - \bar{x})^2$
3	1	3	-17.847	318.51541	318.51541
8	9	72	-12.847	165.04541	1485.40869
13	12	156	-7.847	61.57541	738.90491
18	13	234	-2.847	8.10541	105.37032
23	16	368	2.153	4.63541	74.16654
28	11	308	7.153	51.16541	562.81950
33	6	198	12.153	147.69541	886.17245
38	2	76	17.153	294.22541	588.45082
43	2	86	22.153	490.75541	981.51082
	72	1,501			5741.31946

The mean is:

$$\bar{x} = \frac{\Sigma fx}{\Sigma f} = \frac{1,501}{72} = 20.847$$

and the standard deviation is given by:

$$s = \sqrt{\frac{\Sigma f(x - \bar{x})^2}{\Sigma f}} = \sqrt{\frac{5741.31946}{72}}$$

$$= \sqrt{79.74055}$$

$$= 8.930$$

Using the calculation formula the workings are rather shorter:

Mid-points

(x)	f	fx	fx^2
3	1	3	9
8	9	72	576
13	12	156	2,028
18	13	234	4,212
23	16	368	8,464
28	11	308	8,624
33	6	198	6,534
38	2	76	2,888
43	2	86	3,698
	72	1,501	37,033

Using the mean of 20.847, the standard deviation is:

$$s = \sqrt{\frac{\sum fx^2}{\sum f} - \bar{x}^2} = \sqrt{\frac{37,033}{72} - (20.847)^2}$$

$$= \sqrt{514.34722 - 434.59741}$$

$$= \sqrt{79.74981}$$

$$= 8.930$$

Once again, there are slight differences in the figures due to rounding.

Finally, if an assumed mean of 23 is used the workings are as follows (it is a good idea to choose one of the mid-points as the assumed mean):

Mid-points (x)	f	d (= x - 23)	fd	fd²
3	1	-20	-20	400
8	9	-15	-135	2,025
13	12	-10	-120	1,200
18	13	-5	-65	325
23	16	0	0	0
28	11	5	55	275
33	6	10	60	600
38	2	15	30	450
43	2	20	40	800
	72		-155	6,075

then:

$$\bar{d} = \frac{\sum fd}{\sum f} = \frac{-155}{72} = -2.153$$

and the standard deviation is given by:

$$s = \sqrt{\frac{\sum fd^2}{\sum f} - \bar{d}^2} = \sqrt{\frac{6,075}{72} - (-2.153)^2}$$

$$= \sqrt{84.375 - 4.63541}$$

$$= \sqrt{79.73959}$$

$$= 8.930$$

7.10.6 Standard deviation for continuous, grouped data

When we have a frequency table for a continuous variable we use the same approach and formula as for the discrete case. The only alteration is that, again, no adjustment to the class intervals is necessary.

Consider the sweet box weights example:

Weight of package (in grams)	Frequency
Under 490	1
490 but less than 495	3
495 but less than 500	12
500 but less than 505	22
505 but less than 510	8
510 or over	2
	48

To work out the standard deviation, we will again need to treat the open-ended intervals as having the same width as their adjacent intervals. The calculations for the definition formula are:

Mid-points

(x)	f	fx	x - $\bar{x}$	(x - $\bar{x}$)^2	f(x - $\bar{x}$)^2
487.5	1	487.5	-14.06	197.6836	197.6836
492.5	3	1,477.5	-9.06	82.0836	246.2508
497.5	12	5,970.0	-4.06	16.4836	197.8032
502.5	22	11,055.0	0.94	0.8836	19.4392
507.5	8	4,060.0	5.94	35.2836	282.2688
512.5	2	1,025.0	10.94	119.6836	239.3672
	48	24,075.0			1,182.8128

The mean is:

$$\bar{x} = \frac{\Sigma fx}{\Sigma f} = \frac{24,075}{48} = 501.56 \text{ grams}$$

and the standard deviation is :

$$s = \sqrt{\frac{\Sigma f(x - \bar{x})^2}{\Sigma f}} = \sqrt{\frac{1,182.8128}{48}}$$

$$= \sqrt{24.64193}$$

$$= 4.964$$

If the calculation formula is used, the workings are:

Mid-points (x)	f	fx	fx²
487.5	1	487.5	237,656.25
492.5	3	1,477.5	727,668.75
497.5	12	5,970.0	2,970,075.00
502.5	22	11,055.0	5,555,137.50
507.5	8	4,060.0	2,060,450.00
512.5	2	1,025.0	525,312.50
	48	24,075.0	12,076,300.00

then the standard deviation is:

$$s = \sqrt{\frac{\Sigma fx^2}{\Sigma f} - \bar{x}^2} = \sqrt{\frac{12,076,300}{48} - \frac{24,075}{48}^2}$$

$$= \sqrt{251,589.58 - 251,564.94}$$

$$= 24.64$$

$$= 4.964$$

If we use an assumed mean of 502.5 then the calculations are:

Mid-points (x)	f	d (= x - 502.5)	fd	fd²
487.5	1	-15	-15	225
492.5	3	-10	-30	300
497.5	12	-5	-60	300
502.5	22	-0	-0	0
507.5	8	5	40	200
512.5	2	10	20	200
	48		-45	1,225

The mean difference $\bar{d}$ is:

$$\bar{d} = \frac{\Sigma fd}{\Sigma f} = \frac{-45}{48} = -0.9375$$

and the standard deviation is then:

$$s = \sqrt{\frac{\Sigma fd^2}{\Sigma f} - \bar{d}^2} = \sqrt{\frac{1,225}{48} - (-0.9375)^2}$$

$$= \sqrt{25.52083 - 0.87891}$$

$$= 24.64193$$

$$= 4.964$$

7.68

7.10.7 Features of the standard deviation

The standard deviation has the following properties:

(a) It is fairly easy to calculate.

(b) It makes use of every value in the distribution.

(c) It is ideal for mathematical processing.

(d) It is the basis of further statistical developments.

(e) It can be distorted by extreme values.

(f) It is almost impossible to visualise what the figure for standard deviation represents.

Example 7.13

Find the standard deviation for the following sets of data:

(a) The number of new firms commencing trade, per month, in a metropolitan district were recorded each month for a year as:

   0,3, 2, 2, 1, 0, 1, 1, 5, 2, 1, 6

(b) A firm has recorded the number of applicants for posts it advertises. The figures are given in the following table:

Applicants	Frequency
1-5	17
6-10	38
11-15	19
16-20	13
21-25	5
over 25	1
	93

(c) The lengths of steel bars gave the following frequency distribution:

Length (in metres)	Frequency
Under 1.95	4
1.95 but less than 2.00	12
2.00 but less than 2.05	27
2.05 but less than 2.10	28
2.10 but less than 2.20	61
2.20 but less than 2.50	25
2.50 or over	3
	160

7.69

Solution

(a) For these figures:

$$\Sigma x = 24 \qquad \Sigma x^2 = 86$$

The mean is:

$$\bar{x} = \frac{\Sigma x}{n} = \frac{24}{12} = 2$$

The standard deviation is:

$$s = \sqrt{\frac{\Sigma x^2}{n} - \bar{x}^2} = \sqrt{\frac{86}{12} - 2^2}$$

$$= \sqrt{7.1667 - 4}$$

$$= 3.1667$$

$$= 1.78 \text{ (to 2 decimal places)}$$

(b)

Mid-points (x)	f	fx	fx²
3	17	51	153
8	38	304	2,432
13	19	247	3,211
18	13	234	4,212
23	5	115	2,645
28	1	28	784
	93	979	13,437

The mean is:

$$\bar{x} = \frac{\Sigma x}{n} = \frac{979}{93} = 10.52688$$

and the standard deviation is calculated as:

$$s = \sqrt{\frac{\Sigma fx^2}{\Sigma f} - \bar{x}^2} = \sqrt{\frac{13,437}{93} - (10.52688)^2}$$

$$= \sqrt{144.48387 - 110.81520}$$

$$= \sqrt{33.66867}$$

$$= 5.802$$

(c) Remembering to treat the open-ended intervals as having the same widths as their adjacent intervals, the calculations are:

Mid-points (x)	f	fx	fx^2
1.925	4	7.700	14.8225
1.975	12	23.700	46.8075
2.025	27	54.675	110.7169
2.075	28	58.100	120.5575
2.150	61	131.150	281.9725
2.350	25	58.750	138.0625
2.650	3	7.950	21.0675
	160	342.025	734.0069

The mean is:

$$\bar{x} = \frac{\sum x}{n} = \frac{342.025}{160} = 2.138 \text{ metres}$$

and the standard deviation is given by:

$$s = \sqrt{\frac{\sum fx^2}{\sum f} - \bar{x}^2} = \sqrt{\frac{734.0069}{160} - \frac{342.025}{160}^2}$$

$$= \sqrt{4.58754 - 4.56957}$$

$$= \sqrt{0.01797}$$

$$= 0.134 \text{ metres}$$

7.11 Comparison of measures of dispersion

Three measures of dispersion or spread have been discussed in the previous sections. By far the most commonly used of these measures is the standard deviation and this is because much of further statistical work (which we do not need to cover) develops from it.

All the measures increase in size as the data values become more spread. The range is sometimes used as a 'quick' method for finding spread but is only usually used where we have few data values. The least used is the mean deviation even though it is probably the easiest to understand. The standard deviation is usually quoted whenever the mean is used as measure of location.

7.12   Skewness

7.12.1   Definition

Skewness is a measure of whether a distribution of values is symmetrical or whether there is a 'tail' of values to one side or other. If there is a long tail of values towards the higher values this is called positive skewness, if the tail is towards the lower values this is called negative skewness.

7.12.2   Illustrations of skewness

The easiest way to identify whether a set of frequency data (whether discrete or continuous) is skewed or not is to draw a histogram. Its shape will tell us whether we have positively or negatively skewed data, or whether the data is symmetrical.

(a)   Symmetrical data

Suppose we have measured the lengths of 100 steel strips. The results were:

Length (in metres)	Frequency
9.80 but less than 9.90	3
9.90 but less than 10.00	17
10.00 but less than 10.10	30
10.10 but less than 10.20	30
10.20 but less than 10.30	17
10.30 but less than 10.40	3
	100

The histogram is:

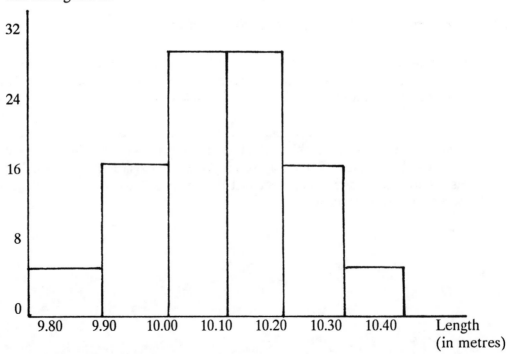

As can be seen the two 'ends' of the distribution drop at the same rates. This is an exactly symmetrical distribution. In practice distributions are very rarely exactly symmetrical. We look for the histogram being fairly symmetrical.

(b) Positive skewness

Suppose we have the following table of annual salaries for employees of a company:

Annual salary (£)	Number of employees
2,000 to < 4,000	2
4,000 to < 6,000	46
6,000 to < 8,000	183
8,000 to < 10,000	96
10,000 to < 12,000	40
12,000 to < 14,000	21
14,000 to < 16,000	13
16,000 to < 18,000	7
18,000 to < 20,000	3
20,000 or over	1
	412

then the histogram looks like this:

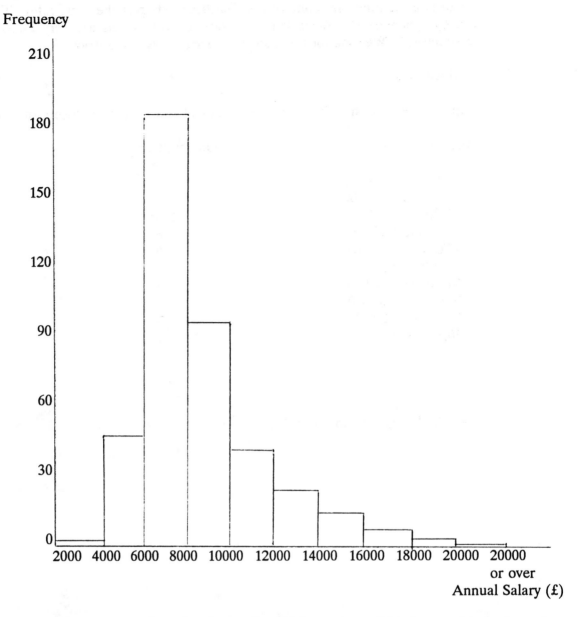

and we can see there is a long tail of higher values. This is a positively skewed set of data.

(c)   Negative skewness

Suppose we have recorded the journey times between two factories in the following table:

Journey time (minutes)	Frequency
20 but less than 25	1
25 but less than 30	4
30 but less than 35	7
35 but less than 40	15
40 but less than 45	28
45 but less than 50	9
50 or over	1
	65

then the histogram looks like this:

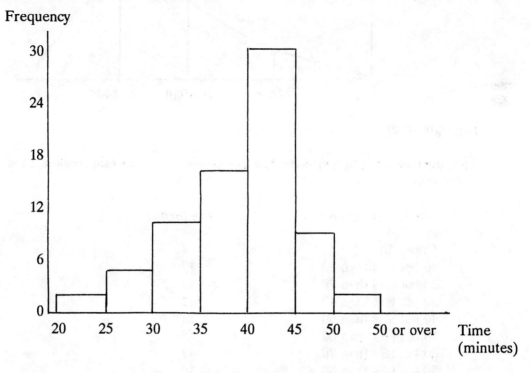

As can be seen the heights of the columns increase slowly from the lower values reaching a peak but then dropping very quickly from the peak. This is lop-sided with a long tail at the lower values so the data is negatively skewed.

When we have a symmetrical set of data then the mean, median and mode are at more or less the same value.

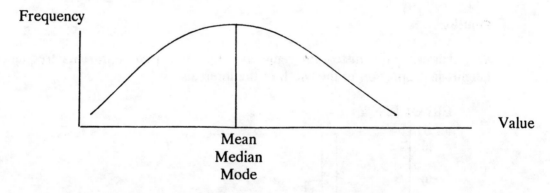

If, however, we have positively skewed data, then the mode has a lower value than the median which in turn has a lower value than the mean.

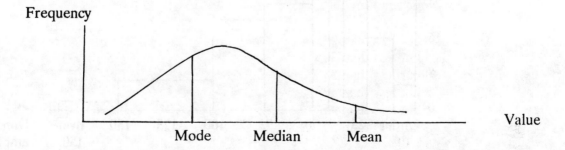

Finally, if we have negatively skewed data then the mode has a higher value than the median which in turn has a higher value than the mean.

0176z

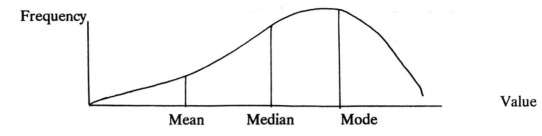

Example 10.20

The number of employees within companies in a certain region gave the following distribution:

Number of employees	Frequency
Under 10	4
10 but less than 20	12
20 but less than 20	28
30 but less than 40	47
40 but less than 50	35
50 but less than 60	55
60 but less than 70	42
70 but less than 80	16
80 but less than 90	6
	245

Draw a histogram and decide whether the data is skewed or symmetrical.

Solution

When drawing the histogram remember that the area represents frequency so adjust heights in proportion to the width of the intervals.

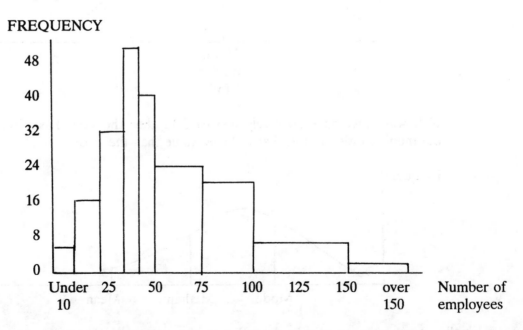

This has a long tail to the higher values, it is positively skewed.

7.13 Normal distribution

7.13.1 Introduction

If a continuous graph is drawn through a histogram we obtain a frequency curve and for a continuous variable this can be a smooth curve. This curve is called a probability density curve and the most commonly used is the 'normal' curve. This is a name rather than implying other curves are in some way odd!! The normal distribution curve is a symmetrical, bell-shaped graph like the diagram below:

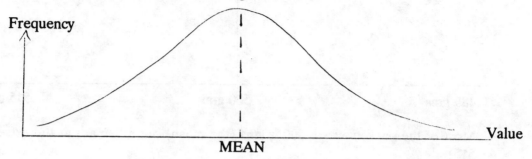

To specify the normal distribution curve we need two numbers:

(a)   the arithmetic mean of the population; and
(b)   the standard deviation of the distribution.

The normal curve is symmetrical about the arithmetic mean and the standard deviation determines how flat or peaked the distribution curve is. Many measurements in practice follow a normal distribution and so it is widely used for finding probabilities.

7.13.2 The area under the curve

The normal tables are used to find the probability of certain things happening, it may be the probability a person earns between £5,000 and £10,000 per annum, it may be the probability a component is over 2 cm in length and so on.

We could measure the area under the normal curve in many different ways. However, we are interested in the probability that a member of a population has a certain value and so we shall consider the area under the curve from this point of view.

Consider the weights of packets of butter produced by a machine. The lightest weighs 485 grams and the heaviest 515 grams. Assuming that the distribution is normal we might obtain the distribution as follows:

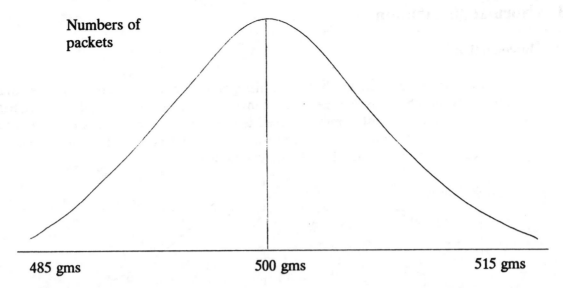

Numbers of
packets

485 gms   500 gms   515 gms

Most of the packets weigh 500 grams (the mean) but a few are at the extremes (485 and 515).

Remember that the total probability of something occuring is one (a packet of butter is bound to weigh between 485 and 515 grams), so we can say that the total area under the curve is one (any packet of butter is bound to weigh between 485 grams and 515 grams and so the total population must all lie under the curve). It also follows that the area under the curve to the left of the mean (the probability that a packet will weigh less than 500 grams) is 0.5, and the area under the curve to the right of the mean (the probability that a packet will weight more than 500 grams) is also 0.5.

7.13.3   Normal tables

The normal curve has the property that the area from the mean to a fixed number of standard deviations away from the mean is always the same regardless of the value of the standard deviation.

Consider the following two normal distributions:

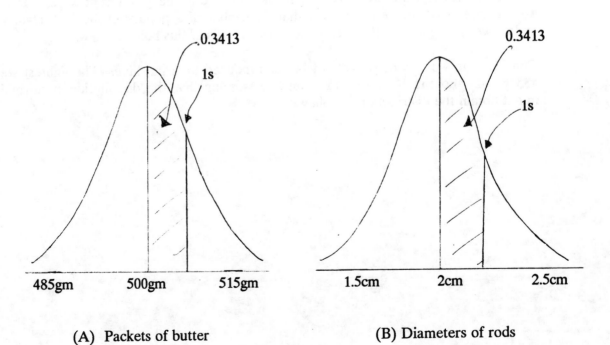

(A) Packets of butter   (B) Diameters of rods

Machine (A) produces 5,000 packets of butter per week that are normally distributed as shown with

> mean = 500 grams
> s (standard deviation) = 5 grams (say)

Machine (B) produces 2,000 rods per week that are normally distributed with

> mean = 2 cm
> s = 0.16 cm

No matter how different the products, the means of their distributions or their standard deviations, it is nevertheless the case that:

(a) the area under the curves between the mean and 1 standard deviation above the mean is 0.3413 (ie 34.13 % of the total area) in both cases.

(b) the area under the curves between the mean and 2 standard deviations above the mean is 0.4772 (ie 47.72% of the total area) in both cases.

(c) the area under the curve between the mean and 3 standard deviations above the mean is 0.4987 (ie 49.87% of the total area) in both cases.

Notes

1   These proportional or percentage amounts are given in the normal tables in the introduction. These tables give the area under the curve between the mean and any number of standard deviations above the mean up to 3.09 standard deviations.

2   Because the normal curve is symmetrical about the mean, the same tables also give the area under the curve below the mean.

3   Note that the area under the curve 3 standard deviations either side of the mean accounts for 0.9974 (0.4987 + 0.4987) of the population, ie 99.74% of the population is within 3 standard deviations of the mean.

Consider the tables in the introduction. 'Z' is the letter that stands for the number of standard deviations that a particular value is above (or below) the mean. Thus if a value is one standard deviation above the mean, the area under the normal curve between the mean and the value is 34.13%, representing a probability of 0.3413. Similarly, if the value is 1.14 standard deviations above (or below) the mean, the area under the curve would be 37.29% of the total area representing a probability of 0.3729.

7.13.4   Converting a value into a number of standard deviations

Suppose we know that the weights of packets of butter follow a normal distribution with average weight 500 grams and standard deviation 4 grams. If we pick a packet of butter at random, what is the chance its weight will be between 505 and 510 grams?

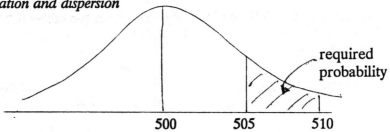

Note that the tables do not give the area under the curve between the mean and a value (505 grams or 15 cms etc); the tables only give the area between the mean and a number of standard deviations above the mean. Thus we have to convert the relevant values into a number of standard deviations.

Consider the area under the curve between the mean and 505 grams. This distance represents 505 - 500 = 5 grams.

$$
\begin{array}{lll}
\text{If} & 4 \text{ grams} = & 1 \text{ sd} \\
& 1 \text{ gram} = & 1/4 \text{ sd} \\
\text{Therefore} & 5 \text{ grams} = & 5/4 \text{ sd}
\end{array}
$$

In general therefore to convert a distance on the horizontal axis to a number of standard deviations we say:

$$\text{distance} = (\text{value - mean}) \text{ grams}$$

$$\text{no. of standard deviations} = \frac{\text{value - mean}}{\text{standard deviation}}$$

The number of standard deviations so calculated is the 'z-value' that is looked up in the tables.

The z-values in this illustration are therefore:

$$z = \frac{505-500}{4} = 1.25 \qquad \text{for the lower limit}$$

$$z = \frac{510-500}{4} = 2.5 \qquad \text{for the upper limit}$$

In our example we look up z = 1.25 and obtain the value of the area from the tables 0.3944:

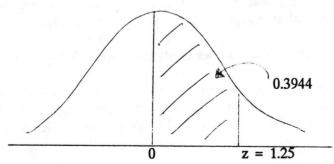

and if we look up z = 2.5 we obtain the area from the tables 0.4938:

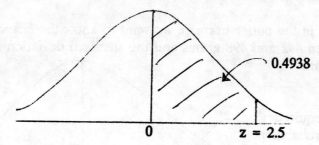

Combining the two pictures we have:

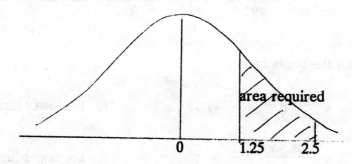

and the area we require is:

0.4938-0.3944 = 0.0994

This means that the probability of a packet weighing between 505 grams and 510 grams is 0.0994 or 9.94%.

Example 7.14

Look up the following z-values and find the corresponding probabilities from the tables:

(a)   z = 3.00.

(b)   z = 1.60.

(c)   z = 1.83.

(d)   z = 0.46.

(e)   z = 0.08.

Solution

(a)   0.4987.

(b)   0.4452.

(c)   0.4664.

(d)   0.1772.

(e)   0.0319.

7.13.5   Illustration

Now, suppose in the butter example we want to know the chance that a packet of butter weighs between 492 and 498 grams and the standard deviation is 5 grams. We have the following picture:

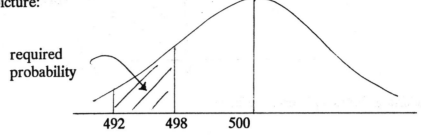

The z-values for the limits are:

$$z = \frac{492-500}{5} = -1.60 \qquad \text{for the lower limit}$$

$$\text{and} \quad z = \frac{498-500}{5} = -0.40 \qquad \text{for the upper limit}$$

The probability we require is:

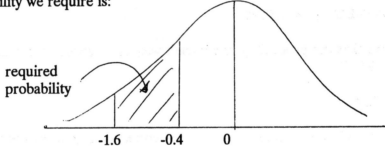

Using the symmetry of the normal distribution, when we get a negative limit we look it up in the tables as if it were positive to obtain the area from -z to zero. For these two limits looking up the tables gives:

For z = 1.6 the table value is 0.4552 so the area from -1.6 to zero is 0.4552

z = 0.4 the table value is 0.1554 so the area from -0.4 to zero is 0.1554

and the probability we require is:

$$0.4452 - 0.1554 = 0.2898$$

7.13.6 Illustration

If we want to know the chance a packet of butter will weigh between 495 and 507 grams with a standard deviation of 5 grams, then we require:

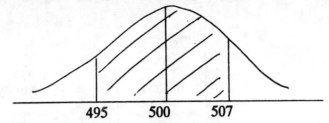

Working out the z-values for the limits we obtain:

$$z = \frac{495-500}{5} = -1 \qquad \text{for the lower limit}$$

$$z = \frac{507-500}{5} = 1.4 \qquad \text{for the upper limit}$$

so the probability we require is:

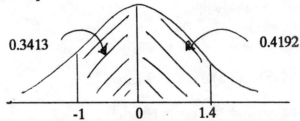

Looking up z = 1 in the tables will give us the area from -1 to zero. This value is 0.3413. Then looking up z = 1.4 in the tables gives us the area from zero to 1.4. This value is 0.4192. The probability we require is:

$$0.3413 + 0.4192 = 0.7605$$

Notice that we subtract the values obtained from the tables when the z-values have the same sign but add values if the z-values have different signs.

7.13.7 Illustration

The final situation we may have to deal with is the chance a packet of butter weighs more than 503 grams. We require:

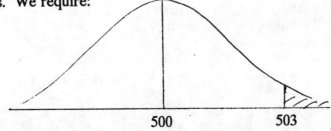

Working out the z-value for the one limit we obtain:

$$z = \frac{503-500}{5} = 0.6$$

The probability from the tables corresponding to this z-value is 0.2257. This is the area from 0 to z but we want the area above z. We know zero splits the normal distribution symmetrically, ie, 0.5 each side.

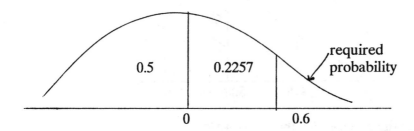

The probability we require is then:

$$0.5 - 0.2257 = 0.2743$$

Example 7.15

The lengths of steel pipes average 25 cm with standard deviation 0.5 cm. What is the probability a particular pipe will be:

(a)   between 25.3 cm and 26.5 cm in length;

(b)   between 23.7 cm and 24.6 cm in length;

(c)   between 24.5 cm and 26.0 cm in length?

Solution

(a)   The z-values are:

$$z = \frac{25.3-25.0}{0.5} = 0.6 \qquad \text{(lower limit)}$$

$$z = \frac{26.5-25.0}{0.5} = 3.0 \qquad \text{(upper limit)}$$

Looking up z = 0.6 gives 0.2257; and

z = 3.0 gives 0.4986

so the probability required is:
$$0.4986 - 0.2257 = 0.2729$$

(b)   The z-values are:

$$z = \frac{23.7-25.0}{0.5} = -2.6 \qquad \text{(lower limit)}$$

$$z = \frac{24.6-25.0}{0.5} = -0.8 \qquad \text{(upper limit)}$$

Looking up   z = 2.6 gives 0.4953; and
           z = 0.8 gives 0.2881

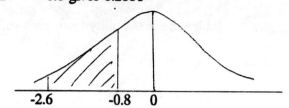

so the probability required is:

$$0.4953 - 0.2881 = 0.2072$$

(c)   The z-values are:

$$z = \frac{24.5-25.0}{0.5} = -1.0 \qquad \text{(lower limit)}$$

$$z = \frac{26.0-25.0}{0.5} = 2.0 \qquad \text{(upper limit)}$$

Looking up   z = 1.0 gives 0.3413; and
           z = 2.0 gives 0.4772

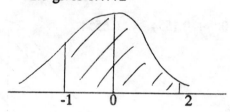

so the probability required is:

$$0.3413 + 0.4772 = 0.8185$$

Example 7.16

For the steel pipes with average length 25 cm and standard deviation 0.5 cm, what is the chance a particular pipe will be:

(a)   over 25.9 cm in length;

(b)   less than 25.2 cm in length;

(c)   less than 23.8 cm in length;

(d)   over 24.1 cm in length?

Solution

(a) The z-value for the limit is $\dfrac{25.9\text{-}25.0}{0.5} = 1.8$

From the tables the probability from zero to 1.8 is 0.4641.

The probability required is:

0.5 - 0.4641 = 0.0359

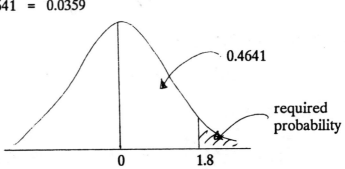

(b) The z-value for the limit is $\dfrac{25.2\text{-}25.0}{0.5} = 0.4$

From the tables the probability from zero to 0.4 is 0.1554.

The probability required is:

0.5 + 0.1554 = 0.6554

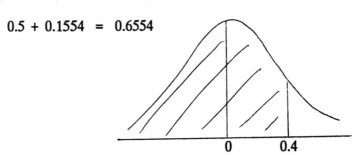

(c) The z-value for the limit is $\dfrac{23.8\text{-}25.0}{0.5} = -2.4$

From the tables the probability from zero to -2.4 is 0.4918.

The probability required is:

0.5 - 0.4918 = 0.0082

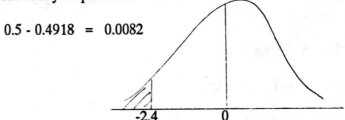

(d) The z-value for the limit is $\dfrac{24.1\text{-}25.0}{0.5} = -1.8$

From the tables the probability from zero to -1.8 is 0.4641.

The probability required is:

0.5 + 0.4641 = 0.9641

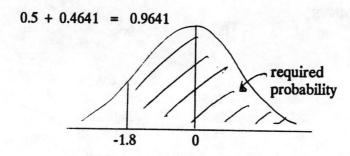

required probability

-1.8   0

Example 7.17

The wages distribution for a company is as follows:-

WEEKLY WAGE (£)	NUMBER OF EMPLOYEES
Under 50	0
50 but less than 75	17
75 but less than 100	53
100 but less than 125	58
125 but less than 150	42
150 but less than 200	18
200 or over	2
	___
	190

Find the range and the standard deviation for weekly wage.

Solution

The range is the difference between the bottom limit of the lower interval and the top limit of the higher interval. The first interval with a frequency is '£50 - £75' so the bottom limit of this interval is £50. The last interval with a frequency is '£200 or over'. As this is an open-ended interval treat it as if it had a width equal to its adjacent interval, ie, treat it as '£200 - £250' so the top limit is £250. This gives a range of:

RANGE = 250 - 50 = £200

To find out the standard deviation we carry out the following calculations:

MID-POINTS (x)	f	fx	fx^2
37.5	0	0	0
62.5	17	1,062.5	66,406.25
87.5	53	4,637.5	405,781.25
112.5	58	6,525.0	734,062.50
137.5	42	5,775.0	794,062.50
175.0	18	3,150.0	551,250.00
225.0	2	450.0	101,250.00
	190	21,600.0	2,652,812.50

Using the calculation formulae for mean and standard deviation:

$$\bar{x} = \frac{\Sigma fx}{\Sigma f} = \frac{21,600.0}{190} = £113.6842$$

and

$$s = \sqrt{\frac{\Sigma fx^2}{\Sigma f} - \bar{x}^2} = \sqrt{\frac{2,652,812.5}{190} - (113.6842)^2}$$

$$= \sqrt{13,962.171 - 12,924.100}$$

$$= \sqrt{1,038.07}$$

$$= £32.22$$

Example 7.18

A machine produces an average of 2,500 items per hour with standard deviation of 100 items per hour. What is the chance that the number of items produced on the machine in an hour will be:

(a)   between 2,600 and 2,700 items;

(b)   between 2,350 and 2,575 items;

(c)   over 2,425 items;

(d)   under 2,475 items?

Solution

We know that $\mu = 2,500$, $\sigma = 100$

(a)   We require $Pr(2,600 < x < 2,700)$ so firstly we must standardise the limits.

z-value for the lower limit is:

$$\frac{2,600-2,500}{100} \quad = \quad 1 \text{ and from tables, area is } 0.3413$$

z-value for the upper limit is:

$$\frac{2,700-2,500}{100} \quad = \quad 2 \text{ and from tables, area is } 0.4772$$

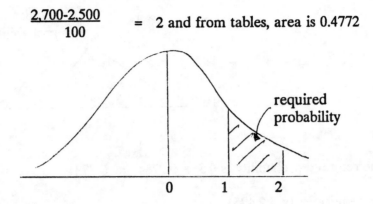

Required probability is 0.4772 - 0.3413 = 0.1359

(b)   We require Pr (2,350 < x < 2,575) so firstly standardise the limits.

z-value for the lower limit is:

$$\frac{2,350-2,500}{100} \quad = \quad -1.5 \text{ and from tables, area is } 0.4332$$

z-value for the upper limit is:

$$\frac{2,575-2,500}{100} \quad = \quad 0.75 \text{ and from tables, area is } 0.2734$$

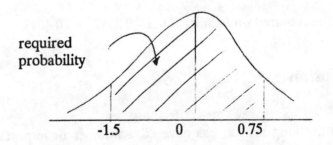

The required probability is 0.4332 + 0.2734 = 0.7066

(c)   We require Pr ($x \geq 2,425$).

The z-value for this limit is:

$$\frac{2,425-2,500}{100} = -0.75 \text{ and from the tables, area is } 0.2734$$

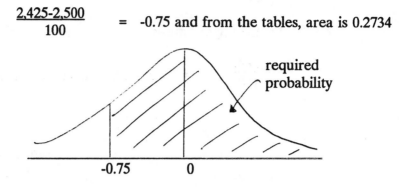

The required probability is $0.5 + 0.2734 = 0.7734$

(d)   We require Pr ($x \leq 2,475$).

The z-value for this limit is:

$$\frac{2,475-2,500}{100} = -0.25 \text{ and from the tables, area is } 0.0987$$

The required probability is $0.5 - 0.0987 = 0.4013$

7.14   Conclusion

This rather long session has covered a number of important statistical measures. You should be able to

●   calculate and contrast the three measures of central tendency

As for dispersion, there are many different statistics available, the most important of which are

●   standard deviation

●   quartile deviation

7.15 Questions

7.15.1 Objective test questions

(1)   The mean of 250 items of grouped data is to be found. With an assumed mean of 45 and a class interval of 10, the net sum of differences from the assumed mean in class intervals is 50. The mean is

A   47

B   50

C   70

D   95

(2)   A sample of a thousand people is selected at random and they are found to have incomes in the following ranges

Income (£)			Number
0	to under	5,000	120
5,000	to under	10,000	410
10,000	to under	15,000	385
15,000	to under	20,000	85

The median income to the nearest £5 is

A   £9,605

B   £9,635

C   £9,675

D   £10,000

(3)   The arithmetic mean of seven numbers is 12.429, and the sum of the squares of those numbers is 2,575. The standard deviation of the numbers is

A   14.6

B   18.9

C   49.2

D   49.9

7.15.2 Written test questions

7.1 Pay increase

During the pay negotiations the management of a company made the following offer to the representatives of the workers:

Pay increase (£)	Percentage of workers who will receive such an increase
2.50	46
3.00	24
4.00	15
9.60	15

An argument ensues as to the interpretation of the 'average' pay increase which has been offered. Perform any necessary calculation and explain why the argument arises.

7.2 Mekon

The Mekon Production Company have produced the following table showing weekly production for a period of 200 weeks.

Production output (000s units)			Number of weeks
40	to under	60	10
60	"	80	25
80	"	100	36
100	"	110	28
110	"	120	30
120	"	140	34
140	"	160	28
160	"	180	9
			200

(a) Draw the histogram representing these data.

(b) Find the arithmetic mean and the standard deviation of production.

(c) State in which classes the median and the mode will lie and suggest circumstances where:

(i) the median; and
(ii) the mode

may be more useful than the arithmetic mean.

(d) Estimate the mode using a histogram.

7.3 South Yorkshire

The monthly unemployment figures (males and females) in South Yorkshire in 1978 were as follows (to nearest thousand):

Month	J	F	M	A	M	J	J	A	S	O	N	D
No unemployed	35	34	33	34	33	37	41	42	39	37	36	35

Source: Manpower Services Commission

Evaluate the mean, median and mode number of unemployed for 1978.

Suppose it was found that the July and August figures had failed to include school leavers registering at offices in a particular area. If the correct figures for July and August should be 43 and 44 respectively, what effect would this have on the measures of location found earlier. Justify your conclusions.

7.4   Three shifts

Items are produced to a target dimension of 32.5mm on a single machine. Production is carried out on each of three shifts, each shift having a different operator, A, B and C. It is decided to investigate the accuracy of the operators. The results of a sample of 100 items produced by each operator are as follows:

Dimension of items (mms)

Operator	32.1	32.2	32.3	32.4	32.5	32.6	32.7	32.8	32.9
A	1	6	10	21	36	17	6	2	1
B	0	0	7	25	34	27	6	1	0
C	3	22	49	22	4	0	0	0	0

(a)   Determine by means of appropriate statistical measures which of the operators is:

   (i)   the most accurate in keeping to the target; and
   (ii)   the most consistent in his results.

(b)   Explain why the mean of the dimension produced by each operator is an inadequate guide to his performance.

7.5   Plastic containers

The capacity of a batch of plastic containers averages 1,000 cc. The standard deviation is 20 cc. What is the chance a container chosen at random will have capacity:

(a)   under 1,012 cc;
(b)   between 1,005 and 1,008 cc;
(c)   between 992 and 1,003 cc;
(d)   over 998 cc?

SESSION 8

Correlation and regression

By now, you should be familiar with graphs of all shapes and sizes. In this session we revert to the simplest of them all - the straight line. We shall see how to establish a relationship between two variables and how to assess its strength.

8.1 Correlation

8.1.1 Introduction

This study session covers two topics - correlation and regression - which are closely linked. They are both concerned with relationships between two variables (sets of figures) where changes in one variable are accompanied by changes in another. For example, if information were collected on the ages of husbands and wives it would be found that, in general, the older husbands were married to the older wives although there will obviously be exceptions. Furthermore there is no exact mathematical relationship in this case. It is not possible to say that because a man of 30 is married to a woman of 28 that a man twice as old (ie, 60) will be married to a woman of 56, and indeed no exact rule exists. It is simply known that, generally, older men are married to older women. This rather nebulous type of relationship can be investigated and, hopefully, quantified by the techniques of correlation and regression.

8.1.2 Correlation

The theory of correlation enables us to measure the overall strength of the relationship between two variables, such as height and weight of a person. For your examination, you need only understand 'simple' correlation where the relationship is linear (this will become clear in the following paragraph) and only two variables are involved. However, in its more advanced forms, correlation is a very important tool for the statistician.

8.1.3 Scatter diagrams

Presented with some pairs of measurements for two variables (eg, height and weight), we can make a rough estimate of the correlation between them by plotting all the known values on a graph. This is called a **scatter diagram** because we examine it to determine how widely the points are scattered over it. If all the points appear to lie about a straight line we have linear correlation, whereas if the points appear to lie along a curved path the correlation is curvilinear.

If the points are scattered at random over the graph with no particular pattern emerging we say the variables are uncorrelated. Some examples of scatter diagrams are given in the following paragraph.

8.1.4 Examples

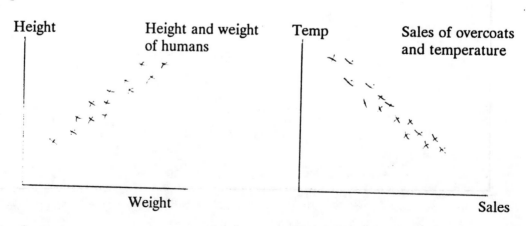

Positive linear correlation

Negative linear correlation

Output of crops
and hours of sunshine

Road casualties and
sugar imports

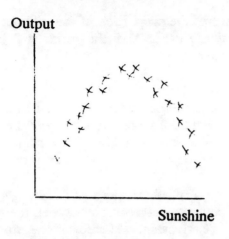

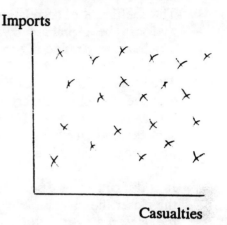

Curvilinear correlation

No correlation

The curvilinear correlation is only given as an example but the theory is outside the scope of your syllabus.

8.1.5 Quantitative methods

By direct observation of the scatter diagram we can determine in a **qualitative** manner how well a given line describes the relationship between the variables. However if we wish to deal with the problem of scattering of the data about a line in a **quantitative** manner we need to investigate a measure of correlation.

8.2 Correlation coefficient

8.2.1 Pearsonian measure

There are many different measures of correlation but the one most commonly used is called Pearson's product moment coefficient of correlation (r). The formula for this measure can be expressed in many different ways, some of the most common being listed below. There is obviously no need to remember them all as they are only different ways of writing down the same expression and will all give exactly the same answer.

8.2.2 Formulae

$$1 \quad r = \frac{\text{covariance (x, y)}}{\Sigma x \ \Sigma y} = \frac{\Sigma (x - \bar{x})(y - \bar{y})}{\sqrt{\Sigma (x - \bar{x})^2 \ \Sigma (y - \bar{y})^2}}$$

$$2 \quad r = \frac{n\Sigma xy - \Sigma x \ \Sigma y}{\sqrt{[n \ \Sigma x^2 - (\Sigma x)^2][n\Sigma y^2 - (\Sigma y)^2]}}$$

8.2.3 Interpretation

It is easy to see that all of the preceding formulae are symmetrical in x and y. This emphasises the fact that, for the purposes of measuring correlation, it does not matter which of the variables is chosen as x and which as y.

(**Note:** This is different from regression where it is important to identify the independent and dependent variables and label them x and y respectively.)

The coefficient of correlation simply measures the proportion of the value of one variable that can be **explained** by knowledge of the other and the result will be the same whichever way round the variables are chosen.

The values of the correlation coefficient range from -1 to +1. A magnitude of 1 implies that the variables are perfectly correlated and the points on a scatter diagram will lie on the same straight line. If r = +1 this line will have a positive slope and the variables are said to be perfectly positively correlated. Conversely if r = -1 the slope of the line is negative and there is perfect negative correlation. If r = 0 then there is no correlation.

It is difficult to give such exact interpretation to other values of r although, in all cases, the closer the magnitude of r is to 1 the better the correlation between the variables and the closer to zero, the less strong the relationship. Moreover the strength of the relationship is not proportional to r so that an r of 0.9 does not indicate twice as strong a relationship as one of 0.45. The full interpretation of values of r depends on many factors, one of the most important being the sample size or number of pairs of observations (n). The larger the sample considered the more reliable the result will be.

8.2.4 Illustration

x	y			
1	1	$\bar{x} = \dfrac{\sum x}{n}$	$= \dfrac{28}{7}$	$= 4$
2	2			
3	6			
4	7	$\bar{y} = \dfrac{\sum y}{n}$	$= \dfrac{63}{7}$	$= 9$
5	10			
6	16			
7	21			

$\sum x = 28 \quad \sum y = 63$

$x - \bar{x}$	$(x - \bar{x})^2$	$y - \bar{y}$	$(y - \bar{y})^2$	$(x - \bar{x})(y - \bar{y})$
-3	9	-8	64	24
-2	4	-7	49	14
-1	1	-3	9	3
0	0	-2	4	0
1	1	1	1	1
2	4	7	49	14
3	9	12	144	36
	28		320	92

$$r = \frac{\sum(x - \bar{x})(y - \bar{y})}{\sqrt{\sum(x - \bar{x})^2 \; \sum(y - \bar{y})^2}} = \frac{92}{\sqrt{28 \times 320}} = 0.972$$

Although the sign can be taken as either positive or negative where a square root is used, it is easy to see from the original data that the two variables tend to increase together and therefore any correlation will be positive.

A value of 0.972 is very close to 1, indicating that the correlation is very high. However with a sample size as small as 7 the result may not be statistically significant. Statistical tables exist giving significant values of r for various sample sizes but this is of more use for practical rather than examination work.

8.2.5 Spurious correlation

It is possible to calculate the correlation coefficient for any two variables where corresponding pairs of values are given and it is important to realise that high correlation between two variables does not imply that a cause and effect relationship exists between them.

There could well be a high correlation between ice cream sales and bikini sales but this does not prove that you could achieve higher ice cream sales by starting a sales drive on bikinis. There is a common cause behind the high correlation here, namely changes in the seasons and the associated weather. Correlation is not synonymous with causation.

In some cases high correlation has been proved between two variables where not even a common cause for the variations can be found. For example, there has been high correlation between the annual number of TV licences issued and the annual admissions into mental institutions. This is known as spurious correlation.

8.3 Regression

8.3.1 Introduction

When demonstrating linear correlation on scatter diagrams in an earlier part of this session, a straight line approximation for the relationship between the variables was plotted on the graph. The line was fitted by inspection of the points on the diagram with a view to producing what might be called a 'line of best fit'. A more formal approach to producing a line of best fit is known as the method of least squares and the resulting line is called the regression line. Before investigating the method it may be advisable to briefly revise the general equation and properties of a straight line.

8.3.2 Straight lines

The general equation of a straight line is $y = bx + a$ where a and b are constants for any given line. The constant **b** determines the slope or gradient of the line, while **a** gives the point at which it cuts the y axis. If these two constants are known, the line is fixed and may be plotted on a graph. For example, consider $y = -2x + 1$.

The gradient is -2 (ie, the line slopes backwards with a gradient of 2 : 1) and it cuts the y axis at $y = 1$.

The easiest way to plot a given line is to:

(a)   set $x = 0$ and determine y;

(b)   set $y = 0$ and determine x;

(c)   joint these two points and extend the line on either side as far as required.

In the above example:

when x = 0 y = 1

and   when y = 0 -2x + 1 = 0, ie, x = $^1/2$

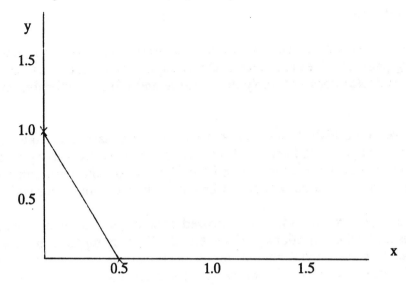

If you are still not very confident about drawing straight lines you should invent a few simple ones and draw them from practice. You must be able to draw a straight line on a graph from an equation because most examination questions on regression ask for the regression line to be drawn.

8.3.3   Method of least squares

Before launching into the technical details of the theory, consider the figures used for calculating the correlation coefficient in the previous section to relate to seven different plants of the same species as shown below:

Age of plant (weeks)	1	2	3	4	5	6	7
Height of plant (cms)	1	2	6	7	10	16	21

These figures may be plotted on a scatter diagram but obviously the pattern will depend on which variable is plotted on which axis.

The technique of regression, unlike correlation, requires a particular choice of variables for the x and y axes, the rule being:

x axis - independent variable
y axis - dependent variable

It is therefore necessary, before proceeding further, to establish which of the variables in the above example depends on the other. You should have no difficulty in convincing yourself that the height of the plant is dependent upon its age rather than the other way round. Thus the age will be plotted along the horizontal (x) axis and the height along the vertical (y) axis.

With the variables chosen this way round, the resulting regression line enables a forecast to be made for the **dependent** variable from a given value of the **independent** variable. This regression line must not be used to make predictions in the opposite direction, ie, to forecast a value for the **independent** variable from a given value of the **dependent** variable.

The resulting scatter diagram is as shown:

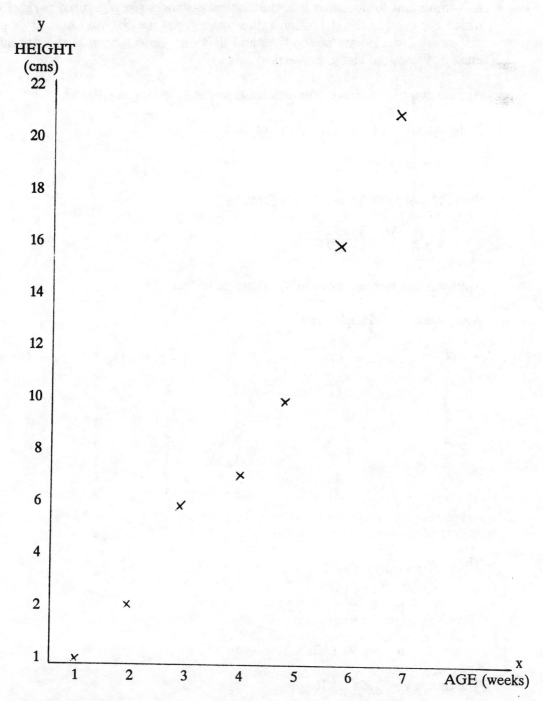

It would be impossible to draw one straight line which passes through all these points but, from the pattern on the graph, it seems reasonable to accept a straight line as an approximation for the relationship between the two variables. This is reinforced by the value of the correlation coefficient (previously calculated as +0.972) which implies high positive correlation.

8.3.4   Criterion and calculation

The criterion by which the regression line is fixed leads to its alternative name of 'least squares line' and also helps to emphasise the importance of choosing the dependent and independent variables correctly.

Of all the straight lines which may be drawn, the regression line is the one such that the sum of the squares of the **vertical** distances of the scatter points from the line is minimised.

8.7

It is important to note that it is the vertical distances (ie, measured parallel to the y axis) which are used in the definition rather than the more obvious shortest or perpendicular distances of the points of the line, and it is for this reason that the dependent variable must be measured along the vertical axis.

Application of the above criterion leads to the following results.

If the equation of the regression line is:

$$y = bx + a$$

then the constants 'a' and 'b' are given by:

$$b = \frac{\Sigma(x - \bar{x})(y - \bar{y})}{\Sigma(x - x)^2} \qquad a = y - b\bar{x}$$

Applying this to the figures in the example we get:

Age (weeks)   Height (cms)

x	y	x - x	y - y	$(x - x)^2$	(x - x) (y - y)
1	1	-3	-8	9	24
2	2	-2	-7	4	14
3	6	-1	-3	1	3
4	7	0	-2	0	0
5	10	1	1	1	1
6	16	2	7	4	14
7	21	3	12	9	36
				28	92

Thus

$$b = \frac{92}{28} = 3.29$$

$$a = 9 - (3.29 \times 4) = -4.16$$

The line is y = 3.29x - 4.16.

8.3.5 Interpolation and extrapolation

One important reason for calculating the equation of a regression line is to enable estimations to be made for values of the dependent variable corresponding to given values of the independent variable. These estimates are likely to be reliable provided that the chosen value of the independent variable is within the range of values given in the data. Using the regression line for extrapolation outside these limits, however, can produce misleading results since it does not follow that the variables continue to be approximately linearly related beyond the given range.

To illustrate this, consider the following examples using the regression line calculated above:

(a)   What would be the expected height of a plant aged $5^1/2$ weeks?

y = 3.29x (- 4.16)   where x = 5.5

y = 13.94 cms

(b)   What would be the expected height of a plant aged $^1/2$ week?

y = 3.29x (- 4.16)   where x = 0.5

y = -2.52 cms

(c)   What would be the expected height of a plant aged 100 weeks?

y = 3.29x (- 4.16)   where x = 100

y = 324.84 cms

Although answer (a) seems reasonable, the results of (b) and (c) look rather peculiar. In (b) we might expect that a plant had not germinated within $^1/2$ week and therefore would have a height of zero, but a negative figure does not make sense. Similarly the result of (c) might be rather alarming if this were a house plant!

We conclude that the regression line is a good approximation for the relationship between the age and height of this type of plant over the first seven weeks of life, although for an age of less than one week the equation gives negative heights which might sensibly be interpreted as zero. The relationship may be assumed to continue beyond seven weeks but we are not justified in making this assumption without being given more information. In practice, a plant would be expected to reach a maximum height and stop growing. Even before maximum height is attained, the rate of growth may slow down considerably compared with growth in the early stages of its development. Great care must therefore be taken when interpreting extrapolated results.

8.4   Step by step illustration 1

Plot the following data on a scatter diagram and comment on the pattern shown:

OUTPUT (thousands of units)	COST OF PRODUCTION (£000s)
5	11.8
7	14.7
9	18.5
11	24.0
13	26.2
15	30.1

Calculate the regression line of the total cost on output and hence estimate the fixed and variable costs of production.

Solution

To plot the scatter diagram we must first determine which variable is x and which is y (we must get them the right way round because the regression line is also required).

We can say that costs are dependent on output:

therefore   cost of production - y (dependent variable)
output - x (independent variable)

The scatter diagram is as follows:

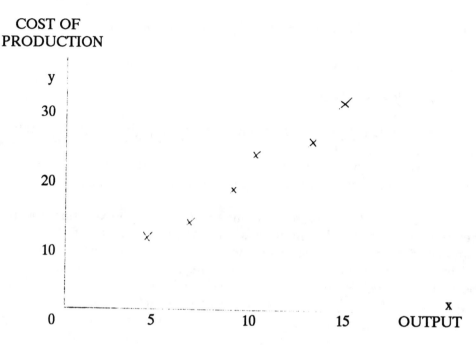

COST OF
PRODUCTION

The scatter diagram shows that the points group very closely about a straight line and thus indicates that there is a very strong positive linear association between level of output and cost of production.

Regression line

x	y	x - x̄	y - ȳ	(x - x̄) (y - ȳ)	(x - x̄)^2
5	11.8	-5	-9.08	45.40	25
7	14.7	-3	-6.18	18.54	9
9	18.5	-1	-2.38	2.38	1
11	24.0	+1	3.12	3.12	1
13	26.2	+3	5.32	15.96	9
15	30.1	+5	9.22	46.10	25
				———	——
				131.50	70

$\bar{x} = 10 \qquad \bar{y} = 20.88$

$$b = \frac{\Sigma(x - \bar{x})(y - \bar{y})}{\Sigma(x - \bar{x})^2} = \frac{131.50}{70} = 1.88$$

$$a = \bar{y} - b\bar{x} = 20.88 - (1.88 \times 10)$$

$$= 2.08$$

8.10

Regression line is

$$y = 1.88x + 2.08$$

Thus fixed cost $= £2,080$

variable cost $= £1,880$ per 1,000 units

8.5 Step by step illustration 2

(a) The following data shows the total payroll value and total value of output for ten industrial plants each manufacturing the same product. Calculate the correlation coefficient.

Super Manufacturing Co Limited
Payroll and value of Product X's output

Plant	Total payroll	Total value of Product X's output
	£ (thousands)	£ (thousands)
1	5	8
2	3	6
3	7	8
4	4	5
5	8	9
6	2	6
7	6	5
8	8	11
9	6	9
10	7	10

(b) What is the purpose of finding the correlation coefficient in respect of the above data and what does the value of the coefficient signify?

Solution

(a) Here the dependent variable is production (since this is likely to depend on the level of pay). The Pearson product-moment correlation coefficient is then found as follows:

Plant	Payroll (£000s) x	Production (£000s) y	x- x	y - y	(x - x) (y - y)	(x - x)²	(y - y)²
1	5	8	-0.6	0.3	-0.18	0.36	0.09
2	3	6	-2.6	-1.7	4.42	6.76	2.89
3	7	8	1.4	0.3	0.42	1.96	0.09
4	4	5	-1.6	-2.7	4.32	2.56	7.29
5	8	9	2.4	1.3	3.12	5.76	1.69
6	2	6	-3.6	-1.7	6.12	12.96	2.89
7	6	5	0.4	-2.7	-1.08	0.16	7.29
8	8	11	2.4	3.3	7.92	5.76	10.89
9	6	9	0.4	1.3	0.52	0.16	1.69
10	7	10	1.4	2.3	3.22	1.96	5.29
	56	77			28.80	38.4	40.10

$$x = 5.6 \qquad y = 7.7$$

Correlation coefficient =

$$\frac{\Sigma(x - \bar{x})(y - \bar{y})}{\sqrt{\Sigma(x - \bar{x})^2 \, \Sigma(y - \bar{y})^2}} \qquad = \quad \frac{28.8}{\sqrt{38.4 \times 40.1}} \quad = \quad 0.734$$

(b)   The purpose of calculating the coefficient of correlation for the data given in the question is to ascertain whether or not there is a relationship between changes in payroll and the value of the output of Product X; the coefficient also shows the degree of relationship if one exists.

If there is a known relationship, management can use it to predict the likely effect on production of changes in the value of the payroll from month to month.

The value of the correlation coefficient can range from -1, signifying perfect and inverse correlation (eg, a 10% increase in price being accompanied by a similar decrease in demand) to +1, signifying perfect and positive correlation (eg, a 10% increase in wages). The closer to zero is the calculated coefficient, the lower is the degree of relationship between the variables being compared.

In the present example, the value of the coefficient is 0.734. This shows that there is a positive relationship between the payroll and the output of Product X, but the degree of correlation is not particularly high. (If the payroll had consisted of wages paid under a strict piece-rate system, with no guaranteed basic weekly rate, the value of the coefficient would have been +1.)

8.6   Step by step illustration 3

Determine the correlation coefficient for the following figures:

	x	y
1976	10	20
1977	60	25

Explain why your answer comes to the figure it does. What conclusion can you draw from this exercise regarding the interpretation of the correlation coefficient for small samples?

Solution

The correlation coefficient is found as follows:

x	y	$x - \bar{x}$	$y - \bar{y}$	$(x - \bar{x})(y - \bar{y})$	$(x - \bar{x})^2$	$(y - \bar{y})^2$
10	20	-25	-2.5	62.5	625	6.25
60	25	+25	+2.5	62.5	625	6.25
				125.0	1,250	12.50

$\bar{x} = 35 \qquad \bar{y} = 22.5$

$$ r = \frac{\Sigma(x - \bar{x})(y - \bar{y})}{\sqrt{\Sigma(x - \bar{x})^2 \; \Sigma(y - \bar{y})^2}} = \frac{125}{\sqrt{1,250 \times 12.5}} = +1 $$

This answer must seem rather strange when you look at the original figures. It implies perfect correlation but the original figures do not appear to be at all correlated. However, if the scatter diagram were drawn it would be obvious why there is perfect correlation. With only two points in the diagram, the line of best fit is bound to go through both of them and in any case where all the points on the scatter diagram lie on the line of best fit there is perfect correlation.

The conclusion is that the value of r will be reasonably close to 1 for small samples but, as the sample size increases it becomes increasingly more difficult to find a line of best fit which lies close to all the points on the scatter diagram and the value of r diminishes. Thus high values of r (close to 1) are more significant for large samples than for small ones.

8.7   Conclusion

Establishing a regression equation is a simple arithmetic exercise but care needs to be taken in allocating the x and y variables.

Calculation of the correlation coefficient is not difficult but again, care must be taken with its interpretation.

8.8 Questions

8.8.1 Objective test questions

(1) A student gained 50% in a 'mock' examination but was unable to sit the final examination due to illness. The following information is available relating to the performances of the other candidates:

Average mock mark $(\bar{m})$ = 41%   Average final mark $(\bar{f})$ = 43.2%

$$\sum(m - \bar{m})^2 = 2,780 \qquad \sum(f - \bar{f})^2 = 3,125$$

$$\sum(m - \bar{m})(f - \bar{f}) = 2,500$$

What is the 'least squares' regression line estimate of the mark the absent candidate would have obtained in the final examination?

A   46.44%
B   47.12%
C   51.30%
D   54.45%

(2)

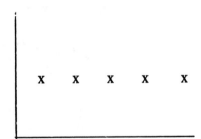

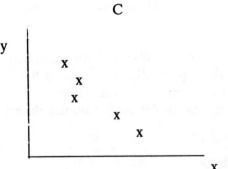

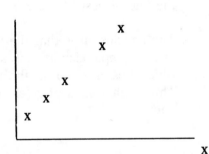

The above scatter diagrams represent five pairs of values for the variables x and y. Which diagram indicates a correlation coefficient of zero?

A   (A)
B   (B)
C   (C)
D   (D)

(3) A large number of pairs of values for two variables, x and y, are noted and the correlation coefficient is calculated to be approximately 0.5. The appropriate regression line for the variables is given by y = a + bx.

Which of the following is the correct conclusion?

A A value of y, given x, can be predicted with 50% accuracy
B 25% of the variation in y can be explained by variation in x
C 25% of the data will lie on the regression line
D 50% of the variation in y can be explained by variation in x

8.8.2 Written test questions

8.1 Freight

Figures for delivery charges on a fixed volume of freight but over different distances have been compiled by a company's accountant as follows:

Distance (100s miles)	6	13	27	15	9	11	21	14	12
Delivery charge (£)	49	93	159	115	66	90	139	98	88

Determine the regression line for these data and interpret the two regression constants 'a' and 'b'. Hence estimate the delivery charge for the same volume of freight on a 2,000 mile journey.

8.2 Vide and Feldt

Vide and Feldt Limited is a printing company whose main output is romantic novels. They wish to investigate how the cost of printing these books varies with the size of book.

Details have been obtained of the costs of producing ten books of varying size and these are given below:

NUMBER OF PAGES	COST (£)
362	142
264	174
285	195
451	260
363	234
418	246
300	161
492	296
338	220
464	287

(a) Represent the above data on a graph and comment on any observed features of the graph.

(b) Use the method of least squares to derive a linear relationship between book size (x) and cost (y) in the form y = bx + a.

    (c)   Explain the constants 'a' and 'b' in this particular equation.

    (d)   Estimate from your equation the cost of a proposed book of 550 pages and comment on the reliability of your estimate.

8.3   Miners

For the period 19X1-X7, the coal production, number of miners killed underground and average weekly earnings of underground workers were as follows:

Year	Coal production (million tons)	Persons killed underground	Average weekly earnings (in £s)
19X1	153	84	23.34
19X2	140	82	24.93
19X3	133	66	28.35
19X4	109	57	31.96
19X5	127	74	36.56
19X6	97	37	38.46
19X7	115	55	58.65

By plotting appropriate scatter diagrams comment on the association between coal production and number of persons killed, and between coal production and average weekly earnings.

8.4   Petrol stations

Ten petrol stations (A-J) which are situated in areas of similar traffic density are ranked according to quality of service, rank 1 indicating best service. The price of the petrol sold at each garage and the average weekly petrol sales are given below:

Station	Quality of service	Petrol price (£ per gallon)	Sales (hundreds of gallons)
A	3	1.66	47
B	7	1.71	20
C	4	1.70	23
D	8	1.65	36
E	2	1.67	36
F	5	1.67	31
G	10	1.72	33
H	9	1.69	28
I	1	1.67	42
J	6	1.68	24

    (a)   Using Pearson's correlation coefficient, determine whether the price of petrol or quality of service appears to be the more important factor in determining the volume of petrol sales, or whether neither appears to be important.

    (b)   For what reason do you think that the above analysis has been confined to areas of similar traffic density?

SESSION 9

Time series analysis

In this session we shall consider more complicated relationships between two variables. One of the variables will be 'time' and we shall see that time series analysis involves identifying four components of the series for further analysis.

9.1   Introduction

9.1.1   A time series is a set of values for some variable (eg, monthly production) which varies with time. The set of observations will be taken at specific times, usually at regular intervals. Examples of figures which can be plotted as a time series are:

(a)   monthly rainfall in London;

(b)   daily closing price of a share on the Stock Exchange;

(c)   weekly sales in a department store.

The following graph shows the birth rate in the Netherlands from 1956-1960.

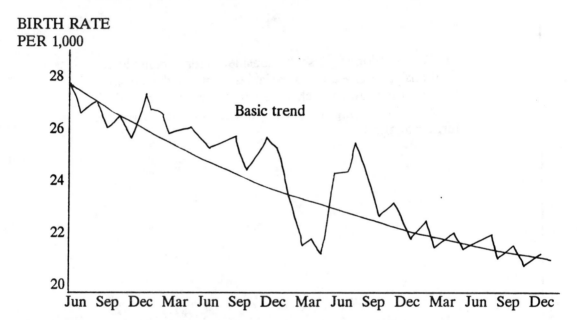

In such a graph each point is joined to the next by a straight line hence the typically 'jagged' appearance. Do not make the mistake of trying to construct a smooth curve which will pass through all the points on a time series graph. You will find it practically impossible and, in any case, it is incorrect to do so. In fact, the only reason for joining the points at all is to give a clearer picture of the pattern, which would be more difficult to interpret from a series of dots.

9.1.2   **Time series analysis**

The graph of a time series may be useful for investigating what happened in the past but the real importance of studying a time series is trying to use it to **forecast** what will happen in the future. In other words the past information is recorded, analysed and projected into the future to help with production planning, staff recruitment, etc.

9.2   Characteristic movements

9.2.1   Analysis of time has revealed certain characteristic movements or variations, some or all of which are present to varying degrees. These movements are sometimes called the **components** of the time series. Analysis of these components is essential for forecasting purposes. The four main types of components are:

(a)   long-term movements or basic trend;
(b)   cyclical movements;
(c)   seasonal movements;
(d)   irregular or random movements.

To illustrate these features, the figures below show the graphs of the components of a time series as they are built up into the graph of the complete time series.

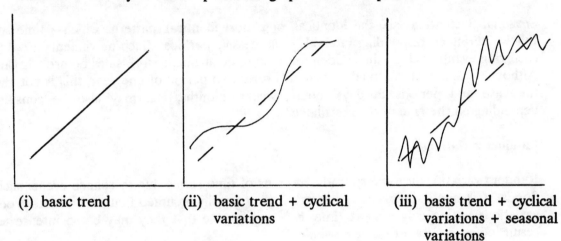

(i) basic trend

(ii) basic trend + cyclical variations

(iii) basis trend + cyclical variations + seasonal variations

9.2.2   **Basic trend**

The basic trend refers to the general direction in which the graph of a time series appears to be going over a long interval of time. This movement can be represented on the graph by a trend curve or line. Three of the most common basic trends are:

(a)   parabolic trend;
(b)   arithmetic trend;
(c)   compound interest trend (semi-logarithmic).

Trend curves for these are illustrated below.

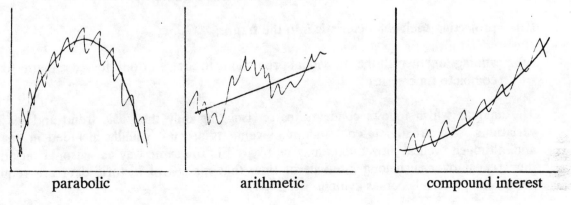

parabolic

arithmetic

compound interest

9.2.3 Cyclical variations

Cyclical variations refer to long-term oscillations or swings about the trend line or curve. These cycles may or may not be periodic, ie, they do not necessarily follow exactly similar patterns after equal intervals of time. In business and economic situations movements are said to be cyclical if they recur after time intervals of more than one year. A good example is the trade cycle, representing intervals of prosperity, recession, depression and recovery.

For cyclical variations to be apparent, data must be available over very long periods of time since the periods of oscillation are so long. This is impractical for examination questions and for that reason the calculation of cyclical variations is ignored in this session although you must, of course, realise that they exist.

9.2.4 Seasonal variations

Seasonal fluctuations are the identical, or almost identical, patterns which a time series follows during corresponding intervals of successive periods. Such movements are due to recurring events such as the sudden increase in department store sales before Christmas. Although, in general, seasonal movements refer to a period of one year, this is not always the case and periods of days, hours, weeks, months, etc, may also be considered depending on the type of data available.

9.2.5 Random variations

Random variations are the sporadic motions of time series due to chance events such as floods, strikes, elections, etc. Although it is ordinarily assumed that such events produce variations lasting only a short time, it is conceivable that they may be so intense as to result in new cyclical or other movement.

By their very nature they are unpredictable and therefore cannot play a large part in any forecasting but it is possible to isolate the random variations by calculating all other types of variation and removing them from the time series data. It is important to extract any significant random variations from the data before using them for comparative purposes.

9.3 Analysis

9.3.1 The analysis of a time series consists of:

(a) breaking the series down into its characteristic variations;

(b) projecting each characteristic into the future;

(c) adding together all the individual projections to arrive at one forecast figure for the complete time series.

The analysis which follows concentrates on isolating only the basic trend and seasonal variations. As already stated, random movements are not usually included in analysis and, although cyclical movements may be treated in the same way as seasonal variations, they repeat over such long intervals of time that masses of historic data are required before the pattern becomes evident.

9.3.2   Isolating the trend

You may have noticed that a trend curve was drawn in on the time series graph in paragraph 9.1.1. Indeed one way, admittedly not very scientific, of isolating the trend is imply to draw it in freehand on the graph. This is not usually good enough for examination purposes and the two common methods are:

(a)   using moving averages.

(b)   calculating the line of best fit using regression analysis;

The least squares line of best fit, being a straight line, will only be reasonably accurate if the trend is approximately linear. This can be determined from the graph of the time series. An example is given in Section 9.4 of this session. We will concentrated on the method of moving averages which can be used whether the trend is linear or not.

9.3.3   Moving averages

By using moving averages of **appropriate order**, the variations in a time series can be eliminated leaving a 'smoothed' set of figures which is taken as the trend. It is important that the correct order is chosen for the moving average otherwise the result will not be as good as it should be. For instance, if there are seasonal variations present in a time series and the pattern is repeated every fourth period then moving averages of order 4 should be used for the best results.

This may become clearer as you follow through the simple example in the next paragraph.

9.3.4   Which order?

The following rather contrived series is made up of two components, a simple seasonal variation of period 4 (ie, that recurs every fourth period) and an arithmetic trend. Notice how different results are obtained from the different order moving averages.

Trend	Variation	Time Series (actual data)	Order 2	Order 3	Order 4
				Moving averages	
1	2	3			
			4		
2	3	5		$4^1/3$	
			5		$4^1/2$
3	2	5		5	
			5		$5^1/2$
4	1	5		$5^2/3$	
			6		$6^1/2$
5	2	7		7	
			8		$7^1/2$
6	3	9		$8^1/3$	
			9		$8^1/2$
7	2	9		9	
			9		$9^1/2$
8	1	9		$9^2/3$	
			10		$10^1/2$
9	2	11		11	
			12		$11^1/2$
10	3	13		$12^1/3$	
			13		$12^1/2$
11	2	13		13	
			13		
12	1	13			

The moving average of order 4 is the only one which captures the steadily increasing property of the original trend. It is therefore important to examine the figures before choosing which order moving average to use.

9.3.5 Centred averages

You may have been wondering about the peculiar positioning of the moving averages in the last paragraph. In fact each average has been written exactly opposite the middle of the figures from which it has been calculated. This results in the moving averages of **even** order being suspended half way between two of the original figures. In the next stage of the analysis it is essential that the moving averages are exactly aligned with the original figures which necessitates a centring process as demonstrated in the following example.

Example 9.1

Given the following production data for 19W7-X7, calculate the four year moving averages and four year centred moving averages.

Year	Data	4 year moving total	8 year moving total	8 year centred moving average (trend)
19W7	50.0			
19W8	36.5			
		174.0		
19W9	43.0		336.9	42.1
		162.9		
19X0	44.5		327.4	40.9
		164.5		
19X1	38.9		318.6	39.8
		154.1		
19X2	38.1		302.4	37.8
		148.3		
19X3	32.6		299.4	37.5
		151.1		
19X4	38.7		305.2	38.2
		154.1		
19X5	41.7		314.4	39.3
		160.3		
19X6	41.1			
19X7	38.8			

The figures in the final column are now an estimate of the trend.

9.3.6 Disadvantages

Although an extremely simple method of finding the trend, moving averages have certain disadvantages:

(a) data at the beginning and end of the series are lost - therefore the moving averages do not cover the complete period;

(b) the moving averages may generate cycles or other movements that were not present in the original data;

(c) the averages are strongly affected by extreme values. To overcome this a 'weighted' moving average is sometimes used giving the largest weights to central items and small weights to extreme values.

9.3.7 Seasonal variations

Having isolated the trend we are going to consider a way of dealing with the seasonal variations. This uses an additive model where variations are expressed in absolute terms with above and below average figures designated by plus and minus signs respectively. The method can be based on a trend produced by any method.

The workings which follow are based on an additive time series model. This states that the four components of a time series (T = trend; S = seasonal variation; C = cyclic variation; R = random variation) are expressed as absolute values which are simply added together to produce the actual figures,

ie, Actual data = T + S + C + R.

For unsophisticated analysis over a relatively short period of time C and R are ignored. Random variations are ignored because they are unpredictable and would not normally exhibit any repetitive pattern, whereas cyclic variations (long term oscillations) are ignored because their effect is negligible over short periods of time. The model therefore simplifies to:

Actual data = T + S

9.3.8 Calculating the seasonal variation

The seasonal variation is simply the difference between the actual data and the trend. Rearranging the above equation we obtain:

S = Actual data - T

Example 9.2

Year/qtr	1	2	3	4
1	73	99	93	126
2	81	114	108	148
3	91	121	117	154
4	106	131	135	175
5	134	149		

Solution

Step 1: Calculate the trend and the seasonal variation.

(a)		Value (b)	4 quarter moving total (c)	8 quarter moving total (d)	Trend (T) (d)/8 (e)	Seasonal Variation (S) (b-e) (f)
1	1	73				
	2	99				
			391			
	3	93		790	98.75	-5.75
			399			
	4	126		813	101.625	+24.375
			414			
2	1	81		843	105.375	-24.375
			429			
	2	114		880	110	+4
			451			
	3	108		912	114	-6
			461			
	4	148		929	116.125	+31.875
			468			
3	1	91		945	118.125	-27.125
			477			
	2	121		960	120	+1
			483			
	3	117		981	122.625	-5.625
			498			
	4	154		1006	125.75	+28.25
			508			

9.8

(a)		Value (b)	4 quarter moving total (c)	8 quarter moving total (d)	Trend (T) (d)/8 (e)	Seasonal Variation (S) (b-e) (f)
4	1	106		1034	129.25	-23.25
			526			
	2	131		1073	134.125	-3.125
			547			
	3	135		1122	140.25	-5.25
			575			
	4	175		1168	146	+29
			593			
5	1	134				
	2	149				

Step 2: Average the seasonal variations.

Now we can tabulate the variations for each quarter.

Year qtr	1	2	3	4
1	-	-	-5.75	+24.375
2	-24.375	+4.00	-6.00	+31.875
3	-27.125	+1.00	-5.625	+28.25
4	-23.25	-3.125	-5.25	+29.00
5	-	-	-	-
Sum	-74.75	+1.875	-22.625	+113.5
Average	-24.917	+0.625	-5.656	+28.375

The purpose of the averaging, shown above, is to find one representative seasonal variation for each quarter. This will then enable both forecasting and deseasonalisation of the original data to be carried out.

Step 3: Deseasonalisation of data

Having isolated the seasonal variations we are now in a position to deseasonalise the original data by removing these variations. After data have been deseasonalised they still include trend, cyclical and random movements. The trend has already been found and can now be removed from the deseasonalised data to leave only cyclical and random movements (residual variations).

Year + quarter		Original data	Average seasonal variations	Deseasonalised data	Trend	Residual variations (cyclical & random)
1	3	93	-5.656	98.656	98.75	-0.094
	4	126	+28.375	97.625	101.625	-4.0
2	1	81	-24.917	105.917	105.375	+0.542
	2	114	+0.625	113.375	110.0	+3.375
	3	108	-5.656	113.656	114.0	-0.344
	4	148	+28.375	119.625	116.125	+3.5
3	1	91	-24.917	115.917	118.125	-2.208
	2	121	+0.625	120.375	120.0	+0.375
	3	117	-5.656	122.656	122.625	+0.031
	4	154	+28.375	125.625	125.75	-0.125
4	1	106	-24.917	130.917	129.25	+1.667
	2	131	+0.625	130.375	134.125	-3.75
	3	135	-5.656	140.656	140.25	+0.4
	4	175	+28.375	146.625	146.0	+0.625

9.4 Step by step illustration 1

Graph the following sales figures as a time series.

Sales of Priceless Arts Limited

Year	Turnover (£10,000s)
19X0	10
19X1	12
19X2	14
19X3	11
19X4	15
19X5	14
19X6	12
19X7	14
19X8	16
19X9	14

Using the method of least squares fit a straight line trend to these sales figures, plotting the trend on your graph. What is the purpose of estimating a trend for such data? Discuss the possibility of suing the trend line for purposes of estimating sales in 1980.

Solution

To plot any time series the variable (turnover in this case) is recorded on the vertical axis, with time on the horizontal axis. The plot of this data is thus as follows:

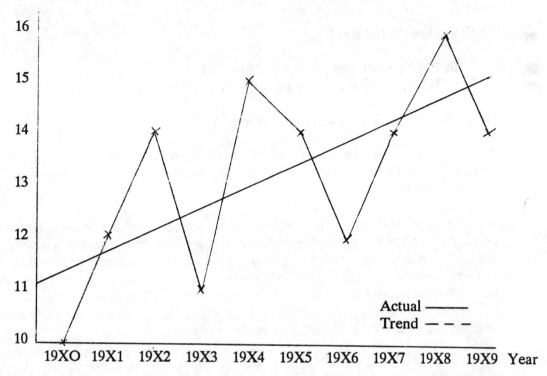

To find the trend line using the method of least squares we must specify which is the dependent and which is the independent variable. In time series the variable is always y and time x. Instead of using 19X0, 19X1, etc, as x, we number the years 1, 2, 3, etc. The trend is thus found in the following manner:

Year Turnover

x	y	x - x̄	y - ȳ	(x - x̄) (y - ȳ)	(x - x̄)^2
1	10	-4.5	-3.2	14.4	20.25
2	12	-3.5	-1.2	4.2	12.25
3	14	-2.5	0.8	-2.0	6.25
4	11	-1.5	-2.2	3.3	2.25
5	15	-0.5	1.8	-0.9	0.25
6	14	0.5	0.8	0.4	0.25
7	12	1.5	-1.2	-1.8	2.25
8	14	2.5	0.8	2.0	6.25
9	16	3.5	2.8	9.8	12.25
10	14	4.5	0.8	3.6	20.25
55	132			33.0	82.5

x̄ = 5.5   ȳ = 13.2

$$b = \frac{\Sigma(x - \bar{x})(y - \bar{y})}{\Sigma(x - \bar{x})^2} = \frac{33}{82.5} = 0.4$$

$$a = y - b\bar{x} = 13.2 - (0.4 \times 5.5) = 11.0$$

Regression line is:

$$y = 0.4x + 11$$

To fit the line on the graph

in 19X0 x = 1 and y = 0.4 + 11 = 11.4
in 19X9 x = 10 and y = 0.4 x 10 + 11 = 15

Hence the dotted line shown on the graph.

The trend line shows the course which data have followed over a period. For example, despite fluctuation in turnover upwards and downwards during the ten years 19X0-19X9 the trend has been upwards.

It would be absurd to use the trend line from such a small set of data, spanning only 10 years, to produce a forecast figure for five years later than the last known figure. The method of producing a trend line is not very sophisticated and should only be used to produce forecasts into the immediate future. Extrapolation of the trend a long way into the future cannot possibly give a reliable estimate. Tax legislation, budgets, the economic climate and many other factors could drastically change the pattern of sales over a five year period invalidating any forecast made at present.

9.5 Step by step illustration 2

The following data shows the number of cash receipts per day for a company over four working weeks:

Week/Day	1	2	3	4	5
1	8	12	15	10	9
2	10	13	17	15	16
3	17	23	25	21	21
4	26	30	32	34	35

Plot the data on a graph. Calculate the trend using 5-day moving averages and superimpose this trend on your graph.

Solution

The 5-day moving average trend is simply found by adding up the figures in fives and dividing by five. No centring is required.

Week/day		Receipts	5-day moving total	Trend
1	1	8		
	2	12		
	3	15	54	10.8
	4	10	56	11.2
	5	9	57	11.4

Week/day		Receipts	5-day moving total	Trend
2	1	10	59	11.8
	2	13	64	12.8
	3	17	71	14.2
	4	15	78	15.6
	5	16	88	17.6
3	1	17	96	19.2
	2	23	102	20.4
	3	25	107	21.4
	4	21	116	23.2
	5	21	123	24.6
4	1	26	130	26.0
	2	30	143	28.6
	3	32	157	31.4
	4	34		
	5	35		

The trend values and the actual receipts are plotted on the following graph.

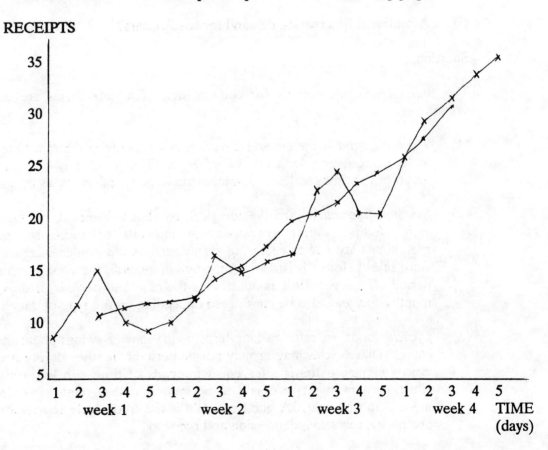

9.6 Step by step illustration 3

Explain the four characteristic movements of a time series. With which characteristic movement would you mainly associate each of the following:

(a) A fire in a factory delaying production for 3 weeks?

(b) An era of prosperity?

(c) An after-Easter sale in a department store?

(d) A need for increased wheat production due to a constant increase in population?

(e) The monthly number of inches of rainfall in a city over a 5 year period?

(f) A recession?

(g) An increase in employment during summer months?

(h) The decline in the death rate due to advances in science?

(i) A steel strike?

(j) A continually increasing demand for smaller cars?

Solution

The characteristic movements (or components) of a time series are explained in the session.

(1) *The basic trend* is the general direction in which the graph of a time series appears to be going over a long interval of time. The trend may be represented on the graph of the times series as a smooth curve or in special cases by a straight line.

(2) *Seasonal fluctuations* are the identical, or almost identical, patterns which a time series follows during corresponding intervals of successive periods. Such movements are due to recurring events such as the sudden increase in department store sales before Christmas. Although, in general, seasonal movements refer to a period of one year, this is not always the case and periods of days, hours, weeks, months, etc, may also be considered depending on the type of data available.

(3) *Cyclical variations* refer to long term oscillations or swings about the trend line or curve. These cycles may or may not be periodic, ie, they do not necessarily follow exactly similar patterns after equal intervals of time. In business and economic situations movements are said to be cyclical if they recur after time intervals of more than one year. A good example is the trade cycle representing intervals of prosperity, recession, depression and recovery.

(4) *Random variations* are the sporadic motions of time series due to chance events such as floods, strikes, elections, etc. Although it is ordinarily assumed that such events produce variations lasting only a short time it is conceivable that they may be so intense as to result in new cyclical or other movement.

For the situations listed the following are the main characteristic movements with which they would be associated:

(a)   Random variation.

(b)   Cyclical variation.

(c)   Seasonal variation.

(d)   Trend.

(e)   Seasonal variation.

(f)   Cyclical variation.

(g)   Seasonal variation.

(h)   Trend.

(i)   Random variation.

(j)   Trend.

9.7   Conclusion

It is important that you can identify the trend and seasonal variations using the method of moving averages. Make sure that you can also explain the nature of the four components of a time series giving one or two practical examples in each case.

9.8 Questions

9.8.1 Objective test questions

(1)   In what order should the following be placed to show movements that can be described as a trend, seasonal variation, cyclical variation and random variation respectively?

1   The pattern of the number of cars going over Battersea Bridge in London each hour during a working day.

2   The decline in the infant mortality rate due to improvements in intensive care treatment.

3   Changes in house prices in the North relative to the Retail Price Index.

4   The increase in buildings insurance claims due to the worst storms to hit England in history.

A   2, 3, 1, 4
B   2, 1, 3, 4
C   3, 4, 1, 2
D   3, 1, 2, 4

(2)   Which of the following statements concerning the trend of a time series is incorrect?

A   The more exact method of linear regression for isolation of the trend is always preferable to the moving average method
B   The trend may be linear or a curve
C   The method of moving averages can always be used whatever the shape of the underlying trend
D   Extraction of the trend can be by the same method whether the additive or proportional model is to be used

(3)   The following represents quarterly output for a product

	March	June	September	December
Year 1	100	104	110	109
Year 2	102	108	112	108

The trend figures that would be obtained by centred moving averages of order 4 would be

A   105.75, 106.25, 107.25, 107.75, 107.5
B   106, 106.75, 107.5, 107.625
C   212, 213.5, 215, 215.25
D   423, 425, 429, 431, 430

9.8.2   Written test questions

9.1   New cars

The table below shows the total number of UK new car registrations and the number of cars produced in the UK for the home market for 19X0-Y0:

Year	Total Registrations of new cars in UK (1,000s)	UK Car Production for the Home Market (1,000s)
19X0	1,097	918
19X1	1,302	1,027
19X2	1,663	1,308
19X3	1,645	1,142
19X4	1,234	938
19X5	1,166	736
19X6	1,256	768
19X7	1,285	753
19X8	1,561	728
19X9	1,676	678
19Y0	1,460	574

(a)   Plot the two time series on a single graph and in each case comment on the pattern in the data.

(b)   From the given data, express UK car production as a percentage of total new car registrations (ie, as a percentage of total car sales) for each year.   Plot these percentages on a suitable graph and comment on the pattern in this data.

9.2   Cigars

The production of small cigars in the USA over a ten-year period is shown in the following table:

YEAR	NUMBER OF SMALL CIGARS (millions)
1	98
2	92
3	80
4	89
5	84
6	69
7	68
8	68
9	58
10	64

(a) Graph the above time series.

(b) Calculate the equation of a least squares trend line fitting the data, indicate what the trend value is at year 1 and year 10 and insert the trend line on your graph.

(c) Estimate the production of small cigars for year 12.

(d) Comment on the validity of projecting the trend of such a series.

9.3 Commodities

The following data show the quarterly indexes of wholesale prices of a group of commodities.

| | Quarter | | | |
	1	2	3	4
Year 1	195	189	183	183
Year 2	220	216	210	210
Year 3	230	227	222	222
Year 4	265	259	255	254
Year 5	320	315	310	312

(a) Calculate the seasonal variations and use them to correct the data and so obtain 'seasonally adjusted' figures.

(b) Chart the original and adjusted figures on the same graph.

(c) What does this graph indicate?

9.4 TV licences

The following data is the number of black and white television licences sold in the United Kingdom from 19X4 to 19X9 inclusive:

Year	19X4	19X5	19X6	19X7	19X8	19X9
Number of Licences (millions)	10.61	9.38	8.43	7.37	6.52	5.56

(a) Plot this data on a graph and comment on the pattern observed.

(b) The data below are the number of colour TV licences sold over the same period:

Year	19X4	19X5	19X6	19X7	19X8	19X9
Number of Licences (millions)	6.82	8.29	9.57	10.72	11.97	12.71

Is there any evidence to support the statement that the rate of decrease in black and white licences has been compensated for by the increase in colour licences?

SESSION 10

Probability

Probability is potentially a complicated topic, but for this syllabus only the simpler aspects are introduced.

We shall begin by explaining the basic laws of probability and consider their application to straight forward problems.

10.1   Introduction

Risk is faced when the probabilities of particular future events can be objectively quantified. For example, insurance companies can calculate with a high degree of precision the probability that a particular proportion of a population will die before the age of 35. The probability is quantified on the basis of a large number of historical observations.

For many business decisions there will not be a large number of observations available. A new product launch is a unique event which is unlikely to be repeated in the same way. Management may make subjective estimates of the probabilities that the launch will be a success or a failure, but the probabilities are based on managers' judgement and experience. When the probabilities of particular future events can only be subjectively quantified, the condition of uncertainty is faced.

Often information is presented to managers on which they are to base a decision which reflects only one possible view of the future: a 'most likely' estimate. This may result in managers giving inadequate consideration to the risk factor or at least having no information readily available on the implications for the company if the 'most likely' estimate is not realised. Managers' decisions may be improved if they estimate, or have made available to them, alternative forecasts with the associated probabilities of them occurring.

The aim of this session is to explain and demonstrate the application of the basic notion of probability and techniques which might be employed in allowing for risk and uncertainty in decision-making.

10.2   Definition

There is no generally accepted definition of probability. However, expressed in simple terms, probability expresses the chance of some event occurring. If you were told: 'There is a 50% chance of rain tomorrow', you would know exactly what was meant. An alternative way of saying the same thing is: 'The probability of rain tomorrow is 0.5'.

Probability is a way of expressing the percentage chance of something happening and is expressed as a number between 0 and 1.

(a)   If an event will definitely occur, then the probability of that event occurring is 1:

   eg, if you have a pet goldfish, the probability that it will die is 1. Written in shorthand notation:

   P (pet goldfish will die) = 1.

(b)   If an event will certainly not occur, then the probability of that event occurring is zero:

   eg, P (pet goldfish would survive 1 week out of water) = 0.

10.3 Laws of probability

10.3.1 Introduction

There are several laws relating to probability that you need to understand.

We shall now consider some of the basic laws of chance (probability):

(a) first law: law of proportions;
(b) second law: multiplication law;
(c) third law: addition law.

These sound rather pompous and complicated when stated in English but the numerical examples should prove that they are only stating the obvious.

10.3.2 Law of proportions

(a) *Definition*

Whenever some action can have more than one result, then the probability of any one of them occurring in a single test will be the proportion which that particular result bears to all possible results.

(b) *Explanation*

(i) This is a fairly obvious law. For example, an ordinary die used in games has six sides numbered from 1 to 6. If the die is not weighted (unbiased) it is equally likely that any one of the six sides will land face uppermost when the die is thrown. Therefore the probability of any one number being thrown is 1/6.

(ii) Again, there are four aces in a normal pack of 52 playing cards. The probability of an ace (ie, any ace) being drawn in a random selection is therefore 4/52 = 1/13.

(iii) Lastly, if a box contains 50 black balls, 20 white balls and 30 red balls and one ball is selected at random from the box then:

P (black) = 50/100 = 1/2
P (white) = 20/100 = 1/5
P (red)   = 30/100 = 3/10

10.3.3 Multiplication law (AND)

(a) *Definition*

Whenever some action can have more than one result then the probability of getting any particular combination of results in a fixed order from two or more **independent** tests (consecutive or simultaneous) will be the product of their individual probabilities.

(b)   *Explanation*

The AND stresses that two or more things must happen for the multiplication law to apply. Also the results must be independent of each other, in other words one outcome must not affect any others.

To illustrate the law, suppose that two dice are thrown consecutively.   The outcomes of each throw are completely independent. If a four is thrown on the first dice it will in no way affect what will happen on the second one.

Thus the probability of obtaining a four on the first die and a six on the second is given by

$$P \text{ (4 on 1st AND 6 on 2nd)} = P(\text{4 on 1st}) \times P(\text{6 on 2nd})$$
$$= 1/6 \times 1/6$$
$$= 1/36$$

(c)   *Example*

If the probability of selling 1,000 units of A is 0.6, and the probability of selling 1,000 units of B is 0.3 (they are not mutually exclusive), the probability of selling 1,000 units of A and 1,000 units of B is:

$$(0.6 \times 0.3) = 0.18$$

10.3.4   Addition law (OR)

(a)   *Definition*

Whenever some action can have more than one result, then if all possible results are mutually exclusive, the probability of alternative results occurring in a single test will be the sum of their individual probabilities.

(b)   *Explanation*

(i)   The word OR is given in brackets to emphasise that the addition law applies where alternatives can occur.

(ii)   The possible results must be mutually exclusive; that is, if one result occurs then the others cannot occur.

(c)   *Example*

The probability that a single throw of a die will produce a 2 or a 5 is calculated as:

$$P(2) = 1/6 \quad P(5) = 1/6$$

$$P(2 \text{ OR } 5) = P(2) + P(5) = 1/6 + 1/6 = 1/3$$

(e)   *Review of example*

Note that because there are two possible outcomes, the chance of one of them occurring is increased; their individual probabilities are added together.

10.3.5   Extension to addition law

It was emphasised that the addition law, as stated above, only holds when the events are mutually exclusive but a similar result can be produced for non mutually exclusive events. For example, in a survey regarding the number of people in a certain area who smoke cigarettes or drink beer, it was ascertained from a sample of 1,000 people interviewed that 400 smoke and 500 drink beer. However, it would be wrong to conclude from this that:

(i)   40% of the sample smoked cigarettes but did not drink beer;
(ii)   50% of the sample drank beer but did not smoke;
(iii)   10% of the sample neither smoked nor drank beer.

The important point is that the events of smoking and drinking beer are not mutually exclusive - some people do both.

On closer examination we might discover, that 300 of the persons interviewed were teetotal and non smokers, while 200 of the sample smoked and drank beer. The easiest way to visualise this is by drawing a Venn diagram in which the total sample is represented by the rectangle and the smokers and drinkers each by a circle. Since the events are not mutually exclusive, the two circles will overlap and the common area represents those in the sample that both smoke and drink. The area of the rectangle outside the circles represents teetotal, non-smokers.

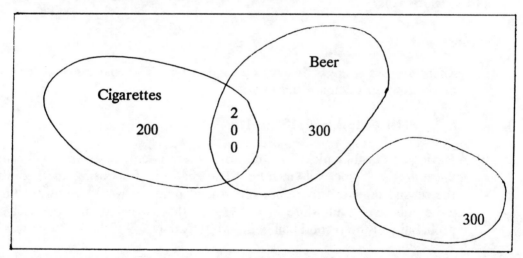

From this it should be obvious what would happen if we used the addition law incorrectly to say:

P(smoke OR drink) = P(smoke) + P(drink) = 0.4 + 0.5 = 0.9

We have effectively included the people who both drink and smoke twice; once with the smokers and once with the drinkers. If we subtract the proportion who both drink and smoke just once then the problem is solved and the formula for two events which are not mutually exclusive is:

P(smoke OR drink)   = P(smoke) + P(drink) - P(smoke AND drink)
                    = 0.4 + 0.5 - 0.20
                    = 0.70

10.3.6   Illustration

If the probability of selling 1,000 units of A is 0.6, and the probability of selling 1,000 units of B is 0.3, the probability of selling 1,000 units of A or 1,000 units of B is:

0.6 + 0.3 - 0.18 = 0.72

You may like to think of it as follows. Consider a 10 day selling period: on 6 days you expect to sell 1,000 As and on 3 days you expect to sell 1,000 Bs; on how many days do you expect to make a sale of either A or B? Not 9, because you may sell 1,000 As and 1,000 Bs on the same day.

10.3.7   Conditional probability

The addition and multiplication laws can be extended to deal with events which are not independent as long as great care is taken. The best examples of this could arise from sampling without replacement.

Example 10.1

Imagine a box containing five black balls, two white balls and three red balls. Two balls are to be selected from the box by sampling without replacement - in other words the first ball is not replaced before the second is selected. What is the probability of picking out two white balls?

Solution

(a)   There are two white balls out of a total of ten. The chances of picking a white ball on the first occasion are therefore:

P(1st white) = 2/10 = 1/5

(b)   Having successfully picked a white ball, there is only one white ball remaining and there are only nine balls in total. The chances of choosing another white ball on the second draw are therefore one out of nine. It would be misleading simply to write this as P(2nd white) = 1/9 as that does not tell the full story. The probability of the second ball being white is only 1/9 if the first one was also white.

The correct way to express this conditional probability is 'the probability that the second is white **given that** the first was also white' and in shorthand notation this is written:

P(2nd white | 1st white) = 1/9

The vertical line means 'given that'.

(c)   The question asked for the probability that the first was white and the second was white. By the multiplication law:

P(1st white AND 2nd white) = P(2nd white | 1st white) x P(1st white)

= 1/9 x 1/5

= 1/45

10.4 Application of probability theory: expected values

10.4.1 Introduction

One of the most useful applications of probability theory in business is the calculation of expected values. This enables management to predict a possible future outcome given a knowledge of the probabilities associated with the various possible outcomes.

Example 10.2

Possible future levels of demand with their associated probabilities are given in the following table:

Demand in units per annum	Probability
10,000	0.1
20,000	0.15
30,000	0.25
45,000	0.30
50,000	0.20

Calculate the likely annual demand.

Solution

The method relies on weighted averages. The calculation is as follows:

Demand in units	x	Probability	=	Conditional values
10,000	x	0.1	=	1,000
20,000	x	0.15	=	3,000
30,000	x	0.25	=	7,500
45,000	x	0.30	=	13,500
50,000	x	0.20	=	10,000
		Expected value	=	35,000 units

The most likely outcome (45,000 units) is given the greatest weight. The other possible outcomes are given their appropriate weights and the 'expected value' results.

10.4.2 Limitations of expected value

The main limitations of expected value are:

(a) The expected value is an average and therefore only really applicable when there will be repeated trials or decisions. Many business decisions are 'one-offs' however.

(b) The probabilities employed will often be subjective estimates by managers and therefore influenced by the personalities (optimistic, pessimistic) and objectives of the individuals making the estimates.

(c)   Although the EV provides an average of the future values it does not measure the degree of possible variation around the average.

10.5   Step by step illustration 1

A card is drawn from a pack of 52 playing cards. Find the probability that the card is:

(a)   a club;
(b)   not a club;
(c)   a king or a queen;
(d)   a ten or a red card.

If two cards are drawn from the pack simultaneously, find the probability that both are aces if:

(e)   no replacement takes place;
(f)   the first card is replaced before the second is drawn.

Solution

This is a simple example which illustrates the laws of probability well, even though you could probably answer it without the laws.

(a)   Using the law of proportions, P(club) = 13/52, since there are 13 club cards in a pack of 52 playing cards.

(b)   If there are 13 clubs in the pack, then there must be 52-13 = 39 none clubs. Therefore again by the law of proportions P(not club) = 39/52.

This example is simple, yet important. Using the fact that P(not a club) = 1 - P(club) (known as the compliment law) is a very useful tool in more complicated questions.

(c)   Using the addition law,

P(king or queen)   = P(king) + P(queen) since the two are mutually exclusive

                                  = 4/52 + 4/52

                                  = 8/52 or 2/13

(d)   Using the addition law

P(ten or red card)   = P(ten) + P(red card) - P(ten and red card) because the 2 events are not mutually exclusive

                                  = 4/52 + 26/52 - 2/52

                                  = 28/52 or 7/13

(e)   Using the multiplication law, if the first card is not replaced before the second is drawn then, on the second selection of a card there are only 51 in the pack. Thus,

P(both aces)   =   P(1st is an ace **and** second is an ace)

                       =   P(first is an ace) x P(second is an ace/first was an ace)

                       =   4/52 x 3/51

                       =   12/2652   =   0.0045

(f)   If the first card is replaced before the second is drawn then there are still 52 cards in the pack. Therefore using the multiplication law

P(both aces)   =   P(1st is an ace **and** second is an ace)

                       =   P(1st is an ace **and** second is an ace)

                       =   4/52 x 4/52

                       =   16/2704   =   0.0059

10.6   Step by step illustration 2

In a factory, 35% of employees are female and 51% of the employees belong to a union. Also it is known that 10% of the employees are female union members. If an employee is chosen at random, what is the probability that this person is either a woman or a union member?

Solution

We are given the following probabilities (using the law of proportions)

P(female employee)	= 0.35
P(union member)	= 0.51
P(female **and** union member)	= 0.10

Hence, using the addition law

P(female or a union member)

=   P(female) + P(union member) - P(female and union member) since the events are not mutually exclusive

=   0.35 + 0.51 - 0.10

=   0.76

10.7   Step by step illustration 3

A gambler has a 0.3 chance of winning £100, a 0.2 chance of winning £200, a 0.1 chance of winning £300 and a 0.4 chance of losing. If the gambler loses he has to pay £200. What is the gambler's expected return?

Solution

We are given the following information:

P(winning £100)	=	0.3
P(winning £200)	=	0.2
P(winning £300)	=	0.1
P(losing)	=	0.4

The gambler's expected return on placing a bet is found by multiplying these probabilities by the corresponding cash return.

Return (£)	x	Probability	=	Conditional Value
100	x	0.3	=	30
200	x	0.2	=	40
300	x	0.1	=	30
-200	x	0.4	=	-80

Therefore the gambler's expected return = 30 + 40 + 30 - 80

= £20

10.8 Conclusion

We have only skimmed the surface of probability here and you will come across more advanced aspects as your studies progress.

For the moment make sure that you have understood and learnt both the addition and multiplication laws of probability.

10.9 Questions

10.9.1 Objective test questions

Use the information given below to answer questions 1, 2, 3 and 4.

Four playing cards are drawn, without replacement, from a standard pack of 52.

(1)   What is the probability that the four cards are all spades?

  A   .00235
  B   .00264
  C   .00391
  D   .01056

(2)   What is the probability that the four cards are all of the same suit?

  A   .00264
  B   .00939
  C   .01056
  D   .01562

(3)   What is the probability that a heart, club, diamond and spade are drawn in that order?

  A   .00235
  B   .00264
  C   .00391
  D   .00440

(4)   What is the probability that a heart, club, diamond and spade are drawn in any order?

  A   .10550
  B   .09375
  C   .05633
  D   .01758

(5)   A batch of forty radiator caps contain three which are defective. A mechanic selects two caps at random and without replacement from the batch. The probabilities that (i) one cap, and (ii) neither cap is defective respectively are

  A   (i)   .071   (ii)   .854
  B   (i)   .075   (ii)   .856
  C   (i)   .139   (ii)   .833
  D   (i)   .142   (ii)   .854

(6)   In a box there are 80 red balls, 150 green balls and 320 black balls. If three balls are picked out without replacement what is the probability that they will consist of two green balls and one which is either red or black?

        A   .0540
        B   .1621
        C   .1623
        D   .3242

Use the following information to answer questions 7 and 8

The contents of two packets of vegetable seed are identical except that the one from garden centre P contains three times as many seeds as that from garden centre Q. It is found that 12% from P and 8% from Q do not germinate.

All the seeds are sown.

(7)   The proportion of non-germinating seeds from the total sown is

        A   8%
        B   9%
        C   10%
        D   11%

(8)   Assuming all seeds are mixed together and planted, the probability of one failing being from Q is

        A   .08
        B   .10
        C   .18
        D   .20

10.9.2   Written test questions

10.1   Defectives

A lot consists of 16 articles; 10 are good, 4 have slight defects and 2 have major defects.

(a)   One article is drawn at random. Find the probability that:

        (i)   it has no defects;
        (ii)   it has no major defects;
        (iii)   it is either good or has major defects.

(b)   Two articles are selected at random without replacement. Find the probability that:

        (i)   both are good;
        (ii)   both have major defects;
        (iii)   at least one is good;
        (iv)   at most one is good;
        (v)   exactly one is good;
        (vi)   neither has major defects; and
        (vii)   neither is good.

10.2   Investments

Two equally priced investments are available. The possible net returns are shown in the table below, with the associated probabilities:

Net returns (£s)	Probability of return Investment A	Investment B
-3,000	0	0.1
-2,000	0	0.2
-1,000	0.1	0.1
0	0.2	0.1
1,000	0.3	0.1
2,000	0.2	0.2
3,000	0.2	0.1
4,000	0	0.1

Which investment is preferable?

10.3   Strike

A firm is facing the possibility of a strike occurring at one of its main plants. Considering only two points (realistically more would be used) management assesses the following:

1   An offer of 14 per cent pay increase yields:

chance of being accepted outright	= 0.3
chance of a strike lasting one week	= 0.2
chance of a strike lasting two weeks	= 0.3
chance of a strike lasting three weeks	= 0.2

2   An offer of 20 per cent pay increase yields:

chance of being accepted outright	= 0.5
chance of strike lasting one week	= 0.25
chance of strike lasting two weeks	= 0.25

Given that the increase in the wage bill per 1 per cent increase is £500 per week and that any agreement will last for one year (52 weeks) from the time the offer is made and also that the estimated cost of a strike is £200,000 per week, made up of lost production, lost orders, goodwill, etc, which offer should the management make?

10.4   Fruit machine

A fruit machine has three windows behind each of which is a wheel which spins at random, and independently of the other wheels, when a player feeds a 10p coin into the machine and pulls the handle. Each wheel has 5 pictures around the circumference one of which is a bunch of cherries and the other four are plums. The player wins or loses depending on the arrangement of pictures showing through the windows when the wheels stop spinning as follows:

	Position			Win type	Money paid out of machine
	1	2	3		
	cherries	cherries	cherries	A	£5.00
2	cherries in any position			B	£0.50
	cherries	plum	plum	C	£0.30
	any other arrangement			Lose	

(a)   What proportion of the time can the machine be expected to show:

   (i)   win type A;

   (ii)   win type B; and

   (iii)   lose?

(b)   Given that the machine shows a winning arrangement what is the probability that it is a win type A?

(c)   To what figure should the payment on win type A be adjusted, if this is the only alteration made, so that a player will break even in the long run?

SESSION 11

Sampling, significance testing and quality control

In this session we introduce the important theory of sampling and the distribution of sample means. Once again, at this stage only a very basic knowledge will be required.

In addition, the practical aspects of collecting sample data is covered.

11.1 Collection of data

11.1.1 Introduction

In many situations where we require information it is impossible to collect all the necessary facts. We may wish to know, for instance, average annual salary for all females currently employed in the United Kingdom. It would be totally impractical to try and find each appropriate individual annual salary and then average them. Instead we might select a suitable sample of females currently employed and average their annual salaries. This average would be our estimate for the overall average annual salary of females currently employed.

In other instances the data we require might already have been collected in part or fully by someone else. It may well be that we can use this data ourselves.

The problems we have here are:

(a)   if we have to obtain survey data, how do we obtain it?; or

(b)   if data has already been collected by someone else how do we make use of it?

11.1.2 Population and sample

Before setting out on an exercise involving collection of data we must decide what data or figures we wish to collect. This may seem rather obvious but take the following situation: You are required to determine average annual turnover of companies in the engineering sector.

Firstly, does this mean all companies in the world, only the EEC or can we assume we are only concerned with the United Kingdom? Secondly, are we to consider all types of engineering or a specific type of engineering? Do we want all companies with any interest in the engineering sector or only those whose interest is in this sector alone? How are we to describe turnover? Should it be in numbers of individual products or services sold, or in overall money terms or some other description?

As you can see, care must be taken at this stage. The first step is to decide what the aim is in collecting data. When we have decided exactly what we are trying to establish we can determine what items or people or companies or other sources we need to collect data from. The whole group of items or people we are concerned with is called the **population**. As we have already mentioned it is unlikely that we would collect data from all the members of a population, but rather from a selection of the population. The group of members of a population from whom we collect data is called the **sample**.

Suppose we wish to establish average earnings per month of college lecturers, we might go to one or two colleges and ask those lecturers we meet what their monthly earnings are. In this situation the population would be all college lecturers and the sample would be those college lecturers who actually told us their monthly salary.

The word 'population' does not only refer to people. Consider a situation where we wish to find the average contents of bottles stored in a warehouse. As there are several thousand crates of bottles within the warehouse we decide to measure the contents of a few of the bottles chosen from some of the crates. In this instance the population is every bottle in the warehouse and the sample is the group of bottles whose contents we actually measure.

Example 11.1

Determine the population and sample in each of the following situations:

(a) The average number of hours worked per week by employees within a large company is required. All employees at one of the company's factories have had their weekly hours recorded and these figures are to be used as an estimate for the company as a whole.

(b) A company produces a batch of 100,000 electrical components. Management wish to know the average length of these components, so 500 of the components are chosen and are measured for length.

(c) A company has six factories producing television sets. The company wishes to know the average weekly output per factory for last year and has collected, for each factory, their production figures for each week of last year.

Solution

(a) The population is every person employed by the company. The sample is all the employees at the one factory checked.

(b) The population is the batch of 100,000 electrical components. The sample is the 500 components which have been measured for length.

(c) Here, the population would be a list of the weekly output figures for each of the factories and for each week of last year. This is the information that has been collected as the sample. In this situation the population and the sample are the same, the sample is all the members of the population.

11.1.3 Sampling methods

If we decide that collecting data from a whole population is inappropriate then we need to choose a sample. But how do we select our sample? There are many methods of sampling used. Our aim is to obtain as fair and representative a sample as we can manage within the limitations of cost, time and required accuracy. Suppose we wish to determine the average annual earnings of adult employees in the United Kingdom. Before we can consider the sample we are going to use we need a list of the population to be investigated. This list is called the **sampling frame**. This is not always easy to establish but if we assume such a list is available how do we decide which members of the population to sample?

(a) **Simple random sampling**

Simple random sampling is a sampling method where every member of a population has an equal chance of being chosen in the sample. One way this can be achieved is by numbering every member of a population, putting their numbers in a hat or drum, mixing the numbers up and drawing out numbers of those to be in the sample. In practice, this exercise would generally be carried out by use of a computer. If a sample is to be 'fair' it is necessary for some form of random sampling to be used.

In our example above, if we selected a random sample then those people chosen would be spread all round the United Kingdom and it might turn out to be very costly and time-consuming to collect our data. However, if this were acceptable we may wish to improve the accuracy of our results.

(b) **Stratified random sampling**

If our population consists of a collection of different groupings then we can extend the idea of random sampling so that our population is split into these sub-groups and a random sample taken from the different sub-groups (or strata as they are called). If a population does have sub-groups within it then this is the most reliable method of sampling. It is usual for the sample size for each sub-group to be in proportion to the size of the sub-group to the population.

In our example an obvious sub-grouping to introduce is sex. Our sample should reflect the relative proportions of men and women within the working population. So, if our total sample size is 200 and the working population has 70% men, 30% women, our sample rather than being a random sample of 200 employees will be a random sample of 140 male employees and a random sample of 60 female employees. The proportions in the combined sample reflect the proportions in the working population.

We do not need to stop at one sub-grouping. We may wish to bring in other categories such as age and social status. If we used age then we may know the following proportions in the working population:

		MEN	WOMEN
	18 30	27%	16%
Age	30 50	23%	6%
(Years)	50 or over	20%	8%
TOTAL		70%	30%

then our sample would need the following numbers in each sub-group:

		MEN	WOMEN
	18 30	54	32
Age	30 50	46	12
(Years)	50 or over	40	16

With stratified random sampling we are open to the same problems of sampling cost and sampling time as with simple random sampling.

(c)   **Multi-stage sampling**

If the expense and/or time involved in carrying out a simple or stratified random sampling are excessive then a possible alternative is to use **multi-stage sampling**. In multi-stage sampling we select a few areas which we believe are representative of the population as a whole. We then take a random sample within each of these areas. It is hoped this will reduce the cost and time involved in collecting the data required but we lose some of the reliability of our results as a consequence.

In our example the random sample chosen (whether simple or stratified) may well involve people from all over the United Kingdom. If we adopt multi-stage sampling we may decide that the working populations of Ayr, Cardiff, Derby, Leeds and Portsmouth are representative of the working population as a whole. We would then take random samples but only in these locations.

(d)   **Cluster sampling**

We can take multi-stage sampling a step further and say that certain areas are representative of the population as a whole and we will sample everyone in these areas (rather than taking a random sample). The idea is that costs and time can be reduced even further by adopting this approach but once again we lose further reliability in our results.

In our example we could no longer choose areas such as Cardiff and sample everyone there, rather we would need to isolate streets or groups of streets within a location. We then sample all people from those streets who are employed.

(e)   **Quota sampling**

Quota sampling is a rather different approach. You specify how many people or items within a certain group you want to be sampled (set a quota) and then collect your data from anyone or anything fitting into the required category until the quota is filled. This method is widely used by interviewers encountered in town centres, it is also the least accurate of sampling methods.

In our example we might ask an interviewer to stand in Bedford town centre and question a certain number of men and women concerning their annual income.

(f)   **Systematic sampling**

Systematic sampling is a method used where we sample each 10th or 100th or 834th item or person (or any other interval we may wish to use). This is a method widely used in quality control of items produced. It can be a dangerous method to use if not applied carefully.

In our example suppose we decide to sample every fourth house on a particular street. It may be that one side of the street is four-bedroomed, detached houses, the other side two-bedroomed cottages. Using our systematic sampling method we would only obtain information from one side of the street which would not be representative of the street as a whole.

Sometimes attempts are made to make this sampling method random. This is usually done by choosing the first item or person randomly and then sampling at the chosen interval. Continuing our example, we would choose to start with house 1, 2, 3 or 4 at random, then sample every fourth house. If we chose house 3, then we would continue with house 7, 11, 15, etc. This is acceptable provided that the interval is not in phase with some difference in characteristics in the population.

Example 11.2

What type of sampling is being employed in the following situations:

(a)   A company wishes to launch a new product on a pilot basis in just one of its twenty-three sales areas. The company has no preference as to which area should be used so all their names are put in a hat and mixed, then one drawn out and this area chosen to carry out the pilot launch.

(b)   There are 5,000 items in a ledger which is to be checked. It has been decided to inspect every twentieth entry beginning at the eleventh entry.

(c)   In a storage area crates of a product are kept prior to shipment. To inspect a batch of this product it is decided to check all the contents of two adjacent crates in the storage area.

Solution

(a)   Each sales area has an equal chance of being drawn, there is no sub-grouping of sales areas so this is simple random sampling.

(b)   Every twentieth entry is being checked so sampling is at a regular interval. This tells us that it is systematic sampling.

(c)   Two adjacent crates are being fully inspected so we are carrying out 100% sampling on a small part of our population of product. This means cluster sampling is being used. Notice how cluster sampling can be used on items as well as on people.

11.1.4   Sample survey design

We now consider how to obtain the information we require from those items or people we have chosen to form our sample. There are basically two approaches we can use, direct measurement or questioning.

(a)   **Direct measurement**

Where the information we require can be measured or counted we can arrange for ourselves or someone else to take the necessary measurements directly without recourse to a third party influence. This method has the distinct advantage that accurate measurements can be obtained. It can, however, turn out to be very time-consuming and costly if misused. Further, there are only certain measurements which can be taken directly.

(b)   Questioning

Much information that we may require in a sample survey can only be obtained by questioning people (eg, opinions, age, profession, etc). This method of obtaining information is usually based on a formal questionnaire rather than 'off the cuff' questions and it is very important that a questionnaire is designed properly (see following section 11.1.6). A questionnaire can be administered in several ways but the main three methods used are personally, by post or by telephone.

(i)   *Personal questionnaires* - This method is where an interviewer has a set of questions (the questionnaire) which he or she asks the respondent (person chosen to be in the sample) face-to-face and records the answers. This is a method often adopted in town centres or when interviewers visit the respondent's home or place of work. It has the advantages that the results can be obtained quickly and reliably. However, it can be fairly expensive to employ interviewers and you need to be careful that the interviewer, however unwittingly, does not pass on his or her own opinions to the respondent and so bias the results. Because of the high response rate obtained when using this method it is usually considered the most effective way of obtaining data.

(ii)   *Postal questionnaires* - This method involves sending the respondent a questionnaire which he or she then completes and returns. This method has always been considered as cheaper to use than personal interviews since the main cost is postage. The problem with this method is that the response rate is usually quite low (unless it is a legal requirement to fill in the questionnaire, as it is for the Census of Population). Also, there can be problems if the respondent fails to understand the questions or simply does not answer some of the questions. A further problem which can arise is that only those with strong views will respond to the questionnaire giving an unrepresentative sample. Lately this method has become less popular.

(iii)   *Telephone questionnaires* - This method involves asking the questionnaire via the telephone line. This method, if used at off-peak rates, can be cheaper than the postal questionnaire and usually gives a higher response rate. It has been found to be less efficient than personal interviews but there is a growing trend towards using this approach. There is, however, one major consideration with this method which should not be overlooked. Not everyone has a telephone so the population you are trying to reach should be those who have telephones, otherwise the sample can be unrepresentative.

Example 11.3

What sample survey method should be used in each of the following situations?

(a)   We wish to establish people's reasons for not having a telephone. We have little money available for our survey but wish to contact people from all over the United Kingdom.

(a)   We wish to establish people's reasons for not having a telephone. We have little money available for our survey but wish to contact people from all over the United Kingdom.

(b)   We wish to know the average weight of bars of chocolate being produced in our factory.

(c)   We wish to determine customers' views concerning a new method of delivery that we are considering. The results are required quickly.

Solution

(a)   As we want people's views we will need some sort of questionnaire. Since we are only interested in contacting people without telephones we cannot use telephone questionnaires. As the money available for the survey is very limited personal interviews cannot be used so a postal questionnaire should be used. This will allow us to contact people spread throughout the United Kingdom as required.

(b)   We require a measurement on items produced. Direct measurement should be employed. It may be by means of a weighing scale or automatically by a check weigher.

(c)   We require the views of our customers so a questionnaire should be used. As the results are needed quickly we would not use a postal questionnaire. This leaves a personal questionnaire or telephone questionnaire. For convenience, a telephone questionnaire is likely to be more appealing. This is especially true when customers are contacted by telephone anyway and the questionnaire could be carried out at the same time.

11.1.5   Questionnaire design

If a good response rate, with the required type of answers, is to be achieved from a questionnaire then a great deal of care must be taken in the choice and design of the questionnaire. The following points should be borne in mind:

(a)   Ask as few questions as you can whilst still obtaining the information you require, eg, do not ask people their name or address if they are irrelevant to the investigation.

(b)   Make the questions themselves as short as possible.

(c)   Make the questions as simple as possible.

(d)   Avoid questions that can be ambiguous (if there is a 'wrong' way to interpret a question someone will).

(e)   Do not ask questions leading to a certain answer.

(f)   Do not use questions which involve emotive language.

(g)   Unless you are specifically after personal reactions, do not ask personal questions.

(h)   Make sure the questions being asked are relevant to and can be understood by the person answering them.

(i)   Whenever possible, give people a set of answers to choose from. This will minimise the problems you will encounter when categorising answers. You should, however, allow people the opportunity to give an answer other than those you specify, should they wish to.

(j)   Finally, make the questionnaire look simple and interesting so people will want to answer the questions.

If a questionnaire is to be administered by an interviewer either face-to-face or by telephone, the interviewer should have the following qualities:

(i)   honesty;
(ii)   interest in the questionnaire;
(iii)   accuracy;
(iv)   adaptability;

and should not introduce his or her own views into the questions.

11.1.6   Conducting a survey

When it has been decided that a survey should be carried out the following steps should normally be followed:

(a)   *Define the objectives of the survey:*

You need to decide what information is to be collected and who or what for.

(b)   *Define the target population:*

Decide who or what you wish to obtain information about.

(c)   *Decide on the sampling method:*

Choose which of the methods outlined above is most appropriate to your needs in relation to cost, time, reliability of results.

(d)   *Design questionnaire (if necessary):*

Taking into account the points above decide which questions you want answered and ensure the answers will be the information you require.

(e)   *Carry out a pilot survey:*

However well we think we have designed our survey there will be unforeseen difficulties or problems with it unless we are very fortunate. If we can afford the time and money to carry out a pilot study it will hopefully indicate any such problems and we can take appropriate action.

(f)   *Carry out the main survey:*

Having made any necessary adjustments highlighted by the pilot study, the main survey is carried out.

(g)   *Analyse and present the results:*

When the survey has been carried out and the results collected together they must then be analysed to see what they tell us. This analysis should be followed by a clear presentation of the results.

11.2   Significance testing

11.2.1   Introduction

For the examination, you may need a broad appreciation of significance testing. You will not need to perform any calculations in this area. We therefore take a broad overview of this topic.

11.2.2   Distribution of sample means

Consider all possible samples **of the same size** (n) drawn from a very large population. For each sample the mean can be calculated which will vary from sample to sample. In this manner a frequency distribution of the means of the samples is obtained and is known as 'the sampling distribution of the mean'. This is a confusing term; a better description would be 'the distribution of the means of the samples'.

11.2.3   Practical illustration

Suppose that the height of British adult males is Normally distributed with a mean of 70" and a standard deviation of 3". Now suppose we take samples of 100 men at random from the population and for each sample calculate the average height.

From common sense, you would not expect every sample to give an average height of 70", but you might expect the sample means to be clustered around 70" with some greater and some less. You would probably also expect that, since the original population had a symmetrical (Normal) distribution, the sample means will be symmetrically spread about the population mean. Furthermore there will be many samples which have a mean close to 70" but very few which have a mean as large as 73" or as small as 67".

11.2.4   Histogram of the distribution of the means of the samples

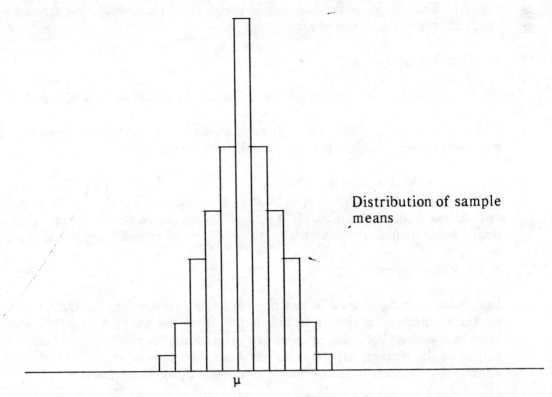

Population distribution

Distribution of sample means

μ

If the distribution of sample means is plotted as a histogram on the same horizontal scale as the original population distribution, the result is as shown in the diagram.

The main feature to note is that the mean of the distribution of the samples is the same as the mean of the distribution of the whole population.

The above histogram clarifies what was said in paragraph 11.2.3, namely that the distribution is spread symmetrically about the population mean. Furthermore the amount of spread or dispersion about the population mean is far less for the sampling distribution than for the population itself. This again should be obvious by considering the following statements.

It is reasonably likely that a member of the population selected at random would have a height of 73" or more.

It is far less likely that a sample of 100 men would have an average height of 73" or more since averaging the heights has a modifying effect.

11.2.5   Significance testing

Significance testing refers to situations where we have a sample and we want to know whether it could have been drawn from a particular population. We want to know whether the characteristics of the sample are similar to or significantly different from the characteristics of the population as a whole.

The argument behind a significance test lies in the fact that the mean of a sample will be one item of the distribution of means of all the samples. We know that the mean of the distribution of all the samples is the same as the mean of the population (which will be known). Thus, if our particular sample comes from that population, its mean should be similar to the mean of the whole population.

11.2.6   Practical illustration

We know that the mean height of the entire population of adult British males is 70".

Suppose a sample of 100 individuals has a mean of 24". We would infer that the sample may have been of children but not adult British males.

Suppose now that a sample of 100 individuals has a mean of 65". There is a probability that they could be adult British males, but the likelihood of that depends on the distribution of the population. If it were a narrow distribution with few very tall or very small people then a sample with a mean of 65" would probably not be adult males.

11.2.7   Another illustration

Significance testing is used in practice to determine whether the output of a particular worker or machine is similar to the output of all the workers or all the machines. By examining the worker's output over, say, a three hour period one can calculate the mean output of the worker, say 20 units per hour, and decide whether that is similar to or significantly different from the output of the workforce as a whole.

11.2.8   Summary

There are fairly complicated techniques for determining mathematically the probability of a sample coming from a particular population. These are outside the syllabus.

11.3   Quality, quality control and inspection

11.3.1   Quality

The quality of a product is a function of consumer preference and expectation.

Quality is determined initially at the design stage. The design processes are influenced by:

(a)   the perceived preferences and expectations of actual or potential consumers;
(b)   the design of competing products;
(c)   the choice of materials;
(d)   manufacturing methods and skills available;
(e)   the return and cost of the required output.

The specification is derived from design but is more influenced by volume and cost factors than is the design itself - the designer for example may see aesthetic merit in metal washers, while the person drawing up the final specification may see cost benefits in plastic ones.

It should be apparent by now that a consideration of product quality extends from the quality of the materials, machines and processes used to make it to the assessment made of it by the customers. Of course a firm can decide on variation in quality standard across a product range recognising that while everyone may wish to possess one of its products their preferences and expectations vary considerably. The important point to remember is that quality is not simply something that is attended to in the production system but a major consideration at all stages of operation and for all functional areas of a manufacturing company.

11.3.2 The role of quality control

Quality control is concerned with the establishment and maintenance of defined quality standards. It is not peculiar to production only - it must also be employed when buying raw material and component supplies and in after sales service. It is, however, central to effective production planning and control to avoid waste in the use of production resources so that goods are produced at the estimated costs, in the quantity wanted and at the required standard of quality. In these ways production helps the company maintain sales, retain the goodwill of its customers and keep an eye on costs and repairs costs arising from warranty or guarantee claims.

Ideally, quality control should be independent of production with reporting lines to the board of directors or the works manager. Where it is not, and all too often it is not, its objectives are bound to be compromised occasionally to achieve some other objective such as raising output or meeting cost targets.

11.3.3 The quality control department - purposes

The quality control department sets quality standards and ensures that they are maintained.

Its purpose are:

(a)   to establish the standard of quality, the product specification;

(b)   to put in place and operate quality control procedures to:

(i)   detect deviations;
(ii)   ensure prompt corrective action;
(iii) provide data and information for review and evaluation;

(c)   to advise management on quality in all its aspects from product design to product use.

11.3.4 The quality control department - specific tasks

Its specific tasks are:

(a)   to undertake pre-production work to identify and eliminate possible sources of manufacturing difficulty;

(b)   to ensure that materials or parts meet the required quality standards during production. This entails close cooperation with the suppliers;

(c) to monitor processed parts at all stages in the production process so that any deviations from quality specification are found before defective parts are produced by:

  (i)   raising the level of awareness of the importance of quality among the work-force - if need be through quality training;

  (ii) training inspectors and testers to assist supervisors to identify sources of quality loss and acquire and use control techniques;

  (iii) sampling finished products;

(d) to conduct special investigations into quality issues and problems.

11.3.5 Inspection

(a) *Definition*

Inspection is the activity or process in which the product is examined at specified points in manufacturing. The purpose of inspection is to identify defective work and prevent its continuation. Inspection should also lead to an accumulation of data about quality variation and deviations so that quality standards can be effectively maintained.

(b) *Types of inspection procedure*

Some factories have a centralised system of inspection based upon inspection shops or departments. Inspection shops are usually required to inspect all goods produced, an arrangement not always conducive to effective inspection because large quantities of goods may be produced before deviations from quality standards are detected. Inspection departments by contrast receive only the work in progress that is to be inspected. Although this arrangement also has disadvantages it does enable a more complete use of the inspector's specialist skills and of types of testing equipment that cannot easily be set up in production areas.

Another type of inspection is the decentralised arrangement under which inspectors patrol the production system, visiting machine stations and work benches to check on quality. This method may often enable an inspector to spot potential causes of deviations from acceptable standards before they occur - defective material, blunt tools, incompetent operatives and environmental problems such as poor lighting, ventilation or heating.

One hundred per cent inspection is sometimes essential as is the case with some products for the aerospace industry for example, when a failure of quality could result in the loss of life and destruction of an aircraft worth millions of pounds. One hundred per cent inspection is of course no guarantee that all poor quality work will be detected; inspectors are human, like the people who make the errors in the first place - they are prone to boredom and fatigue and a consequential loss of concentration. The development of micro-processors has meant that this type of inspection has become more reliable and much less expensive than before.

(c) *Statistical quality control*

Normally, reliable inspection is possible by sampling especially when statistical techniques are employed. In fact statistical quality control is the most common method of inspection used in industry.

Statistical quality control is the appliance of sampling theory to the problem. A small, random sample is taken and inspected. If the sample size measurement criteria are suitably determined, it is then possible to predict with reasonable certainty the quality of the whole batch from which the sample was selected.

11.4 Conclusion

Make sure that you can recall the methods which can be used to select a sample from a large population and be prepared to discuss them. Finally, you should now have a very basic understanding of the potential for significance testing using the properties of the distribution of sample means.

11.5 Questions

11.5.1 Objective test questions

(1) Which of the following would be secondary data for an investigation into the alcohol consumption of UK adults?

A   Statistics computed from the results of a specially commissioned survey

B   Published data derived from information collected by HM Customs and Excise

C   Survey data collected by an independent market research company on behalf of the investigator

D   A summary of responses to questionnaires completed by specially employed enumerators in pubs around the country

(2) Stratified sampling would be most appropriately used when the population:

A   is homogeneous, and is divisible into mutually exhaustive heterogeneous groups

B   is too large to make random sampling practicable

C   is heterogeneous, and is divisble into mutually exhaustive homogeneous groups

D   is listed and each item can be numbered

(3) Below is an extract from a random number table

54	08	18	07	04
68	50	33	31	47
39	90	89	86	77
56	50	45	94	25
59	77	64	59	90

Four employees are to be selected at random from the payroll on which employees are numbered from 00 to 99. Which of the following would **not** be an appropriate set of readings from the table for this purpose?

A   07   31   86   94

B   08   33   86   25

C   54   50   89   94

D   68   08   45   77

Answers

Session 1: Collection of data

Written test answers

1.1　Briggs (Carpets) Limited

The answer here requires recall of the sources of government statistics and the ability to determine which publication gives the answer to each question asked. Little of the information required is likely to be available from other sources. Most of the sources of data have been outlined in paragraph 1.3.4 but a student wanting to attempt such an examination question is advised to look at the government publications mentioned in 1.3.4 (to gain some insight into content).

For points 1-6 mentioned in the letter the following should be included in the reply.

1　Some information may be available in British Business (finding any sections on the carpet industry) but the relevant Business Monitor (PQ419 Carpets in this case) contains most information. It gives the changes in demand for various types of product and Brigg's can thus compare their performance with general sales trends.

2　Information on prices can be found from the Index of Wholesale Prices published in Monthly Digest of Statistics. The IWP gives an indication of changes in the price level of carpets produced in the UK and more detail is again given in the relevant Business Monitor.

3 and 4

　　Some detail on wage rates and hours worked is given in Monthly Digest and the Annual Abstract of Statistics but more detail can be found in the Employment Gazette and the New Earnings Survey.

5　Retail outlets are given in the Census of Distribution (in Business Monitor series) but this is ten yearly and therefore quickly gets out of date. It is now partially replaced by the Annual Retail Inquiry.

6　Statistics on overseas trade are published monthly in Overseas Trade Statistics of the UK (and also from the Customs and Excise Bill of Entry Service).

The letter of reply should also give guidance as to where more information on government statistics can be found, ie, 'Government Statistics - a brief guide to sources' and 'Guide to Official Statistics'.

1.2   Data collection

Listing the advantages and disadvantages is purely recall. Some indication of these was given in paragraph 1.3.5. A more complete list is as follows:

(a)   Direct observation

Advantages:

   (i)   The events are observed and not reported secondhand.

   (ii)   Data is collected while the normal process is in operation, ie, no disruption takes place.

Disadvantages:

   (i)   Cost is high (due to staff training, wages, etc).

   (ii)   It is not always possible to collect data in this way (eg, how often do you decorate?).

   (iii)   For data collection concerning people the results may not be representative (people may behave differently if they know they are being watched).

(b)   Postal questionnaires

Advantages:

   (i)   Low cost (although this is increased by follow-ups).

   (ii)   Large sample size can be obtained easily.

   (iii)   People can take their time and consider answers before replying.

   (iv)   They are free from interviewer bias.

Disadvantages:

   (i)   Poor response rate (20% considered good).

   (ii)   Source of the response is unknown.

   (iii)   No help with difficult questions can be given hence only simple questions can be asked.

   (iv)   The respondents may read the later questions before completing the early ones and so have their answers influenced.

(c)   Interviewing

Advantages:

   (i)   Usually a good response rate.

(ii) More information can sometimes be gained from face-to-face interviews (eg, whether the respondent was reluctant in answering a question).

(iii) Interviewers can provide assistance.

Disadvantages:

(i) Cost is high.

(ii) Answers must be standardised, ie, replies must be recorded in the same manner (staff training).

(iii) Interviewers may be biased in whom they choose as respondents.

(iv) Replies cannot be considered as in postal questionnaires.

(d) **Telephone interviewing**

Advantages:

(i) Low cost.

(ii) Can be carried out quickly.

Disadvantages:

(i) Results may be biased since not everyone has a telephone.

(ii) It is easy to be refused.

(iii) Questionnaire has to be brief.

(iv) Personal contact of face-to-face interviews is lost to some extent.

The second part of the question requires specific methods of data collection to be assigned to specific scenarios. It is not always a clear-cut decision which method is best. The following points should however be included in your answer.

(a) Interviewing would probably be the method used here. Postal questionnaires or telephone interviews are also possible but how do you decide on the respondents. An interview survey carried out in the street using set quotas of types of people to ask is simpler.

(b) Obvious problems arise here in defining 'local'. Once this is done a postal questionnaire would seem appropriate. Bias may arise since the companies with no vacancies may not respond. A telephone survey is an alternative method (but who is the contact in each company?).

(c) Obviously postal questionnaire and telephone interview are not suitable here but a simple questionnaire completed by staff would be a possibility. It may, however, create resentment amongst staff, they may also not know how much time they spend at the machine and would probably underestimate.

Interviewing staff is another possibility and more information may be obtained by such a method. However, resentment is still a problem. Direct observation would thus appear to be appropriate but again this must be done tactfully. An ingenious solution would be to move the machine to somewhere where it can easily be observed by management. This may in fact remove the problem.

Session 2: Tabulation

Written test answers

2.1 Bunny and Hutch

Employees and Wages of Bunny and Hutch Limited 19X4

	Number of employees 1 Jan	31 Dec	Average weekly wage £	Total annual wage bill £
Men	2,088	2,124	121.32	12,884,184
Women	1,871	1,860	87.93	8,177,490
Total	3,959	3,984	105.73	21,061,674

Workings:

Number of women employed at 31 Dec	$= 3{,}984 - 2{,}124 = 1{,}860$
Number of men employed at 1 Jan	$= 2{,}124 - 221 + 185 = 2{,}088$
Number of women employed at 1 Jan	$= 1{,}860 - 97 + 108 = 1{,}871$
Total number employed at 1 Jan	$= 2{,}088 + 1{,}871 = 3{,}959$
Total annual wage bill for men	$= 2{,}124 \times 121.32 \times 50 = £12{,}884{,}184$
Total annual wage bill for women	$= 1{,}860 \times 87.93 \times 50 = £8{,}177{,}490$
Total annual wage bill	$= 12{,}884{,}184 + 8{,}177{,}490 = £21{,}061{,}674$

These estimates of the annual wage bill can be obtained in other ways. In the method shown the wage bill is overestimated for men and underestimated for women since the 31 December figure of total number employed has been used in each case. A cancelling effect thus takes place giving a fairly reliable estimate. We could alternatively have used the 1 January figures of number employed or have averaged the 1 January and 31 December figures.

To calculate the total average weekly wage we could simply add £121.32 to £87.93 and divide by two. This assumes an equal number of men and women employees. Alternatively, since we now have an estimate of the total wage bill, the average weekly wage =

$$\frac{21{,}061{,}614}{3{,}984 \times 50} = £105.73, \text{ again an overestimate.}$$

2.2 **Discrete and continuous**

(a) A discrete variable can only have whole number (or integer) values whilst a continuous variable can have any value within a certain range, ie, a continuous variable can have non-integer or decimal values.

(b) (i) Discrete - the number of passengers is a count and will be a whole number. Fares, however, may include fractions, eg, half fare, etc.

(ii) Continuous - the automatic machine will not produce exactly the same weight for each bag, there will be some inherent variability. The weights of bags can thus have decimal values.

(iii) Continuous - measurement of rainfall can take decimal values.

(iv) Continuous - time taken may be 8.52 seconds, so is continuous. However, in practice, accuracy may be limited and time taken might only be measured to the nearest second, eg, 8, 13, 21 seconds - so discrete.

(v) Continuous - stocks of sugar held will probably be a weight and can thus take any value within a certain range. The variable is not continuous if the sugar is kept as sacks or bags. The number of these is a count and hence discrete.

2.3 **Motor policies**

(a) The region with the highest number of policies held was London and this region also had the largest number of claims made in 1983. The region with the smallest number of policies held was Northern Ireland, although this region had quite a high number of claims, being fifth highest of the eight regions. The smallest number of claims made was in Scotland which had the second smallest number of policy holders.

(b) Since the number of policies held in the different regions varies, more information can be gained by calculating the percentage number of claims per policies held for the eight regions. This is done below:

Region	Claims per policies held (%)
North	8.2
Midlands	7.6
South	6.1
East Anglia	2.5
London	4.3
Wales	1.8
Scotland	1.6
Northern Ireland	10.5

From this table we can see that although London had the highest actual number of claims it was only fourth of the eight regions when the number of policy holders was taken into account. In fact, Northern Ireland has the highest number of claims per policies held. As in (i), Scotland has the best accident record.

2.4   Unemployment

     (a)   Total number of unemployed in the UK on May 9 = 3,240,900. This was 13.4% of the population.

     (b)   Last fall in seasonally adjusted figures was in April 1984.

     (c)   Highest rate of unemployment on May 9 was Northern Ireland, with 20.8% of the population.

     (d)   Unemployment in Yorkshire and Humberside reached 300,000 in September 1984. This level was not maintained for the whole of 1984; in December unemployment in this region fell to 298,800.

     (e)   East Anglia had the lowest number of unemployed in January 1985 with 83,200 (though probably not the lowest **rate** of unemployment).

     (f)   Several categories are excluded from the total number of unemployed (and the problem is made more complicated by quite frequent changes in the method of calculating the figure).

          These include 'temporarily' stopped, those registered for part-time work, severely disabled people, some men aged 60 and over, school leavers between July and September, those registered temporarily ill.

          A second argument put forward is that some people may not register as unemployed but may still be seeking work, ie, concealed unemployment.

Session 3: Frequency distributions

Objective test answers

(1)   B   A describes a histogram, C an ogive and D a Lorenz curve.

(2)   D   A is an independent variable, B continuous and C dependent.

Written test answers

3.1   Pusto Limited

The data here is continuous so suitable class intervals of unit width are '24 but less than 25', etc.

Using tally marks the frequency distribution is thus of the form:

WEIGHT OF PACKET (g)	TALLY MARKS	FREQUENCY
24 but less than 25	1	1
25 but less than 26	1111	4
26 but less than 27	ℍℍ 11	7
27 but less than 28	ℍℍ 1	6
28 but less than 29	ℍℍ ℍℍ 1111	14
29 but less than 30	ℍℍ ℍℍ 1	11
30 but less than 31	1111	5
31 but less than 32	11	2
32 but less than 33	1	1
33 but less than 34	111	3
34 but less than 35	11	2
35 but less than 36	1	1
36 but less than 37		0
37 but less than 38	1	1
		—
		58

Here there are 14 class intervals (more than the maximum of 12) and the last seven class intervals are sparsely populated. It would therefore seem suitable to combine the last seven intervals in some way. One possible way of doing this is as follows:

WEIGHT OF PACKET (g)	FREQUENCY (number of packets)
24 but less than 25	1
25 but less than 26	4
26 but less than 27	7
27 but less than 28	6
28 but less than 29	14
29 but less than 30	11
30 but less than 31	5
31 but less than 36	9
36 and over	1
	—
	58

This has a class interval five times the width of the earlier classes and an open-ended class.

3.2 Socio-economic status

The required two-way frequency distribution is:

Weekly Earnings (£)	Socio-Economic Class						
	A	B	C1	C2	D	E	Total
Less than 80			1	4	7	10	22
80-120		3	5	13	4	1	26
over 120	1	6	8	6	1		22
Total	1	9	14	23	12	11	70

Comments:

The pattern in frequencies is as would be expected. The lower social classes tend to have lower weekly earnings, whereas those in higher socio-economic classes have a tendency to be higher paid.

Workings:

As with ordinary (one-way) frequency distributions it is useful in this example to use tally marks and work through the data just once, thus avoiding the chance of missing values:

Weekly Earnings (£)	A	B	Socio-Economic Class C1	C2	D	E
Less than 80			1	1111	1111 11	1111 1111
80-120		111	1111	1111 1111 111	1111	1
over 120	1	1111 1	1111 111	1111 1	1	

3.3   **Business monitor**

(a)   Using the extract from Business Monitor the rows for the last three class intervals are:

2,500 - 3,999	7	1,935	99.4	21,027	181,450	39.3
4,000 - 7,499	4	1,939	99.6	24,612	206,062	44.6
7,500 and over	7	1,946	100.0	256,091	462,153	100.0

(b)   (i)   In the motor vehicle industry 90.4% of all establishments employ less than 200 employees and these account for 8.8% of all employment.

(ii)   99.1% of establishments employ less than 2,499 employees and these account for 34.7% of all employment. Therefore, 0.9% of all establishments employ 2,500 or more employees and these account for 65.3% of all employment.

Working:

The percentage cumulative frequency for the last three class intervals are found as follows:

$$\text{eg, 2,500 - 3,999} \quad 99.4 \quad = \quad \frac{1,935}{1,946} \times 100 \quad 39.3 \quad = \quad \frac{181,450}{462,153} \times 100$$

3.4   **Office form**

A major problem with this data is that the total number of employees completing each of the forms is different (182 and 110). More information can thus be gained by converting the frequencies to percentages.

TIME TAKEN TO COMPLETE THE FORM IN MINUTES	PERCENTAGE FREQUENCY 81C/A	81C/B
10 but less than 15	2	3
15 but less than 20	11	23
20 but less than 30	25	31
30 but less than 45	27	24
45 but less than 60	13	9
60 but less than 90	10	5
90 but less than 120	8	5
120 and over	4	2
	—	—
	100	102

(This discrepancy is caused by rounding errors.)

Additionally, information can be gained by cumulating frequencies. Again it is sensible to form a cumulative frequency distribution using the percentage figures:

TIME TAKEN TO COMPLETE THE FORM IN MINUTES	CUMULATIVE PERCENTAGE FREQUENCY 81C/A	81C/B
less than 15	2	3
less than 20	13	26
less than 30	38	57
less than 45	65	81
less than 60	78	90
less than 90	88	95
less than 120	96	100

Comments:

Using the percentage frequency distribution we can see that for the form 81C/B the higher percentages of employees are in the class intervals in the first half of the table, ie, a large percentage of employees complete the new form in a short period of time. This contrasts with the form 81C/A, where the percentages are more evenly spread throughout the class intervals with the higher percentages of employees taking longer to complete the form.

The largest percentage of employees (31%) completed 81C/B in 20 but less than 30 minutes whereas the highest percentage (27%) of employees completed 81C/A in 30 but less than 45 minutes.

From the percentage cumulative frequency distribution we see that the above points are reinforced with 57% of employees completing form 81C/B in under 30 minutes compared to only 38% for form 81C/A.

The data thus suggests that the new form 81C/B is an improvement over the old form 81C/A.

Working:

The percentage frequencies are found as follows:

81C/A   81C/B

eg, 10 but less than 15 $\frac{3}{182}$ x 100 = 1.65 $\frac{3}{110}$ x 100 = 2.73

= 2 (approx.)   = 3 (approx.)

This is where the earlier mentioned rounding errors arise.

Session 4: Graphs

Written test answers

4.1   Printer

The two relationships required are:

(i)   Printing: Cost C = 300 + 1.5n   )
) both in pence
(ii)   Photocopier: Cost C = 5n   )

The graph of these equations is then:

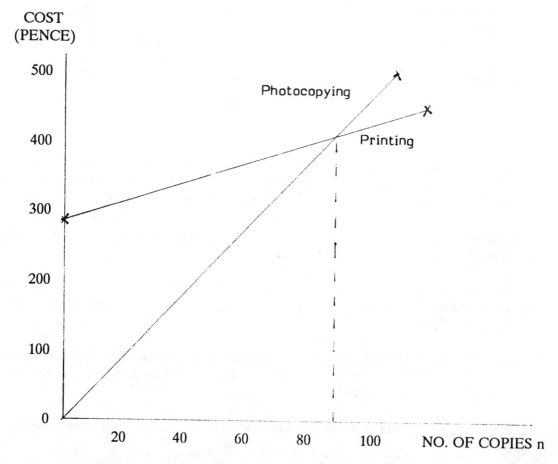

From the graph, the break-even point is when the number of copies taken is (approximately) 86. If less than 86 copies are required photocopying is cheaper, after that number then printing is preferable.

Working:

To plot the two relationships on the graph the following points are required:

Printing	n = 0	C = 300	
	n = 100	C = 300 + 150 = 450	
Photocopier	n = 0	C = 0	
	n = 100	C = 500	

Note that the exact location of the break-even point can be found algebraically by equating the two relationships:

$$300 + 1.5n = 5n$$

$$300 = 3.5n$$

$$\text{therefore } n = \frac{300}{3.5} = 85.7$$

4.2   Ball bearings

A table of values of P for various values of r is required to plot the graph:

r	0.5	1.0	1.5	2.0	2.5	3.0
P	4.75	5	4.75	4	2.75	1

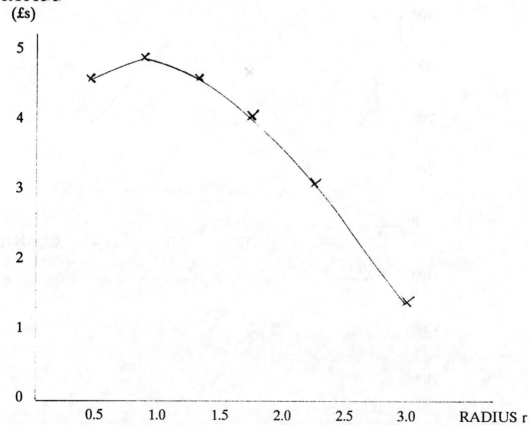

From the graph, profit is maximised when the radius of ball bearings made is 1 mm. For this size ball bearing the profit is £5 per 1,000 ball bearings.

A.11

Answers

4.3   **Product revenue**

(i)   Total costs are given by the relationship:

Total costs   C =   fixed costs + (variable cost per item x quantity produced)

$$C = 400 + 5q$$

(ii)   Profit   =   revenue - total costs

$$= (60q - q^2) - (400 + 5q)$$

$$= 60q - q^2 - 400 - 5q$$

$$= 55q - q^2 - 400$$

(iii)

q	0	10	20	30	40
55q	0	550	1,100	1,650	2,200
$-q^2$	0	-100	-400	-900	-1,600
-400	-400	-400	-400	-400	-400
Profit	-400	50	300	350	200

PROFIT (P)

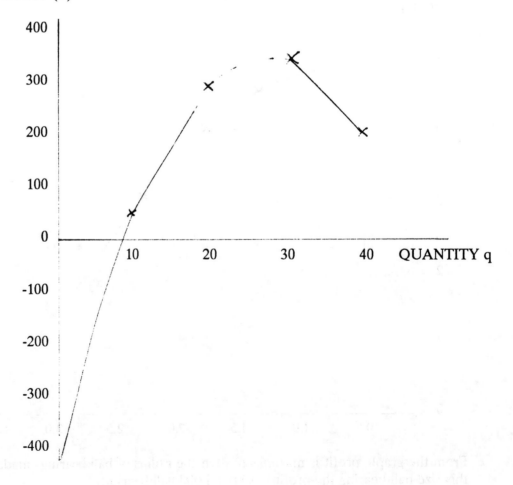

A.12

1134M

This problem illustrates the difficulty in attempting to obtain an optimum point by using graphs alone. By using an interval of 10 on the q axis the maximum point is difficult to obtain accurately - the shape of the graph between q = 20 and q = 30 is uncertain. From the above graph an estimate of maximum profit is when quantity is 27, though more points plotted on the graph would be beneficial.

(The exact answer is in fact q = 27.5!)

4.4   **Agricultural use**

Land available: $\underline{L = 0.645 - 0.001t}$ (W1)

Land required:

t	Land required R
0	0.054
25	0.108
50	0.216
75	0.432
100	0.864

$$\underline{R = 0.054 \times 2^{t/25}}$$ (W2)

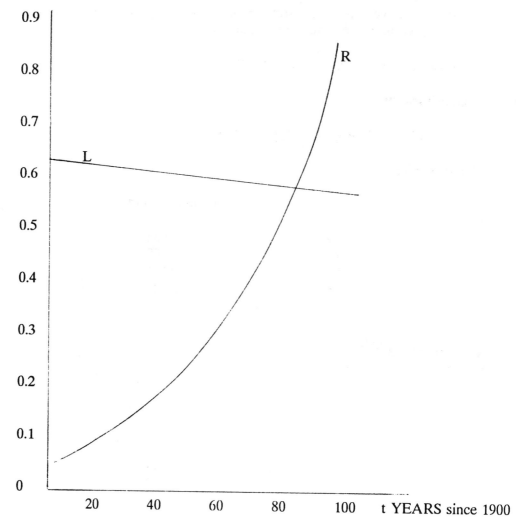

AMOUNT OF LAND
(million hectares)

t YEARS since 1900

From the graph we see that more land is required than is available during 1985.

Workings:

1   To plot the expression for land available, which is a straight line, we need the coordinates:

         t = 0   L = 0.645

         t = 100   L = 0.645 - 0.1 = 0.545

2   The expression for land required is a little difficult to derive if not met before. It is obtained from the table of values by expressing each value as a multiple of 0.054:

t	R				
0	0.054	=	0.054	=	0.054×2^0
25	0.108	=	0.054 x 2	=	0.054×2^1
50	0.216	=	0.054 x 4	=	0.054×2^2
75	0.432	=	0.054 x 8	=	0.054×2^3
100	0.864	=	0.054 x 16	=	0.054×2^4

Session 5: Charts and diagrams

Written test answers

5.1   Energy consumption

We first need to calculate the total energy consumption for each year.

19X1 Total consumption = 139.3 + 151.2 + 28.8 = 319.3
19X9 Total consumption = 129.6 + 139.0 + 71.3 = 339.9

(i)   Component bar chart

UK INLAND ENERGY CONSUMPTION 19X1 + 19X9

UK INLAND ENERGY
CONSUMPTION
(millions of tonnes
of coal equivalent)

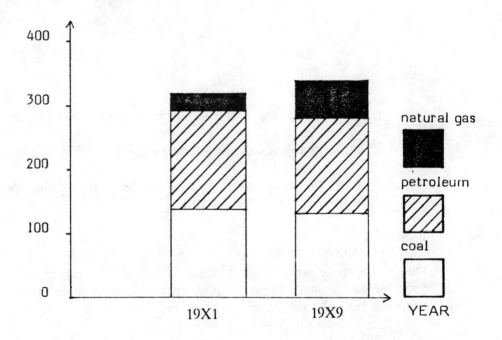

(ii) Compound bar chart

UK INLAND ENERGY CONSUMPTION 19X1 + 19X9

UK INLAND ENERGY
CONSUMPTION
(millions of tonnes
of coal equivalent)

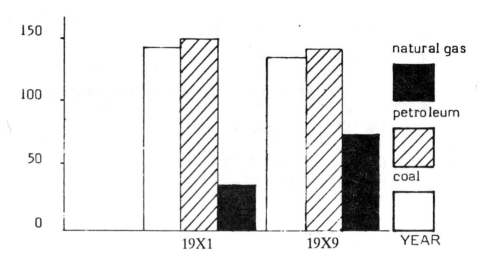

The benefits of both diagrams are:

(a) (i) shows total energy consumption for each year but (ii) does not.

(b) (ii) allows us to use a larger vertical scale than (i), giving increased accuracy.

(c) (ii) shows the trend or change between the years for each energy product. ((i) also shows this trend but not as well.)

5.2   FSS and Co

Due to the quite large number of sub-divisions here, pie charts are suitable. Since the total for each financial year is different we need to scale the two pie charts. The pie chart for 19X3/X4 will have:

$$\sqrt{\frac{750}{620}} = 1.1 \text{ times the radius of that for 19X2/X3.}$$

The pie charts are thus:

VALUE ADDED FOR FSS & CO LIMITED

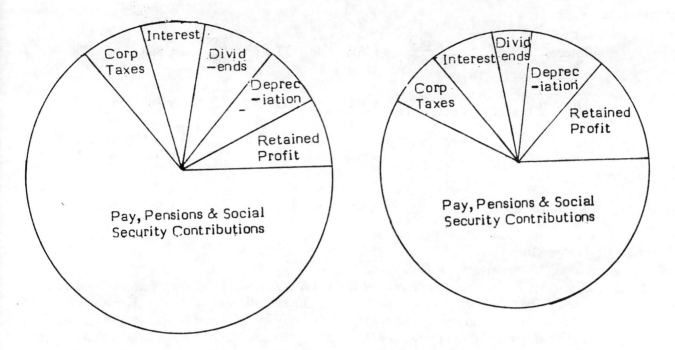

Working:

The proportions and angles used for constructing the two pie charts are:

19X3/X4

	%				Angle		
Pay, etc	$\frac{478.3}{750}$	x 100	= 63.8	$\frac{63.8}{100}$	x 360	=	230
Corp taxes	$\frac{49.4}{750}$	x 100	= 6.6	$\frac{6.6}{100}$	x 360	=	24
Interest	$\frac{53.7}{750}$	x 100	= 7.2	$\frac{7.2}{100}$	x 360	=	26
Dividends	$\frac{58.9}{750}$	x 100	= 7.9	$\frac{7.9}{100}$	x 360	=	28
Depreciation	$\frac{54.6}{750}$	x 100	= 7.3	$\frac{7.3}{100}$	x 360	=	26
Retained profit	$\frac{55.1}{750}$	x 100	= 7.3	$\frac{7.3}{100}$	x 360	=	26
Pay, etc	$\frac{351}{620}$	x 100	= 56.6	$\frac{56.6}{100}$	x 360	=	204
Corp taxes	$\frac{42.4}{620}$	x 100	= 6.8	$\frac{6.8}{100}$	x 360	=	24

A.17

				19X2/X3			
	%				Angle		
Interest	$\frac{48.4}{620}$	x 100	=	7.8	$\frac{7.8}{100}$	x 360	= 28
Dividends	$\frac{32.2}{620}$	x 100	=	5.2	$\frac{5.2}{100}$	x 360	= 19
Depreciation	$\frac{65.3}{620}$	x 100	=	10.5	$\frac{10.5}{100}$	x 360	= 38
Retained profit	$\frac{80.9}{620}$	x 100	=	13.0	$\frac{13.0}{100}$	x 360	= 47

5.3 ICI profits

The diagram shown is a component bar chart with a slight difference from those already seen. Each bar shows the trading profit for a different division. For example, the Agriculture division had a trading profit of £193m in 19X3 and £158m in 19X2. The total height of the bar thus represents the 19X3 figure and the 19X2 figure is included within this. Previous examples have represented these figures with a bar of height £351m (193 + 158).

From the diagram the following points can be noted:

(i)   The future for ICI looks very rosy (the points below illustrate this) since a major recovery in profits has taken place.

(ii)   In 19X3 only the Fibres, Organics and Petrochemicals and Plastics divisions made losses. These were very small and in two of these division the losses were a significant reduction from 19X2 losses.

(iii)   The organics division appears to be the only major problem; making a profit in 19X2 and a loss in 19X3.

(iv)   All other divisions made increased profits in 19X3 (compared with 19X2).

The percentage increases in profits being:

Agriculture	= 22.2%
General chemicals	= 68.3%
Explosives	= 10%
Oil	= 32.9%
Paints	= 17.4%
Pharmaceuticals	= 52.2%

(v)   Overall profit made by ICI

　　　　19X2   £330m
　　　　19X3   £634m

a 92% increase in profits.

5.4   Pydec

The following points in the extract from the company report would give the trades union cause for concern.

Profits:

(i)   The scale of the graph starts at 8 thus distorting the actual change in profits. Profits have in fact fallen from 10.1 to 8.3, ie, 17.8% (it says 'almost 20%' in the report).

(ii)   The vertical scale is presumably profit (labelled 'millions').

(iii)   Is the picture as bad as that painted? The rate of decrease in profits seems to be getting smaller; perhaps levelling out.

(iv)   What does the dotted line mean? Presumably it is a projection but where is the evidence?

Production:

(i)   The scale of the bar chart is OK (but one bar is wider than the other - though this is not obvious).

(ii)   Production has fallen as stated (by 10,000 sets overall) but production at the Leicester factory actually increased.

(iii)   Where are production figures for audio equipment?

(iv)   Report states 'some of our competitors have been doing much better'. Where is the evidence for this?

Wages:

(i)   Report states 'the average wage of all employees rose by £7.23 per week' and claims this is good. What percentage increase is this? What was the rate of inflation?

(ii)   Printing mistake - 'if we compare average wages between 19W5 and 19X0'. But diagrams are for 19W6 and 19X1.

(iii)   The pictogram is misleading. Figures state that wages double, yet the diagram looks like a 4 fold increase took place (twice the length, and twice the width).

Session 6: Other charts

Objective test answers

(1)   D   This is usually used to show cumulative performance over one year in comparison with budget.

(2)   B   This appears on a Lorenz curve.

(3)   A   19X4   19X5   19X6   19X7   19X8
            +9.9%   +9.0%   +8.3%   +7.7%

A decreasing rate of increase

(4)   C   -20.3%   -25.5%   -28.9%   -40.7%

An increasing rate of decline.

Written test answers

6.1   Smith and Brown

Since we are comparing the shapes of two different frequency distributions, frequency polygons are a suitable diagrammatic means of doing this remembering to scale down where wider classes occur. This examination question is simpler than some which you may meet because the total frequency in each case is the same. If the total frequencies are different then the frequencies should be changed to percentages before the diagram is drawn.

The frequency polygons for this data are shown below. They have been drawn on the same axis to allow easier comparison of their shapes.

ANNUAL SALARIES OF EMPLOYEES OF
SMITH LIMITED AND BROWN LIMITED

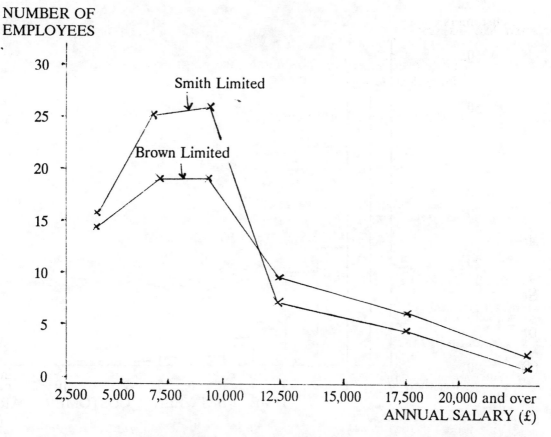

These frequency polygons illustrate the salary distributions of the two companies and are very similar in shape. They show that for both companies, the majority of employees have salaries towards the lower end of the frequency distribution (smaller salaries) as would be expected. However, the polygons also illustrate that Brown Limited has the preferable salary structure (from an employee's point of view). Its frequency polygon is 'flatter' than that of Smith's with a more even distribution of salaries, ie, in general, less employees tend to earn lower salaries and more employees tend to earn higher salaries.

6.2   Bakery shop

To construct the histogram for a frequency distribution of this type requires care in scaling down the heights of blocks of wider class intervals. Here we have two open-ended classes, one class of width $1/2$ minute, four classes of width one minute, one class of width two minutes and a class of width three minutes. The first decision is thus to decide what width of interval to base our heights of blocks on. We could use $1/2$ minute as our base and scale all other class intervals accordingly. However, the usual practice is to use the class interval of the majority of the classes as the base, in this case one minute. The histogram then has the form:

TIME BETWEEN CUSTOMER ARRIVALS AT BAKERY SHOP

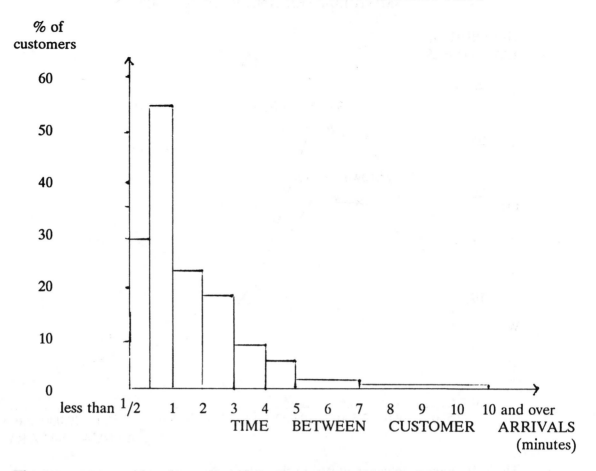

The comments on the shape of the distribution are in this case fairly straightforward. The distribution is 'skewed' so that the majority of inter-arrival times are quite short (less than 3 minutes, say). Fairly infrequently there is a slack period at the bakery shop with longer gaps between customer arrivals.

6.3 **Bakery ogive**

The ogive for this data is as follows:

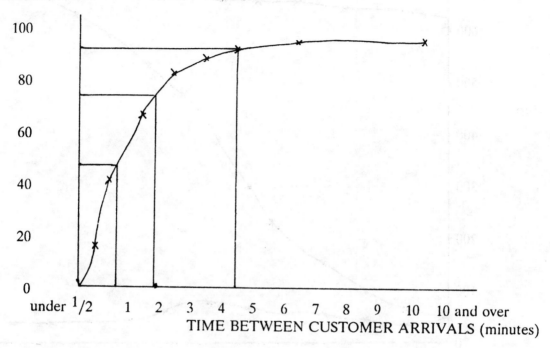

TIME BETWEEN CUSTOMER ARRIVALS AT BAKERY SHOP - OGIVE

From the ogive we find that:

(i)   74% of customers have inter-arrival times of less than $2^1/2$ minutes;

(ii)   approximately 47% of customers have inter-arrival times of between $1^1/4$ and 5 minutes.

Workings:

The following cumulative frequency distribution is required in the construction of the ogive:

TIME BETWEEN CUSTOMER ARRIVALS (minutes)	CUMULATIVE FREQUENCY
less than $^1/2$	15
less than 1	43 (15 + 28)
less than 2	66 (43 + 23)
Less than 3	84 (66 + 18)
Less than 4	92 (84 + 8)
Less than 5	96 (92 + 4)
Less than 7	98 (96 + 2)
Less than 10	99 (98 + 1)
10 and over	100 (99 + 1)

6.4   Z-chart

Z-CHART FOR BENDYBIKES PLC 19X4

Each component of a Z-chart illustrates different aspects of the data. In this case:

(i)   the plot of the actual data (time series plot) shows the seasonal variation. There is a large increase in sales of Bendybikes in the summer months;

(ii)   the cumulative sales plot shows the total sales for 19X4 up to the month of interest, eg, the figure 414 in July indicates that total sales from January to July inclusive have been £4,140,000;

(iii)   the plot of the moving totals has eliminated the seasonal effects and thus shows whether sales are rising or falling. Here they are rising.

Workings:

The calculations used in constructing the Z-chart are:

MONTH	19X3 SALES	19X4 SALES	19X4 CUMULATIVE SALES	MOVING TOTALS
Jan	32	37	37	624 + (37 - 32) = 629
Feb	29	31	68	629 + (31 - 29) = 631
Mar	38	45	113	638
Apr	49	58	171	647
May	57	62	233	652
June	75	79	312	656
July	88	102	414	670
Aug	79	88	502	679
Sept	49	61	563	691
Oct	43	57	620	705
Nov	39	50	670	716
Dec	46	53	723	723
	───			
	624			

6.5   In Great Britain

The semi-logarithmic graphs for these three sets of data are as follows:

VEHICLE LICENSES AND ROAD CASUALTIES

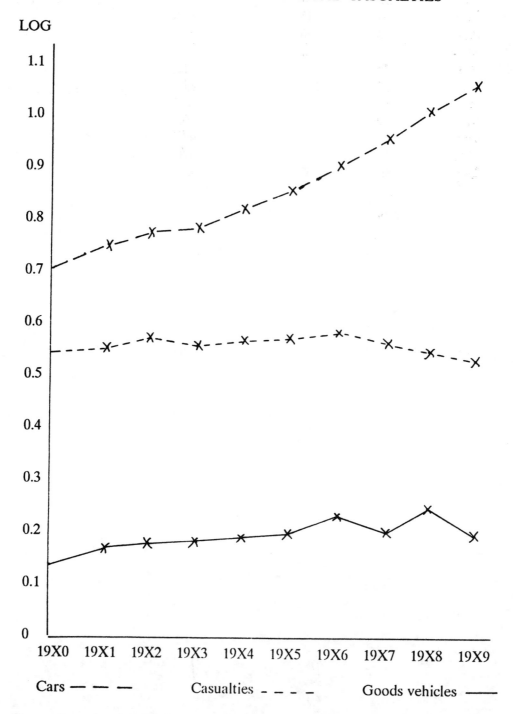

To produce the three lines on the same graph and on a reasonably large scale, 3 has been subtracted from the first two logs and two subtracted from the third one.   This is permissible because a semi-log graph is showing rates of change and not absolute values.

The graph shows that the number of cars licensed increased at a more or less constant rate over the period considered.   This is signified by an upwards sloping straight line.

Over the earlier years the number of goods vehicles increased at a very small constant rate but in 19X6 this levelled off and in later years showed almost complete stability.

The pattern of casualties from road accidents does not entirely fit in with the pattern of the other two sets of figures. Taking the figures for cars and goods vehicles together, there is obviously a constant rate of increase of all vehicles licensed, and yet the curve for casualties shows a slight constant rate of increase up to 19X6 but after that it changed direction and exhibits a slight constant rate of decrease. Of course there are many other factors which would contribute to the reduced accident rate such as more motorways, better road conditions, safer vehicle design and an increase in the use of safety belts.

Workings:

Year	No cars	Log 1	No goods vehicles	Log 2	No casualties	Log 3
19X0	4,972	3.6966	1,378	3.1392	333	2.5224
19X1	5,532	3.7429	1,448	3.1609	348	2.5416
19X2	5,983	3.7769	1,503	3.1770	350	2.5441
19X3	6,560	3.8169	1,522	3.1824	342	2.5340
19X4	7,380	3.8681	1,582	3.1993	356	2.5514
19X5	8,252	3.9166	1,633	3.2130	385	2.5855
19X6	8,922	3.9505	1,661	3.2204	397	2.5988
19X7	9,522	3.9787	1,639	3.2146	392	2.5933
19X8	10,312	4.0133	1,692	3.2284	370	2.5682
19X9	10,825	4.0346	1,640	3.2148	349	2.5428

6.6   Business Monitor II

This is a rather 'extreme' example (although using real data) and gives the following Lorenz curve.

LORENZ CURVE OF OUTPUT AND ESTABLISHMENTS
IN THE MOTOR VEHICLE MANUFACTURING INDUSTRY

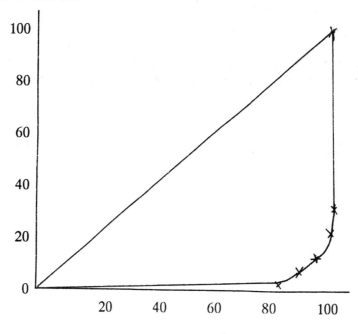

CUMULATIVE %
OF OUTPUT

CUMULATIVE %
OF ESTABLISHMENTS

If we had perfect equality (ie, all size establishments were equally efficient) then the plot of values would follow the straight line. On the other hand, if we had perfect inequality the plot of values would follow the line AB-BC shown on the chart. For the motor vehicle manufacturing industry this is almost the case, the larger establishments generate an enormous proportion of the output.

Workings:

No of Employees	No Establishment	%	Cum.	Net output	%	Cum.
Less than 100	1,658	85	85	99,358	5	5
100 but less than 400	164	8	93	122,887	6	11
400 but less than 1,000	66	3	96	213,681	10	21
1,000 but less than 2,000	34	2	98	206,403	10	31
2,000 but less than 4,000	13	1	99	137,449	7	38
4,000 and over	11	1	100	1,259,810	62	100
	1,946	100		2,039,588	100	

6.7 **Bigga Engines**

The Gantt chart is as below:

GANTT CHART FOR PRODUCTION OF BIGGA ENGINES LIMITED

WEEK 1		WEEK 2		WEEK 3		WEEK 4		WEEK 5	
Fore-cast	Cum. fore-cast	Fore-cast	Cum. fore-cast	Fore-cast	Cum. fore-cast	Fore-cast	Cum. fore-cast	Fore-cast	Cum. fore-cast
100	100	120	220	150	370	150	520	140	660

Actual   Cumulative

Workings:

In constructing the Gantt chart, the actual weekly production figures of Bigga Engines Limited are expressed as a percentage of the forecasted figures:

WEEK	ACTUAL	FORECAST	ACTUAL AS A % OF FORECAST
1	60	100	60
2	96	120	80
3	125	150	83.3
4	150	150	100
5	175	140	125

Session 7: Measures of central tendency and dispersion

Objective test answers

(1)   A

Workings:

$$45 + \frac{50}{250} \times 10 = 47$$

(2)   B

Workings:

Income £'000 (x)	No people (f)	Cum f
0 - 5	120	120
5 - 10	410	530
10 - 15	385	915
15 - 20	85	1,000
	1,000	

Median item (500th) has value lying in range 5 - 10, 380 items in.

Value $\approx 5 + \dfrac{380}{410} (5) = £9,634 \approx £9,635$

(3)   A

Workings:

Using the second σ formula, with A = 0 (ie d = x)

$$\sigma = \sqrt{\frac{\Sigma x^2}{n} - (x)^2} = \sqrt{\frac{2,575}{7} - (12.429)^2}$$

$$\approx 14.6$$

Written test answers

7.1   Pay increase

The argument arises because (at least) measures of average can be used to represent the 'typical' pay increase offered. These being:

$$\text{Mean } \bar{x} = \frac{\sum fx}{\sum f} = \frac{(2.50 \times 46) + (3.00 \times 24) + (4.00 \times 15) + (9.60 \times 15)}{46 + 24 + 15 + 15}$$

$$= \frac{115 + 72 + 60 + 144}{100} = \frac{391}{100} = £3.91$$

Median = £3.00   since $\frac{n}{2}$ = 50 and the 50th value in the cumulative frequency table:

Pay increase	%	CF
2.50	46	46
3.00	24	70
4.00	15	85
9.60	15	100

Mode   = £2.50   since a wage of £2.50 is received by the highest percentage of employees (46%).

These 'averages' are all different thus causing the ensuing argument. Management would be most likely to claim the average wage increase offered was £3.91 (the mean) whilst the representatives of the workers would probably claim the average offer was only £3.00 (the mode).

Answers

7.2   Mekon

(a)   The histogram has the form:

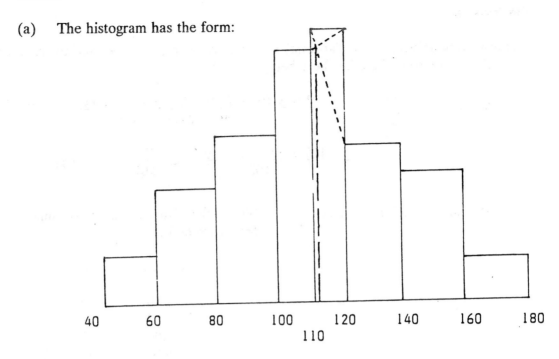

(b)   Using an assumed mean the calculations required are:

Production			f	d	fd	d^2	fd^2	Cumulative frequencies (for (c))
40	to under	60	10	-2	-20	4	40	10
60	"	80	25	-1	-25	1	25	35
80	"	100	36	0	0	0	0	71
100	"	110	28	+0.75	+21	0.56	15.68	99
110	"	120	30	+1.25	+37.5	1.56	46.8	129
120	"	140	34	+2	+68	4	136	163
140	"	160	28	+3	+84	9	252	191
160	"	180	9	+4	+36	16	144	200
			200		201.5		659.48	

An assumed mean of 90 has been used, and the deviations (d) from the assumed mean are measured in terms of a class interval of 20.

A.32   1134M

Arithmetic mean $\qquad \bar{x} = A + \dfrac{\Sigma fd}{\Sigma f} \times CI$

$$= 90 + \frac{201.5}{200} \times 20$$

$$= \underline{110.15} \text{ (000s units)}$$

Standard deviation $\qquad S = \sqrt{\dfrac{\Sigma fd^2}{\Sigma f} - \dfrac{\Sigma fd}{\Sigma f}^2} \times CI$

$$= \sqrt{\frac{659.48}{200} - \frac{201.5}{200}^2} \times 20$$

$$= \sqrt{3.30 - 1.02} \times 20$$

$$= 30.2 \text{ (000s units)}$$

(c) The median is the 100th item.

By looking at the cumulative frequencies, it can be seen that this must lie between 110 and 120.

The mode is the value with the highest frequency. From the histogram it can be seen that this lies in the class 110 to 120.

(i) The median is a useful measure when rank or position is of importance. For example, where a class of students take an exam, it may be more important for a student to know whether his result places him in the top half of the class rather than knowing that his mark is above the average (arithmetic mean). Also the median is not as affected by extreme values as the arithmetic mean.

(ii) The mode is more useful than the arithmetic mean when a measure of central tendency is required to be an actual value that exists in the distribution (although this may not even be true for the mode if data has been grouped beforehand). It is also useful if the most frequently occurring value or the range of values with the highest frequency density is required.

This may be the case, for example, where a shoe manufacturer wishes to know which shoe size is the most common so that he can plan his production accordingly.

(d) The graphical construction for finding the mode is shown on the histogram in the answer to part (a). With the small scale used, it is difficult to quote the answer accurately but the mode appears to be approximately 112,000 units.

7.3   South Yorkshire

Mean number of unemployed:

$$\bar{x} \; = \; \frac{\Sigma x}{n} \; = \; \frac{436}{12} \; = \; 36.3333 \text{ thousand}$$

$$= \; 36333$$

Arranging the data in order of magnitude:

33	33	34	34	35	35	36	37	37	39	41	42

Median number of unemployed $\quad = \quad \dfrac{35 + 36}{2} \; = \; 35.50 \text{ thousand} = 35500$

Mode number of unemployed $\quad = \;$ 33, 34, 35 and 37 thousand

$$= \; 33000, 34000, 35000, 37000$$

If the July and August figures are corrected then the values of the measures are as follows:

Mean number of unemployed:

$$\bar{x} \; = \; \frac{440}{12} \; = \; 36.6667 \text{ thousand}$$

$$= \; 36667$$

Arranging the data in order of magnitude leaves the figures in the same order as earlier:

33	33	34	34	35	35	36	37	37	39	43	44

Therefore median number of unemployed $\quad = \quad \dfrac{35 + 36}{2} \; = \; 35.50 \text{ thousand}$

$$= \; 35500$$

Mode number of unemployed $\quad = \;$ 33, 34, 35, 37 thousand

$$= \; 33000, 34000, 35000, 37000$$

We thus see that the median and mode number of unemployed are unchanged even though the data has changed. Only the mean has reflected the small changes in the data values. This is a major advantage of the mean over the other measures of location.

7.4 **Three shifts**

(a) **Operator A**

Dimension (x)	Frequency (f)	d $\frac{(x - 32.5)}{0.1}$	fd	fd^2
32.1	1	-4	-4	16
32.2	6	-3	-18	54
32.3	10	-2	-20	40
32.4	21	-1	-21	21
32.5	36	0	0	0
32.6	17	1	17	17
32.7	6	2	12	24
32.8	2	3	6	18
32.9	1	4	4	16
	100		-24	206

$$\bar{x} = A + \frac{\Sigma fd}{\Sigma f} \times \frac{1}{10}$$

$$= 32.5 - \frac{24}{100} \times \frac{1}{10}$$

$$= 32.5 - 0.024$$

$$= 32.476 \text{mm}$$

$$S = \sqrt{\frac{\Sigma fd^2}{\Sigma f} - \left(\frac{\Sigma fd}{\Sigma f}\right)^2} \times \frac{1}{10}$$

$$= \sqrt{\frac{206}{100} - \left(\frac{24}{100}\right)^2} \times \frac{1}{10}$$

$$= \sqrt{2.06 - 0.0576} \times \frac{1}{10}$$

$$= 0.142 \text{mm}$$

Operator B

Dimension (x)	Frequency (f)	d $\dfrac{(x - 32.5)}{0.1}$	fd	fd^2
32.3	7	-2	-14	28
32.4	25	-1	-25	25
32.5	34	0	0	0
32.6	27	1	27	27
32.7	6	2	12	24
32.8	1	3	3	9
	100		3	113

$$\bar{x} = A + \frac{\sum fd}{\sum f} \times \frac{1}{10}$$

$$= 32.5 + \frac{3}{1,000}$$

$$= 32.503 \text{mm}$$

$$S = \sqrt{\frac{\sum fd^2}{\sum f} - \left(\frac{\sum fd}{\sum f}\right)^2} \times \frac{1}{10}$$

$$= \sqrt{\frac{113}{100} - \left(\frac{3}{100}\right)^2} \times \frac{1}{10}$$

$$= \sqrt{1.13 - 0.0009} \times \frac{1}{10}$$

$$= 0.106 \text{mm}$$

Operator C

Dimension (x)	Frequency (f)	d $\dfrac{(x - 32.3)}{0.1}$	fd	fd^2
32.1	3	-2	-6	12
32.2	22	-1	-22	22
32.3	49	0	0	0
32.4	22	1	22	22
32.5	4	2	8	16
	100		2	72

$$\bar{x} = A + \frac{\Sigma fd}{\Sigma f} \times \frac{1}{10}$$

$$= 32.3 + \frac{2}{1,000}$$

$$= 32.302\text{mm}$$

$$S = \sqrt{\frac{\Sigma fd^2}{\Sigma f} - \left(\frac{\Sigma fd}{\Sigma f}\right)^2} \times \frac{1}{10}$$

$$= \sqrt{\frac{72}{100} - \left(\frac{2}{100}\right)^2} \times \frac{1}{10}$$

$$= \sqrt{0.72 - 0.0004} \times \frac{1}{10}$$

$$= 0.085\text{mm}$$

(i) The most accurate is the one with mean closest to 32.5mm, ie, operator B.

(ii) The most consistent is the one with smallest standard deviation, ie, operator C.

(b) The mean is a measure of central tendency or location which takes no account of the variability of the values.

A measure of dispersion such as standard deviation, mean deviation, quartile deviation, etc, needs to be used to describe the spread of the values.

Thus the mean alone is an inadequate guide to performance since it can only show a central value but ignores variations around this value. It therefore gives no indication of consistency.

7.5 Plastic containers

We know that $\mu = 1,000$, $\sigma = 20$

(a)

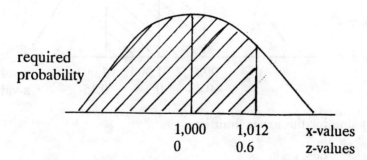

required probability

| | 1,000 | 1,012 | x-values |
| | 0 | 0.6 | z-values |

The z-value for the limit is:

$$\frac{1,012 - 1,000}{20} = 0.6$$

and the value from the table is 0.2257.

The required probability is:

$$0.5 + 0.2257 = 0.7257$$

A.37

(b)

The z-value for the lower limit is:

$$\frac{1,005 - 1,000}{20} = 0.25$$

and the table value is 0.0987.

The z-value for the upper limit is:

$$\frac{1,008 - 1,000}{20} = 0.40$$

and the table value is 0.1554.

The required probability is:

$$0.1554 - 0.0987 = 0.0567$$

(c)

The z-value for the lower limit is:

$$\frac{992 - 1,000}{20} = -0.40$$

and the table value is 0.1554.

The z-value for the upper limit is:

$$\frac{1,003 - 1,000}{20} = 0.15$$

and the table value is 0.0596.

A.38

1134M

The required probability is:

$$0.1554 + 0.0596 = 0.2150$$

(d)

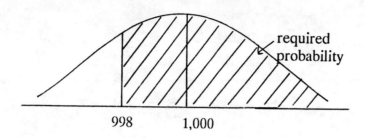

The z-value for the limit is:

$$\frac{998 - 1,000}{20} = -0.1$$

and the table value is 0.0398.

The required probability is:

$$0.5 + 0.0398 = 0.5398$$

Session 8: Correlation and regression

Objective test answers

(1)   C

$$b = \frac{\sum (m - \bar{m})(f - \bar{f})}{\sum (m - \bar{m})^2} = \frac{2500}{2780} \approx 0.9$$

$$a = \bar{f} - b\bar{m} = 43.2 - \frac{2500}{2780}(41) = 6.3$$

The regression line is therefore f = 6.3 + 0.9m

So if m = 50 then f = 6.3 + 0.9(50) = 51.3

(2)   B   As y does not change at all whatever the value of x, then there can be no relationship between the two.

(3)   B   r = 0.5, thus the coefficient of determination, r^2, = 0.25

The coefficient of determination measures the proportion of the variation in the y values (from the average) that could be predicted from the regression line - ie, is explained by the variation of the associated x value from their average.

Written test answers

8.1   Freight

Dependent variable y - delivery charge

Independent variable x - distance

Distance	Charge				
x	y	$x - \bar{x}$	$y - \bar{y}$	$(x - \bar{x})(y - \bar{y})$	$(x - \bar{x})^2$
6	49	-8.2	-50.7	415.74	67.24
13	93	-1.2	-6.7	8.04	1.44
27	159	12.8	59.3	759.04	163.84
15	115	0.8	15.3	12.24	0.64
9	66	-5.2	-33.7	175.24	27.04
11	90	-3.2	-9.7	31.04	10.24
21	139	6.8	39.3	267.24	46.24
14	98	-0.2	-1.7	0.34	0.04
12	88	-2.2	-11.7	25.74	4.84
128	897			1694.66	321.56

$$\bar{x} = \frac{\sum x}{n} = \frac{128}{9} = 14.2 \qquad \bar{y} = \frac{\sum y}{n} = \frac{897}{9} = 99.7$$

Regression line is y = bx + a where 'a' and 'b' are given by:

$$b = \frac{\sum(x - \bar{x})(y - \bar{y})}{(x - \bar{x})^2} = \frac{1{,}694.66}{321.56} = 5.27$$

$$a = \bar{y} - b\bar{x} = 99.7 - 5.27 \times 14.2$$

$$= 24.87$$

Regression line is y $\qquad = 5.27x + 24.87$

Constant a = £24.87 is a fixed charge made on each delivery.
Constant b = £5.27 is a variable charge made for each 100 miles of the journey.

If distance is 2,000 miles

$$x = 20$$

$$y = 5.27 \times 20 + 24.87$$

Therefore delivery charge = £130.27.

8.2   Vide and Feldt

(a)

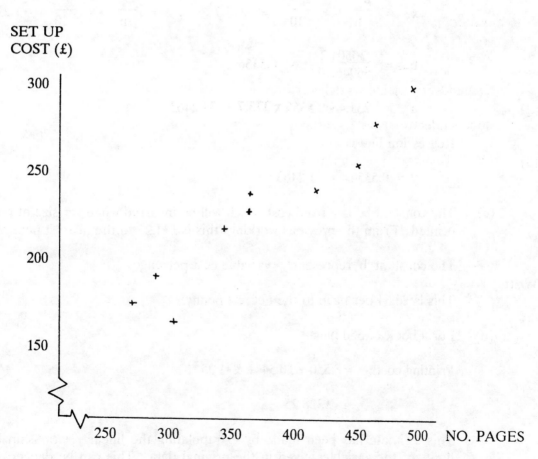

SET UP
COST (£)

NO. PAGES

1   Apart from the point representing a book of 300 pages requiring a set up
        cost of £161, the points look as though they almost lie on a straight line.

2   As may be expected the two variables tend to increase together. Thus longer books result in higher set-up costs.

(b)   Regression line is y = bx + a where 'a' and 'b' are calculated as follows:

$$b = \frac{\Sigma(x - \bar{x})(y - \bar{y})}{(x - x)^2} \qquad a = \bar{y} - b\bar{x}$$

x	y	$(x - \bar{x})$	$(y - \bar{y})$	$(x - \bar{x})(y - \bar{y})$	$(x - \bar{x})^2$
362	241	-11.7	9.6	-112.32	136.89
264	174	-109.7	-57.4	6296.78	12034.09
285	195	-88.7	-36.4	3228.68	7867.69
451	260	77.3	28.6	2210.78	5975.29
363	234	-10.7	2.6	-27.82	114.49
418	246	44.3	14.6	646.78	1962.49
300	161	-73.7	-70.4	5188.48	5431.69
492	296	118.3	64.6	7642.18	13994.89
338	220	-35.7	-11.4	406.98	1274.49
464	287	90.3	55.6	5020.68	8154.09
3737	2314			30501.2	56946.10

$$\bar{x} = \frac{\Sigma x}{n} = \frac{3737}{10} = 373.7 \qquad \bar{y} = \frac{\Sigma y}{n} = \frac{2314}{10} = 231.4$$

$$b = \frac{30501.2}{56946.10} = 0.5356$$

$$a = 231.4 - 0.5356 \times 373.7 = 31.2463$$

Regression line is

$$y = 0.5356x + 31.2463$$

(c)   The constant 'a' is a fixed cost which will be incurred whatever size of book is being printed. From the previous workings this is £31.25 to the nearest penny.

The constant 'b' represents a variable cost per page.

This is £0.54 per page to the nearest penny.

(d)   For a book of 550 pages

Printing cost   = 550 x £0.54 + £31.25

                = £328.25

This estimate has been made by extrapolating the linear relationship beyond the limits of the variables given in the original data. This can be dangerous, because other factors may affect the relationship outside this range which are not apparent from the given figures.

For example, with a book of 550 pages more sophisticated printing and binding machinery may be necessary than for smaller books and this could mean extra cost.

On the assumption that no other factors will influence the costs, the estimate of £328.25 is realistic. However, if any new factors should be considered for books, either to affect the fixed part or the variable part of the cost, then this method should not be used.

8.3   Miners

The scatter diagrams required are as follows:

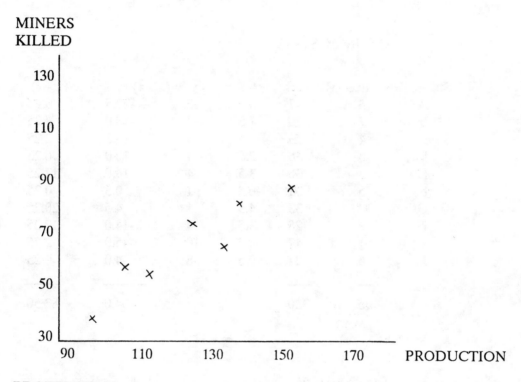

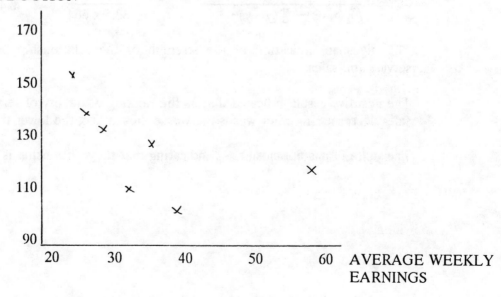

From the scatter diagrams, it appears that there is a strong positive straight line relationship between coal production and the number of miners killed underground. The association between coal produced and average weekly earnings is not as strong. The 19X7 figure deviates significantly from the pattern of other years. If this figure is assumed to be an 'extreme' case and not typical, then the association is quite strong.

The results here are based on seven years' data in total. This is quite a small sample size and means the results on the levels of association are likely to be unreliable.

8.4   Petrol stations

(a)

Quality of Sales

Station	service (x)	(y)	$x - \bar{x}$	$y - \bar{y}$	$(x - \bar{x})(y - \bar{y})$	$(x - \bar{x})^2$	$(y - \bar{y})^2$
A	3	47	-2.5	15	-37.5	6.25	225
B	7	20	1.5	-12	-18.0	2.25	144
C	4	23	-1.5	-9	13.5	2.25	81
D	8	36	2.5	4	10.0	6.25	16
E	2	36	-3.5	4	-14.0	12.25	16
F	5	31	-0.5	-1	0.5	0.25	1
G	10	33	4.5	1	4.5	20.25	1
H	9	28	3.5	-4	-14.0	12.25	16
I	1	42	-4.5	10	-45.0	2.25	100
J	6	24	0.5	-8	-4.0	0.25	64
	55	320			-104.0	82.50	664

$$\bar{x} = 5.5 \qquad\qquad \bar{y} = 32$$

$$r = \frac{\Sigma (x - x)(y - y)}{\sqrt{\Sigma (x - x)^2 \; \Sigma (y - y)^2}} = \frac{-104}{\sqrt{82.5 \times 664}} = -0.44$$

This gives an indication of the strength of the relationship between quality of service and sales.

The negative result indicates that as the ranking of quality of service increases, the sales decrease. In other words the worse the service, the lower the sales.

The value of r is not close to -1 indicating that the relationship is not very strong.

Station   Price   Sales

	(x)	(y)	(x - x̄)	(y - ȳ)	(x- x̄) (y -ȳ)	(x - x̄)²	(y - ȳ)²
A	1.66	47	-0.02	15	-0.30	0.0004	225
B	1.71	20	0.03	-12	-0.36	0.0009	144
C	1.70	23	0.02	-9	-0.18	0.0004	81
D	1.65	36	-0.03	4	-0.12	0.0009	16
E	1.67	36	-0.01	4	-0.04	0.0001	16
F	1.67	31	-0.01	-1	0.01	0.0001	1
G	1.72	33	0.04	1	0.04	0.0016	1
H	1.69	28	0.01	-4	-0.04	0.0001	16
I	1.67	42	-0.01	10	-0.10	0.0001	100
J	1.68	24	0	-8	0	0	64
	16.82	320			-1.09	0.0046	664

$$\bar{x} = 1.68 \qquad\qquad \bar{y} = 32$$

$$r = \frac{\Sigma (x - x)(y - y)}{\sqrt{\Sigma (x - x)^2 \ \Sigma (y - y)^2}} = \frac{-1.09}{\sqrt{0.0046 \times 664}} = -0.624$$

This gives an indication of the strength of the relationship between petrol price and sales.

The negative result indicates that as petrol price increases, sales decrease.

The relationship here is stronger than the one between quality of service and sales, although it is still not a very strong relationship.

Thus, the price of petrol appears to be the more important factor in determining volume of sales.

(b)   If the experiment were not confined to areas of similar traffic density, the results would be very misleading.

Volume of traffic is likely to be the most important factor affecting sales.

Unless areas of similar traffic density were considered it would be impossible to tell whether the variations in sales were due to petrol price or quality of service rather than volume of traffic.

Session 9: Time series analysis

Objective test answers

(1)   B   (Note that seasonal variations don't have to repeat themselves over a period of a year. In this case it is over a day.)

(2)   A   The linear regression method is only appropriate if the underlying trend is approximately linear

Answers

(3)   B   4 qtr moving totals:

$$(100 + 104 + 110 + 109) = 423$$
$$(423 - 100 \text{ (March yr 1)} + 102 \text{ (March yr 2)}) = 425$$
$$(425 - 104 + 108) = 429$$
$$(429 - 110 + 112) = 431$$
$$(431 - 109 + 108) = 430$$

Trend   = (moving totals (order 2) of above)/8
         = (423 + 425)/8, (425 + 429)/8, (429 + 431)/8, (431 + 430)/8
         = 106, 106.75, 107.5, 107.625

Written test answers

9.1   New cars

(a)

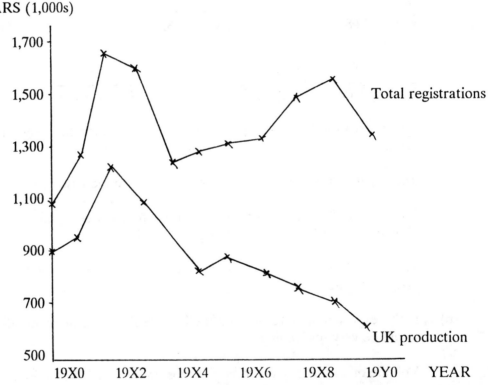

CARS (1,000s)

There is no clear pattern to either time series. Total registrations has an upward trend and seems cyclical. UK production is different before and after 19X5. After 19X5 there is a clear downward fairly linear trend, but before 19X5 there is a cyclic effect similar to total registrations. During the early part of the period 19X0-Y0, UK production accounted for a large share of the market.

(b)   UK car production as a percentage of total market for cars is as follows:

19X0	19X1	19X2	19X3	19X4	19X5	19X6	19X7	19X8	19X9	19Y0
83.7	78.9	78.7	69.4	76.0	63.1	61.1	58.6	46.6	40.5	39.3

UK PERCENTAGE

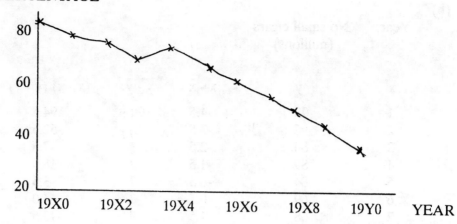

This time series has a much clearer pattern showing a consistent downward trend. With the exception of 19X4, there has been a regular fall in the UK's share of car market.

9.2   Cigars

(a)   Sales of small cigars in USA

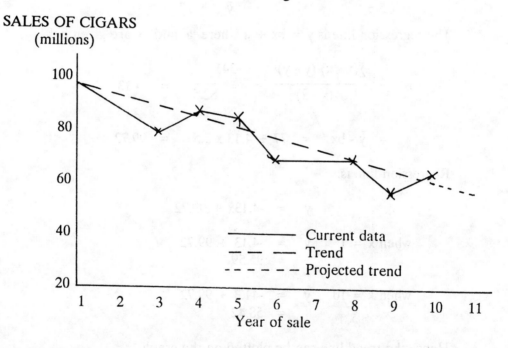

(b)

x	y	x - $\bar{x}$	y - $\bar{y}$	(x - $\bar{x}$) (y - $\bar{y}$)	(x - $\bar{x}$)^2
	Year	No small cigars (millions)			
1	98	-4.5	21	94.5	20.25
2	92	-3.5	15	-52.5	12.25
3	80	-2.5	3	-7.5	6.25
4	89	-1.5	12	-18.0	2.25
5	84	-0.5	7	-3.5	0.25
6	69	0.5	-8	-4.0	0.25
7	68	1.5	-9	-13.5	2.25
8	68	2.5	-9	-22.5	6.25
9	58	3.5	-19	-66.5	12.25
10	64	4.5	-13	-58.5	20.25
55	770			-341.0	82.50

$$\bar{x} = 5.5 \qquad\qquad \bar{y} = 77$$

The regression line is y = bx + a where 'a' and 'b' are given by:

$$b = \frac{\Sigma(x - x)(y - y)}{(x - \bar{x})^2} = \frac{-341}{82.5} = -4.13$$

$$a = \bar{y} - b\bar{x} = 77 + 4.13 \times 5.5 = 99.72$$

Regression line is:

$$y = -4.13x + 99.72$$

$$\text{when } x = 1 \quad y = -4.13 + 99.72$$
$$= 95.59$$

$$\text{when } x = 10 \quad y = -41.3 + 99.72$$
$$= 58.42$$

Hence the trend line can be plotted on the graph.

(c)   Estimated production for year 12 is given by the y value when x = 12

$$y = -4.13 \times 12 + 99.72$$
$$= 50.16$$

(d)   The estimate for year 12 has been achieved by projecting the trend line into the future or extrapolating. It can be dangerous to extrapolate in this way, particularly for periods a long way in the future, as other influencing factors may come into play which did not affect the figures given. For example, the government may raise the tax on small cigars or a report may be published on how smoking may damage your health - both could have a drastic effect on the sales of small cigars.

Extrapolating two years into the future is not too dangerous but to carry the process to its extremes, the trend implies that by year 25 the sales of small cigars will be zero - this is hardly likely!

9.3   Commodities

To obtain the seasonal variations we first need to determine the trend. Since the data is quarterly, a 4-point moving average is used.

(a)

Year	Qtr	(a) Index	4-year moving average	Trend (b) centred moving average	Seasonal variations (a)-(b)
1	1	195			
	2	189			
			187.50		
	3	183		190.63	-7.63
			193.75		
	4	183		197.13	-14.13
			200.50		
2	1	220		203.88	+16.12
			207.25		
	2	216		210.63	+5.37
			214.00		
	3	210		215.25	-5.25
			216.50		
	4	210		217.88	-7.88
			219.25		
3	1	230		220.75	+9.25
			222.25		
	2	227		223.75	+3.25
			225.25		
	3	222		229.63	-7.63
			234.00		
	4	222		238.00	-16.00
			242.00		
4	1	265		246.13	+18.87
			250.25		
	2	259		254.25	+4.75
			258.25		
	3	255		265.13	-10.13
			272.00		
	4	254		279.00	-25.00
			286.00		
5	1	320		292.88	+27.12
			299.75		
	2	315		307.00	+8.00
			314.25		
	3	310			
	4	312			

A.49

	Quarter			
	1	2	3	4
Year 1	-	-	7.63	14.13
Year 2	+16.12	+5.37	-5.25	-7.88
Year 3	+9.25	+3.25	-7.63	-16.00
Year 4	+18.87	+4.75	-10.13	-25.00
Year 5	+27.12	+8.00		
	_____	_____	_____	_____
Sum	+71.36	+21.37	-30.64	-63.01
Average	+17.84	+5.34	-7.66	-15.75

The average seasonal variations may now be used to deseasonalise the data by subtracting the relevant figures from the original data as shown below.

Year	Qtr	(a) Index	(b) Seasonal variation	Deseasonalised data (a)-(b)
1	1	195	+17.84	177.16
	2	189	+5.34	183.66
	3	183	-7.66	190.66
	4	183	-15.75	198.75
2	1	220	+17.84	202.16
	2	216	+5.34	210.66
	3	210	-7.66	217.66
	4	210	-15.75	225.75
3	1	230	+17.84	212.16
	2	227	+5.34	221.66
	3	222	-7.66	229.66
	4	222	-15.75	237.75
4	1	265	+17.84	247.16
	2	259	+5.34	253.66
	3	255	-7.66	262.66
	4	254	-15.75	269.75
5	1	320	+17.84	302.16
	2	315	+5.34	309.66
	3	310	-7.66	317.66
	4	312	-15.75	327.75

(b)   INDEX

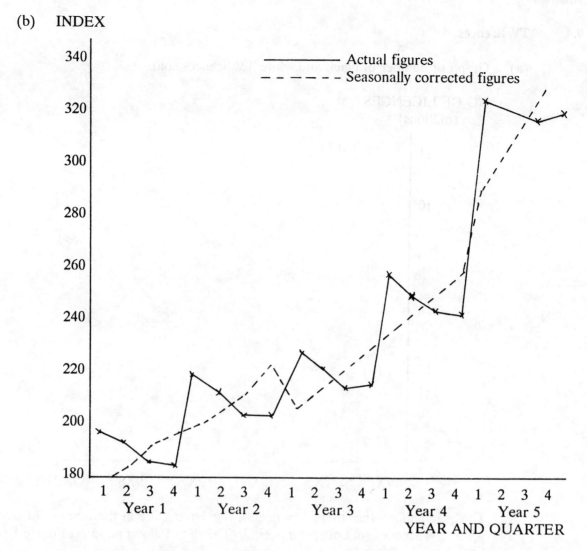

(c)   The graphs show that wholesale prices of this group of commodities were increasing over the period given. The wholesale prices were seasonal with a regular seasonal pattern over the five years. By removing the effect of the seasons we see that, with the exception of one small fall, wholesale prices have been continually rising.

9.4   TV licences

(a)   Graph of number of black and white TV licences sold.

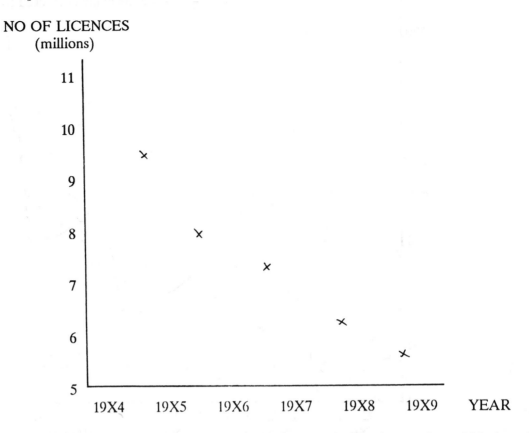

The graph shows that there has been a regular decline in the number of black and white TV licences sold over the period. The data follows an almost perfect straight line.

(b)   The best way of answering this question is to find the total number of licences sold each year and plot this on a graph.

Year	19X4	19X5	19X6	19X7	19X8	19X9
Total Sales	17.43	17.67	18.00	18.09	18.49	18.29

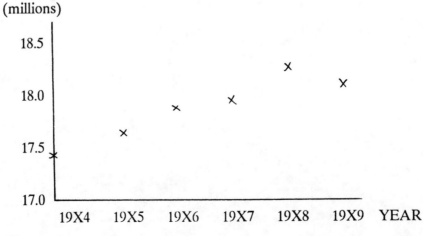

This graph indicates that from 19X4 to 19X8 the total number of TV licences increased each year, giving evidence to the statement made. However, in 19X9 the total number of licences sold fell suggesting that the statement is not true. Figures for 19Y0 would provide evidence as to whether 19X9 was an unusual year.

Session 10: Probability

Objective test answers

(1)   B   13/52 x 12/51 x 11/50 x 10/49

(2)   C   4 x solution to 1 to take account of the four suits that would qualify.

(3)   D   13/52 x 13/51 x 13/50 x 13/49

(4)   A   The four suits could be arranged in 4 x 3 x 2 x 1 = 24 ways, thus the answer to 3 is multiplied by 24, giving .10550.

(5)   D   (i)   defective, non-defective **in that order** has probability 3/40 x 37/39. This needs to be multiplied by 2 as they could be picked in the reverse order;

        (ii)   there is only one arrangement of two non-defectives, thus the probability is just 37/40 x 36/39.

(6)   B   Green, green, non-green in that order has probability 150/550 x 149/549 x (80 + 320)/548.

This needs to be multiplied by 3 to take account of the three positions the non-green could take.

(7)   D   P(from P) = 3/4 P(from Q) = 1/4

P(fails, given from P) = .12

P(fails, given from Q) = .08

P(fails) = P(from P and fails) + P(from Q and fails) (using addition law)

=   P(from P) P(fails/P) + P(from Q) P(fails/Q)

=   .75 x .12 + .25 x .08 = .11 = 11%

(8)   C   Question requires P(from Q/fails)

A table can be formed showing the proportions of seeds falling into each category. Start with any total - say 1,000

| | From garden centre | | |
	P	Q	Total
Germinates	660	230	890
Fails	90	20	110
Total	750	250	1,000

Answers

$$P(\text{from Q/fails}) = \frac{\text{No from Q and fail category}}{\text{Total no of } \textbf{fails}}$$
(by the law of proportions)
$$= 20/110 = 0.18$$

Written test answers

10.1   Defectives

(a)   Let $P(G)$ = Probability article good (ie, no defects)
$P(D)$ = Probability article has major defect
$P(d)$ = Probability article has minor defect

(i) $P(G) = 10/16 = 5/8$

(ii)   If the article has no major defects then it is either good or it has minor defects:

$$\begin{aligned}P(\text{no major defects}) &= P(G) + P(d) \\ &= 5/8 + 2/8 \\ &= 7/8\end{aligned}$$

(iii)   P(either good or has major defects
$$\begin{aligned}&= P(G) + P(D) \\ &= 5/8 + 1/8 \\ &= 3/4\end{aligned}$$

(b)   Let the suffixes 1 and 2 refer to the 1st and 2nd articles respectively. Let $P(G_2 G_1)$ be the probability that the 2nd is good, given that the 1st was good.

(i) $P(G_2 G_1) = 9/15$ since there are now only 15 articles to choose from of which only 9 are good.

Now

$$\begin{aligned}P(\text{both good}) &= P(G_2 G_1) P(G_1) \\ &= 9/15 \times 5/8 \\ &= 3/8\end{aligned}$$

(ii) $$\begin{aligned}P(\text{both major defects}) &= P(D_2 D_1) P(D_1) \\ &= 1/15 \times 1/8 \\ &= 1/120\end{aligned}$$

(iii) $$\begin{aligned}P(\text{at least 1 good}) &= 1 - P(\text{neither good}) \\ &= 1 - 6/16 \times 5/15 \\ &= 1 - 2/16 \\ &= 7/8\end{aligned}$$

A.54

1134M

(iv) P(at most 1 good)   = 1 - P(both good)

= 1 - 3/8 (using (i) above)

= 5/8

(v) Exactly one good article can be produced in one of two ways. Either the first one is good and the second defective or vice versa.

Let P(not good) = P($\bar{G}$) = P(major or minor defects) = 1 - P(G)

The P(exactly 1 good)   = P($\bar{G}_2|G_1$) P(G_1) + P($G_2|G_1$) P(G_1)

= 6/15 x 10/6 + 10/15 x 6/16

= 1/4 + 1/4

= 1/2

(vi) Using the same notation

P(neither has major defects)   = P($\bar{D}_2|\bar{D}_1$) P($\bar{D}_1$)

= 13/15 x 14/16

(vii) P(neither is good)   = P($\bar{G}_2|\bar{G}_1$) P($\bar{G}_1$)

= 5/15 x 6/16

= 1/8

10.2 Investments

We must calculate the expected return on each investment.

Investment A:

Expected return   = (-3,000 x 0) + (-2,000 x 0) + (-1,000 x 0.1)

+ (0 x 0.2) + (1,000 x 0.3) + (2,000 x 0.2)

+ (3,000 x 0.2) + (4,000 x 0)

= 0 + 0 - 100 + 0 + 300 + 400 + 600 + 0

= £1,200

Investment B:

Expected return = (-3,000 x 0.1) + (-2,000 x 0.2) + (-1,000 x 0.1)

+ (0 x 0.1) + (1,000 x 0.1) + (2,000 x 0.2)

+ (3,000 x 0.1) + (4,000 x 0.1)

= -300 - 400 - 100 + 0 + 100 + 400 + 300 + 400

= £400

Investment A has the much higher expected return and from this point of view is therefore preferable.

Additionally, investment A has a much more compact distribution of probabilities. There is no chance of making a loss of £2,000 or £3,000, whereas there is with investment B. However, a drawback with investment A is that there is also no chance of a return of £4,000, but there is a small chance with investment B.

10.3   Strike

If the offer is accepted outright the increased annual cost is:

£500 x 52 x % increase

If there is a strike the cost is £200,000 per week but the increased wages will not be incurred during the period of the strike and thereafter will only be incurred for the remaining weeks of the year (ie, less than 52).

Offer 14%

Expected cost:

		£
0.3 x £500 x 52 x 14		109,200
0.2 (£200,000 + £500 x 51 x 14)		111,400
0.3 (£400,000 + £500 x 50 x 14)		225,000
0.2 (£600,000 + £500 x 49 x 14)		188,600
		£634,200

Offer 20%

		£
0.5 x £500 x 52 x 20		260,000
0.25 (£200,000 + £500 x 51 x 20)		177,500
0.25 (£400,000 + £500 x 50 x 20)		225,000
		£662,500

Comparing costs the company should offer 14%.

10.4   Fruit machine

(a)   (i)   P(win type A)   = 1/5 x 1/5 x 1/5 = 1/125

       (ii)   P(win type B)   = (1/5 x 1/5 x 4/5) Cherry Cherry Plum
                                + (1/5 x 4/5 x 1/5) Cherrry Plum Cherry
                                + (4/5 x 1/5 x 1/5) Plum Cherry Cherry

                                = 12/125

       (iii) P(win type C)   = 1/5 x 4/5 x 4/5

                                = 16/125

       Therefore:

       P(lose)   = 1 - (16/125 + 12/125 + 1/125)

                                = 96/125

(b)   P(type A win)   = P(type A win|win)   P(win)

       1/125   = p x 29/125

       p   = 1/29

       Let the payment for a type A win be £x.

(c)   For a player to break even in the long run, the expected gain must be zero.

       Therefore 0   = -0.1 + x/125 + (12 x 0.5)/125 + (16 x 0.3)/125

       0.1 x 125   = x + 6 + 4.8

       x   = 1.7

       Thus payment should be reduced to £1.70.

Session 11: Sampling, significance testing and quality control

Objective test answers

(1)   B   All the others are examples of primary data, being collected directly for the investigation.

(2)   C

(3)   D   Numbers must be selected systematically from the table. A runs down the fourth column, B and C are diagonals from the second and first numbers on the top row respectively.

Index

The numbers refer to the session and section

STOCKISTS AND DISTRIBUTORS

UK

London

Barbican Business Books, 9 Moorfields, London EC2   Telephone: 01 628 7479

Dillons University Bookshop, 1 Malet Street, London WC1E 7JE   Telephone: 01 636 1577

W & G Foyle, 119 Charing Cross Road, London WC2   Telephone: 01 437 5660

Parks Bookshop, 244 High Holborn, London WC1V 7DZ   Telephone: 01 831 9501

Parks Bookshop, 18 London Road, London SE1 6JX   Telephone: 01 928 5378

Cambridge

Heffers Booksellers, 20 Trinity Street, Cambridge CR2 1NG

Birmingham

Parks Bookshops, 3 Windsor Arcade, Birmingham B2 5LJ   Telephone: 021 233 4969

Hudsons Bookshops, 116 New Street, Birmingham B2

Glasgow

Parks Bookshop, 83 St Vincent Street, Glasgow G2 5TF   Telephone: 041 221 1369

Manchester

Parks Bookshops, 19 Brown Street, Manchester M2 1DA   Telephone: 061 834 4019

Financial Training Courses' Study Packs and Workbooks can also be ordered from any local Financial Training Centre. Ring 01 876 0499 for details.

ABOUT FT COURSES

Financial Training Courses provide the ideal way to study - whatever the student's situation. We provide a flexible, efficient service - designed to adapt to individual needs and to give the best possible chance of success.

- **Study Packs** - At the heart of our courses and programmes are the Financial Training Study Packs; clear, up-to-date texts which are adopted by colleges as set course texts.

- **Workbooks** - Doing the vital job of supporting the Study Packs, each Workbook contains a complete revision programme. Question banks of carefully selected questions ensure familiarity with all parts of the syllabus.

- **Correspondence courses** - Complete learning programmes designed around information you provide. The correspondence course incorporates a unique individual Study Programme, Study Packs, Workbooks, tutors' assistance and practice examinations.

- **Intensive revision courses** - An invaluable back-up to our other material. Personal contact with tutors in intensive classroom situations gives a much greater chance of success. Each course lasts 3 to 5 days, with convenient locations throughout England and Wales from which to choose.

- **Link courses** - We give our comprehensive Link Courses five stars for good reasons. It incorporates all the above elements in addition to providing extra oral tuition. The combination of home study and oral tuition is perfect, as it keeps the student motivated and directly in touch with tutors. Link Courses are our way of making the most of a student's time and chances.

For further information, write or phone us at Financial Training Courses Limited, Parkway House, Sheen Lane, London SW14 8LS. Telephone: 01 876 0499 Fax: 01 878 1749

OVERSEAS

Cyprus

Intercollege of Management & Communication Studies, 17 Heroes Avenue, PO Box 4005, Nicosia

Eire

Hodges Figgis Booksellers, 54 Dawson Street, Dublin
O'Mahoney & Co, 120 O'Connell Street, Limerick

Hong Kong

The Swindon Book Co Ltd, 13-15 Lock Road, Kowloon, Hong Kong

Kenya

Kenya School of Professional Studies, Finance House, Loita Street, PO Box 45531, Nairobi

Malaysia

Stamford Executive Centre, MTUC Building, 19 Jalan Barat, Petaling Jaya, Selangor, Kuala Lumpur
PAAC, First Floor, Wisma ALMA, 2-4 Jalan Manau, 50460, Kuala Lumpur, PO Box 11201

Mauritius

Bernard Yu Sak Kan, 45 Desroches Street, Port Louis, Mauritius

Singapore

Stamford College Group, Stamford Educational Towers, 218 Queen Street, Sinagpore 0718

Sri Lanka

MD Gunesena, PO Box 246, Olcott, Mawatha

Pakistan

Progressive International Agencies, PO Box 8069, Karachi 29

West Indies

Duff's Business College, 4A Marsecaux Road, Kingston, Jamaica
Heinemann Educational Books, 175 Mountain View Avenue, Kingston, Jamaica
Herman Marcano & Associates, 12 Flament Street, Port of Spain, Trinidad
PAL Booksellers Ltd, 213 Belmont Circular Road, Belmount, Port of Spain, Trinidad
School of Accounting and Management, Corner Eastern Main Road, 1-3 McCartly Street, St Augustine, Trinidad